AQA GCSE

FOOD PREPARATION & NUTRITION

Alexis Rickus
Bev Saunder
Yvonne Mackey

HODDER
EDUCATION
AN HACHETTE UK COMPANY

Approval message from AQA

This textbook has been approved by AQA for use with our qualification. This means that we have checked that it broadly covers the specification and we are satisfied with the overall quality. Full details of our approval process can be found on our website.

We approve textbooks because we know how important it is for teachers and students to have the right resources to support their teaching and learning. However, the publisher is ultimately responsible for the editorial control and quality of this book.

Please note that when teaching the AQA GCSE (9-1) in Food Preparation and Nutrition course, you must refer to AQA's specification as your definitive source of information. While this book has been written to match the specification, it cannot provide complete coverage of every aspect of the course.

A wide range of other useful resources can be found on the relevant subject pages of our website: www.aqa.org.uk.

Although every effort has been made to ensure that website addresses are correct at time of going to press, Hodder Education cannot be held responsible for the content of any website mentioned in this book. It is sometimes possible to find a relocated web page by typing in the address of the home page for a website in the URL window of your browser.

Hachette UK's policy is to use papers that are natural, renewable and recyclable products and made from wood grown in sustainable forests. The logging and manufacturing processes are expected to conform to the environmental regulations of the country of origin.

Orders: please contact Bookpoint Ltd, 130 Milton Park, Abingdon, Oxon OX14 4SB. Telephone: (44) 01235 827720. Fax: (44) 01235 400454. Email education@bookpoint.co.uk Lines are open from 9 a.m. to 5 p.m., Monday to Saturday, with a 24-hour message answering service. You can also order through our website: www.hoddereducation.co.uk

ISBN: 978 1 4718 6364 6

© Alexis Rickus, Bev Saunder and Yvonne Mackey 2016

First published in 2016 by
Hodder Education,
An Hachette UK Company
Carmelite House
50 Victoria Embankment
London EC4Y 0DZ

www.hoddereducation.co.uk

Impression number   10 9 8 7 6 5 4 3 2 1

Year   2020 2019 2018 2017 2016

Cover photo © Getty Images/Thinkstock/iStock/Denira777

Illustrations by Aptara

Typeset in India

Printed in Italy

A catalogue record for this title is available from the British Library.

Contents

How to use this book   v

Introduction to AQA GCSE Food Preparation and Nutrition   v

Acknowledgements   vii

Section 1	Food Preparation Skills	1

Skill 1 General practical skills   2

Skill 2 Knife skills   12

Skill 3 Preparing fruit and vegetables   22

Skill 4 Use of the cooker   28

Skill 5 Use of equipment   38

Skill 6 Cooking methods   48

Skill 7 Preparing, combining and shaping   56

Skill 8 Sauce-making   64

Skill 9 Tenderising and marinating   72

Skill 10 Dough   76

Skill 11 Raising agents   88

Skill 12 Setting mixtures   96

Section 2	Food, Nutrition and Health	99

Topic 2.1 Macronutrients   100

Topic 2.2 Micronutrients (and water)   118

Topic 2.3 Nutritional needs and health   145

Section 2 Practice questions   189

Section 3	Food Science	191

Topic 3.1 Cooking of food and heat transfer   192

Topic 3.2 Functional and chemical properties of food   206

Section 3 Practice questions   235

Section 4	Food Safety	237

Topic 4.1 Food spoilage and contamination   238

Topic 4.2 Principles of food safety   262

Section 4 Practice questions   277

Section 5	Food Choice	279

Topic 5.1 Factors affecting food choice   280

Topic 5.2 British and international cuisine   300

Topic 5.3 Sensory evaluation   317

Topic 5.4 Food labelling and marketing   328

Section 5 Practice questions   339

Section 6	Food Provenance	341
	Topic 6.1 Environmental impact and sustainability of food	342
	Topic 6.2 Food production and processing	374
	Section 6 Practice questions	409

Section 7	Preparing for Assessment	411
	Topic 7.1 Non-exam assessment	412
	Topic 7.2 The written exam	439
	Glossary	452
	Index	463

Introduction to AQA GCSE Food Preparation and Nutrition

This book has been written to help you master the skills, knowledge and understanding you need for the AQA GCSE (9–1) in Food Preparation and Nutrition.

This GCSE course focuses on practical cooking skills and will help you develop an understanding of nutrition, food provenance and the working characteristics of food.

The content of the course is divided into five core topics:
1   Food, nutrition and health
2   Food science
3   Food safety
4   Food choice
5   Food provenance

Food preparation skills are integrated into each of these core topics.

Each of these areas will be assessed in the Food Preparation and Nutrition written examination you will complete at the end of the course. (You will find information to help you prepare for the written exam at the end of this book on pages 454–459).

You will also complete two Non-Examination Assessments (NEAs): Food Investigation; and Food Preparation Assessment. (You will find information to help you prepare for these tasks at the end of this book on pages 430–453).

Summary of assessment

Component	Assessment type	Time and marks	% of qualification
Food Preparation and Nutrition	Written examination paper	1 hour 45 minutes 100 marks	50%
Task 1: Food Investigation	Non-examined assessment (NEA)	30 marks	15%
Task 2: Food Preparation	Non-examined assessment (NEA)	70 marks	35%

How to use this book

The book is divided into seven sections.

Section 1: Food preparation skills

Section 1 covers the 12 food preparation skills you will need to understand throughout the course, and provides example recipes that incorporate each skill. These skills are integrated into the practical activities that appear throughout the textbook. You are not expected to work your way through this section of the book from start to finish, but may find it useful to refer to it to find recipes, or when completing the practical activities elsewhere in the textbook.

Sections 2–6: Subject content

Sections 2–6 cover the four areas of subject content you will be tested on in the Food Preparation and Nutrition written exam:

- Section 2 Food, nutrition and health
- Section 3 Food science
- Section 4 Food safety
- Section 5 Food choice
- Section 6 Food provenance

Each section is divided into several topics. Throughout each topic you will find the following features:

Key words

Key words are provided throughout each topic and define all of the important terms you will need to know and understand.

Learning objectives

This box appears at the start of each topic and will tell you what you should know and understand by the end of the topic.

Activity

Activity boxes include short activities your teacher may ask you to complete either in class or at home to help you develop your knowledge and understanding of a topic.

Practical activity

Practical activities are food preparation and cooking tasks that will provide you with opportunities to demonstrate the different food preparation skills and techniques, as well as allowing you to apply your subject knowledge and understanding in a practical context and see how it is relevant to practical food preparation and cooking. You may find it useful to refer to Section 1 Food preparation skills when completing these activities.

Extension activity

These extension tasks will help you to develop your knowledge and understanding of a topic further. They may ask you to complete further research into a topic, demonstrate more complex food preparation and cooking skills and techniques, or consider some of the more challenging aspects of the course.

Check your knowledge and understanding

These are short questions that appear at the end of each topic. They will help you to test your knowledge and understanding of the content covered within the topic.

Practice questions

These questions appear at the end of each section. They will help you to prepare for the written exam.

Section 7: Preparing for assessment

The final section of the book is divided into three topics:

- **Topics 1 and 2** cover the two Non-Examination Assessments: Task 1 Food Investigation and the Task 2 Food Preparation Assessment. They explain the format each assessment will take, how many marks are available for the different aspects of each assessment, and include example work for assessment tasks similar to those you will need to complete.
- **Topic 3** is designed to help you to prepare for the written exam. It includes details on the format of the exam paper, information on the types of questions you will encounter and advice on answering exam questions. It also includes practice questions with some sample answers and commentary.

Acknowledgements

Alexis Rickus: Thank you to Tom and Scott for their support and patience during the writing process.

Bev Saunder: I would like to thank my husband Simon, and my children William and Sophie for being so supportive and self-sufficient giving me the time to write.

Thanks also to Helen, Kim, Helen, James, Anne and Sam for their sound advice throughout the process.

Yvonne Mackey: I would like to thank my mother, Irene for sharing her knowledge of food and nutrition with me from a very early age and for allowing me to cook at home whenever I wanted to.

Also, thank you to Pat Andrews for my ever increasing interest in food safety and enabling me to work in the food industry.

Picture credits:

SECTION 1
Food Preparation Skills

This section includes a range of food preparation and cooking skills that you will need throughout the GCSE course.

You are not expected to work your way through this section from start to finish, but you may find it useful to refer to it when completing the practical activities that appear in other sections of the book, or when preparing for your Food Investigation and Food Preparation Assessment.

This section also includes examples of recipes that use each of the different skills, which can be used for the practical activities throughout the book.

The following food preparation skills are covered in this section:

Skill 1 General practical skills

Skill 2 Knife skills

Skill 3 Preparing fruit and vegetables

Skill 4 Use of the cooker

Skill 5 Use of equipment

Skill 6 Cooking methods

Skill 7 Preparing, combining and shaping

Skill 8 Sauce-making

Skill 9 Tenderising and marinating

Skill 10 Dough

Skill 11 Raising agents

Skill 12 Setting mixtures

SKILL I GENERAL PRACTICAL SKILLS

Weighing and measuring

Most recipes depend on accurate measurements for success, so it is important to be able to weigh and measure accurately. If you are making a cake, for example, and you add too much sugar or too much flour, the results are likely to be poor. However, in some recipes it does not matter so much, for example if you put two onions instead of one in a Bolognese sauce.

Figure 1.1.1 Digital scales will give a more precise and accurate check on weight

Conversion tables

Some recipes use grams (metric); others use ounces/pounds (imperial). Some recipes use both so you have a choice. It is important that you do not use both systems of measurement – one or the other must be used throughout a recipe, as mixing the two could lead to potential errors in the proportion of ingredients in combination.

Measurements are based on weight for solids (dry ingredients) and on volume for liquids (fluid ounces and pints for imperial, millilitres and litres for metric). Table 1.1.1 is a useful guide for approximate conversions from imperial to metric for weight and volume; they have been rounded up or down.

Weight		Volume	
Ounces	**Grams**	**Fluid ounces**	**Millilitres**
1 oz	25 g	1 fl oz	30 ml
2 oz	55 g	2 fl oz	50 ml
3 oz	85 g	5 fl oz ($\frac{1}{4}$ pint)	150 ml
4 oz	115 g	$\frac{1}{2}$ pint	300 ml
5 oz	140 g	$\frac{3}{4}$ pint	425 ml
6 oz	175 g	1 pint	600 ml
7 oz	200 g	$1\frac{3}{4}$ pint	1 litre
8 oz	225 g		
16 oz (1 lb)	450 g		

Table 1.1.1 Conversion table

Equipment

The following equipment is useful for weighing and measuring:

- Kitchen scales – digital/electronic kitchen scales are most widely used.
- Measuring jug – a measuring jug is used to measure liquids; the side of the jug is usually marked with millilitres or fluid ounces or both.
- Measuring cups – some American recipes use cups for dried ingredients such as flour and sugar. Cups should not be used to weigh fat.
- Measuring spoons – these are very useful for measuring an accurate teaspoon or tablespoon. 1 teaspoon is 5 ml, 1 tablespoon is 15 ml.

Figure 1.1.2 Measuring jug

Figure 1.1.3 Measuring cups

Figure 1.1.4 Measuring spoons

Preparing ingredients and equipment

Before you begin cooking, it is extremely important to organise yourself and the area you are cooking in. You will need to organise what equipment and what ingredients you need.

You also need to organise yourself following basic food hygiene and safety rules.

Preparation before starting to cook is called **mis en place**.

A good way to remember how to set up your area ready to cook is the word HATTIE:

> **Key word**
> **Mis en place** means preparation before starting to cook.

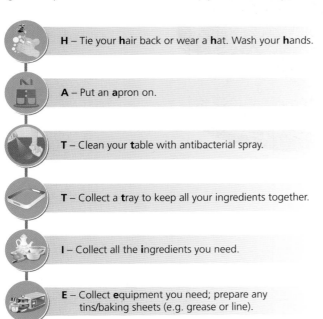

H – Tie your **h**air back or wear a **h**at. Wash your **h**ands.

A – Put an **a**pron on.

T – Clean your **t**able with antibacterial spray.

T – Collect a **t**ray to keep all your ingredients together.

I – Collect all the **i**ngredients you need.

E – Collect **e**quipment you need; prepare any tins/baking sheets (e.g. grease or line).

Figure 1.1.5 Make sure work surfaces are cleaned before cooking

It is always important to use the exact size of tin or dish recommended in the recipe.

● If the tin or dish is too large, then the mixture could spread too thinly and burn or be too crispy in texture.
● If the tin is too small, then the mixture may overflow and spill in the oven and the centre may not cook evenly.

Some tins need preparing before use, mainly to ensure that the mixture does not stick. For example, the tins used to make Swiss rolls need to be lined with non-stick baking paper and greased. Sandwich cake tins need to be lined and greased lightly to stop the cake from sticking to the bottom of the tin.

A light dusting of flour on top of the greased paper can also be added to stop the bottom of the cake becoming too greasy. Non-stick tins may not need to be greased.

Figure 1.1.6 A non-stick cake tin

Selecting and adjusting cooking times

When cooking food, it is best to follow the recipe instructions for a guide to how long it needs to be in the oven. Timing is crucial because you don't want food to be spoilt by overcooking or undercooking.

However, it is also important to learn how to check when food is cooked, and to adjust the cooking time if necessary. Different types of food take different times to cook. It is important to be guided by the recipe, but also to do a visual check and/or a taste test, extending or reducing the cooking time accordingly.

Fish and shellfish

The thickness of the fish will have an impact on the cooking time – thinner fillets cook much quicker than thicker fillets, so the time needs to be adjusted according to the size of the fish.

- For thinner fillets of fish, such as plaice or sole, if the outside of the fish is opaque, the fish is done.
- For thicker fillets, such as salmon or cod, insert a small, thin knife into the thickest part of the fillet to see if it is opaque throughout.

For raw shellfish, boil, sauté or grill them in their shells to keep the most flavour. Raw prawns are grey in colour and turn pink when they are cooked. They cook extremely quickly so you need to watch for the colour change.

Meat and alternatives

Larger joints of meat need long, slow cooking – cooking times are not as precise because they are unlikely to overcook if left in for a few minutes too long.

Smaller cuts, such as steak or burgers, can be grilled more quickly. They can overcook easily so need to be watched while cooking.

Mycoprotein products (i.e. Quorn™) can be cooked using an oven, grill or microwave.

- The instructions on the packet need to be followed, but as a general rule mycoprotein does cook more quickly than meat and poultry.
- You can use mycoprotein mince, pieces and fillets in a recipe in the same way you would meat, just reduce the cooking time slightly.
- For example, mycoprotein mince fries in about 3–5 minutes if using it in a Bolognese sauce.

Bolognese sauce

500 g of mycoprotein

1 onion

50 g mushrooms

1 small pepper

1 clove garlic

400 g tin of chopped tomatoes

1 tbsp of tomato purée

18 ml (1 tbsp) oil

Optional ingredients:

Red/yellow/green pepper

1 courgette

1 carrot

Method

1. Deseed and chop all vegetables into dice. Heat oil and fry the vegetables until soft, approximately five minutes.
2. Add the mycoprotein and stir in.
3. Add all the other ingredients.
4. Decide on whether to add some water and how much – add water (between 125–250 ml).
5. Bring to the boil and simmer for 20 minutes.
6. Adjust seasoning to taste.

Vegetables

Vegetables are usually steamed or boiled and can take as little as 5 minutes to cook. When they are cooked 'al dente' they should be firm to the bite. It is advisable to check vegetables after 3–5 minutes with a knife, as overcooked vegetables lose colour, flavour and nutrients. Continue cooking the vegetables until they are the softness you require.

Pasta and rice

- Pasta and rice are usually placed into water that is already boiling. (Putting pasta and rice into cold water will be less successful and adds to cooking times.)
- Guidance is usually given on the packets because thicker pasta takes longer to cook, and brown rice takes longer than white rice.
- It is useful to check pasta and rice after two-thirds of the cooking time. Continue cooking until it is the softness you require.

Baked products

Generally, individual cakes, breads and pastries cook in a shorter time than large cakes and bread. Larger cakes sometimes need a lower temperature too to avoid the top of the product overcooking.

When it gets near to the cooking time recommended in the recipe, test for readiness regularly.

Figure 1.1.7 Bread baking in an oven

Testing for readiness

You can check whether food is cooked in different ways.

Temperature probe/knife

Raw meats (i.e. chicken and beef burgers) must be cooked thoroughly in order to kill any bacteria present.

To test for readiness, you can use a temperature probe, or use a knife to cut into the thickest point and check that the juices are clear and not pink or bloody.

Figure 1.1.8 A temperature probe

Skewer

When making deep cakes, it is difficult to judge whether the centre is cooked. You can check by inserting a skewer – if the skewer comes out clean, then the cake is cooked. If it is coated with sticky cake mixture, it needs longer in the oven.

Finger/poke test

The finger/poke method is most commonly used to check if small cakes are cooked. When you touch them with a finger, they should feel springy and spongy not liquidy or gooey. Smaller cuts of meat can also be checked by pressing them; the fibres should feel set not soft.

Figure 1.1.9 Skewers

Visual colour check/sound check

Most baked products should be a golden brown in colour. In the case of bread, there is also a sound check – when the bread is turned upside down and tapped with a knuckle, it should sound hollow if it is cooked. When products containing starch, such as bread, cakes and biscuits, are baked in the oven, the dry heat causes the starch to brown (**dextrinisation**). This makes the product look attractive to eat and the depth of the browning is a way in which it can be judged whether the product is cooked.

Taste test

Foods such as rice or pasta can be tasted to check if they are cooked.
- Pasta should be **al dente**, which means firm to the bite.
- Rice should be cooked through: it should be soft and not have a gritty texture.

> **Key words**
>
> **Dextrinisation** is when dry heat turns a starch brown.
>
> **Al dente** means 'firm to the bite', a description of the texture of correctly cooked pasta.

Judging and modifying sensory properties

In order for people to want to eat food, it needs to look and smell appetising. We then judge by taste. The taste buds on our tongues detect four basic flavours in food – sweet, sour, salt and savoury. Personal preferences for food may differ from one person to another and are governed by our taste buds.

As you cook more, you will gradually learn the skills of tasting food to check for flavour, texture and seasoning.

The characteristics of food that affect our organs or senses are known as **organoleptic qualities**. Judging food based on these characteristics is sensory evaluation.

You will learn about sensory testing methods and how to taste food in Topic 5.3 Sensory evaluation. See page 330.

Testing for flavour and seasoning

It is necessary to make sure that the food being cooked retains its taste. Checking its taste is essential during the cooking process, but particularly just before the end of cooking when it may need adjusting by simply adding some seasoning or some herbs or spices. Make sure you use a clean teaspoon when testing flavour.

Changing taste and aroma

An aroma is usually a pleasant smell. It is possible to change the taste and aroma of food by the addition of ingredients, or by the length of cooking time.

Taste and aroma can be changed in the following ways:

Figure 1.1.10 Reduction of wine, stock and cream

- **By infusion** – to **infuse** is to flavour liquid with aromatic ingredients by slowly heating it to boiling point and then allowing it to cool. The flavoured liquid is then called an infusion. When making bread sauce, the milk is infused with cloves, black peppercorns, bay leaf and an onion, before the breadcrumbs are added.
- **By reduction** – a **reduction** is a concentrated liquid formed when it is boiled rapidly; it will concentrate its flavour and colour. Wine and stock can be boiled until syrupy in consistency, and then cream can be added to make a rich reduction.
- **By making a paste** – a paste such as a **beurre manie** is made from equal quantities of butter and flour mixed together to form a soft paste, which is added to liquids to thicken them. The consistency of liquids, gravy and sauces is important: they should not be too thick or too thin.

Changing texture and flavour

Tasting food for texture is as important as testing for flavour. In fact, in many cases, changing the texture of food also changes the flavour. It is important to avoid overcooking foods like rice, pasta and vegetables, so as to achieve the desired texture for a recipe, such as crunchy red pepper or al dente pasta.

The texture of dishes can be changed. Breadcrumbs can be added as a garnish to dishes such as a pasta bake or cauliflower cheese. This will give the dish more texture as it will be crispy and crunchy on top. It will also brown and look attractive.

Meat should be allowed to rest after cooking as this allows the muscle fibres to relax which makes the meat more tender.

When making a product such as crème brûlée, the sugar on the top is heated using the grill or a blow torch; the effect of the heat on the sugar causes it to melt and brown (**caramelisation**). It will burn if too much heat is applied for too long.

Foods such as pastry can be glazed, which will deepen the colour of the top of the pastry and make it look shiny and attractive.

You will learn more about dextrinisation and caramelisation in Topic 3.2 Functional and chemical properties of food. See page 220.

Key words

Organoleptic qualities are the characteristics of food that affect our organs or senses.

Infuse means to flavour liquid with aromatic ingredients by slowly heating to boiling point and then allowing to cool.

Reduction is a concentrated liquid formed when it is boiled rapidly.

Beurre manie is a paste made from equal quantities of butter and flour mixed together, which is added to liquids to thicken them.

Caramelisation is the process of changing the colour of sugar from white to brown when heated.

Presentation and food styling

When eating out, we often judge food by its initial appearance.

Figure 1.1.11 Styled food – duck breast with cherries

Presentation and how the food is styled will improve a dish's **aesthetic** qualities. If food looks delicious, it is likely that the person eating it will think it tastes delicious before they eat it. There are many different ways in which food can be styled and presented to make it look as attractive as possible.

Presentation and how the food is styled will improve a dish's **aesthetic** qualities. If food looks delicious, it is likely that the person eating it will think it tastes delicious before they eat it. There are many different ways in which food can be styled and presented to make it look as attractive as possible.

Garnishes and decorative techniques

Adding a food to a finished dish can improve the aesthetic appearance. Decorations on savoury food are called **garnishes**. Examples of garnishes are sliced tomato, chopped coriander and lemon wedges.

You can learn more about how to prepare garnishes in Section 1, Skill 3 Preparing fruit and vegetables. See page 22.

Key words

Aesthetics is the art of making food look good or attractive, for example by using garnishes on savoury dishes or decorations on sweet dishes.
Garnishes are decorations on savoury food.

AQA GCSE Food Preparation and Nutrition

Decorations on sweet foods are simply called **decorations**. Examples of decorations are grated chocolate, a dusting of icing sugar or cocoa, a strawberry fan, piped cream and chopped nuts.

Accompaniments, such as a sauce or vegetables, also add colour to a dish.

Figure 1.1.12 A styled dessert

Presenting food for serving

It is always important to consider the serving dish and how the food will be placed on the dish. A number of different techniques can be used:

- Use the centre height of the dish – a mound of food will look more attractive than if it is flattened on a plate or serving dish.
- If laying out a plate of biscuits or canapés, arrange them in contrasting rows, as these look attractive.
- Overlap food such as fruit slices or slices of meat, which stops the food looking flat and dull on the plate.
- Keep colours to a minimum – lots of different colours can be overbearing. Using two colours or different shades of a single colour works very successfully.

Portioning

How we portion food and finish it off for presentation is important to make the food look as attractive as possible. Correct portioning of food is important so that each person has the right amount of food to match their nutritional needs and to avoid food wastage.

You will learn portion size and cost when meal planning in Topic 2.3 Nutritional needs and health. See page 148.

Different pieces of equipment are used to portion food, such as:

- a scoop for mashed potato and ice cream
- an individual pie dish for lasagne or shepherd's pie
- individual ramekin dishes for brûlées, mousses, pâtés
- stacking food on plates to add extra shape.

SKILL 2 KNIFE SKILLS

Knives

A selection of small and large kitchen knives and equipment are needed for different purposes. When using knives:

- Always clean the knife after use to avoid cross-contamination.
- Make sure the knife is kept sharp – it causes fewer accidents.
- Use the right-sized knife for the food you are cutting.
- Always store knives carefully in a block or a wrap.
- When carrying a knife always carry it by the handle with the point downwards.

The most common knives used are:

Filleting knife: a thin, flexible, narrow-bladed knife, used to fillet fish.

Cook's knife: a large, general-purpose knife with a deep blade, used for cutting, chopping, slicing and dicing.

Paring knife/vegetable knife: a small, multi-purpose knife, mainly used for slicing and dicing.

Bread knife: a large knife with a serrated blade, used to slice bread, cakes and pastries.

Carving knife: a long, thin-bladed knife used to carve both cooked meats and cold meats.

Figure 1.2.1 A selection of knives

AQA GCSE Food Preparation and Nutrition

Other cutting equipment

- A **corer** is used to remove the core (centre) from fruit, such as apples, pears and pineapples. The corer is pushed into the centre of the fruit and pulled out, taking the core with it as it goes.
- A **peeler** is used to take off a small amount of the outside skin from fruit and vegetables, such as carrots, parsnips and apples.

Figure 1.2.2 Other cutting equipment

Chopping boards

Different coloured chopping boards are used for different preparation tasks:
- A green board is used for salad and fruit.
- A brown board is used for vegetables.
- A red board is used for raw meat and chicken.
- A blue board is used for fish.
- A yellow board is used for cooked meat.
- A white board is used for bread and dairy products.

Figure 1.2.3 Colour-coded chopping boards

Fruit and vegetables

It is important that fruit and vegetables are prepared using the correct equipment, which is usually a paring or office knife, a peeler or a corer and a green cutting board.

There are two techniques for holding and cutting fruit and vegetables when chopping and slicing: **bridge hold** and **claw grip**.

Bridge hold

1   Use your thumb and forefinger and grip either side of the ingredient.
2   Use the knife to slice the ingredient in the gap underneath the bridge formed by your finger and thumb.

Figure 1.2.4a Bridge hold grip

Claw grip

1   With the tips of your fingers and thumb tucked under towards the palm of your hand, hold the ingredient to be cut in a claw-like grip.
2   Hold the knife in your other hand and carefully bring the knife across and slice the ingredient.

Figure 1.2.4b Claw grip

Research and practical activity

Watch the clip on how to chop an onion.

Practise chopping an onion finely.

http://www.jamieshomecookingskills.com/skills-specific.php?skill=howto-videos

Vegetable cuts

Vegetables can be cut into different shapes and sizes according to the dish they are being used for: **julienne**, **brunoise**, **macedoine** and **jardinière**.

> ## Key words
>
> **Julienne** means cutting vegetables into matchstick strips.
>
> **Brunoise** means cutting vegetables into tiny dice from julienne strips.
>
> **Macedoine** means cutting vegetables into medium dice.
>
> **Jardinière** means cutting vegetables into batons.

Vegetable cut	Description	
Julienne (matchstick strips)	1 Cut the vegetable into 2 cm lengths. 2 Cut into thin slices. 3 Cut each slice into thin even-sized strips.	Figure 1.2.5
Brunoise (small dice)	Cut each julienne strip into small dice.	Figure 1.2.6
Macedoine (medium dice)	1 Cut the vegetable into even-sized lengths. 2 Cut the length into 0.5 cm slices. 3 Cut each slice into 0.5 cm strips. 4 Cut the strips into 0.5 cm cubes.	Figure 1.2.7
Jardinière (batons)	1 Cut the vegetables into 1.5 cm lengths. 2 Cut into 3 mm slices. 3 Cut the slices into batons.	Figure 1.2.8

Table 1.2.1 Vegetable cuts

Chicken

Chicken can be bought whole or in portions (pieces). It is possible to cut a whole chicken into portions. This process is also called **jointing**. When just the breast is removed from the chicken, it is called **filleting**.

A whole chicken can be cut into six portions. The portions can be used in a wide variety of dishes; the carcass is generally boiled to make chicken stock.

Raw chickens are often a source of food poisoning bacteria, so it is important to follow hygienic procedures when preparing it to prevent cross-contamination. A red chopping board must be used.

Portioning a chicken

① Cut off the wings

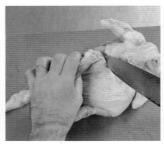

② Cut off the legs cutting around the oyster

③ Remove the feet

④ Separate the thigh from the drumstick

⑤ Trim the drumstick so that it looks neat

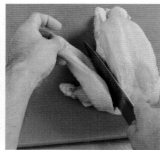

⑥ Remove the breast

Figure 1.2.9 Portioning a chicken

Filleting a chicken using a cook's knife

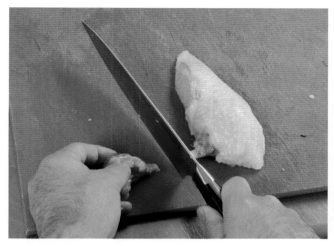

① Trim the breast where the wing was

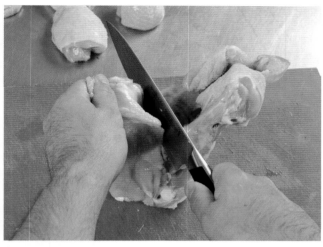

② Cut into the cavity and split the carcass into two. The carcass can be boiled to make stock

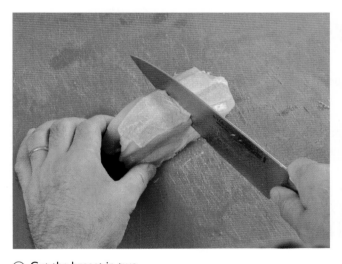

③ Cut the breast in two

Figure 1.2.10 Filleting a chicken

④ The cuts are thighs, wings, breasts, drumsticks and winglets

Meat

Meat is the muscle tissue of animals. In the UK, we mainly eat the meat of these animals:

● pigs – pork, bacon, ham and gammon
● sheep – lamb and mutton
● cows – beef.

Meat does need some preparation before you cook it. Meat is a high-risk food so it is important to follow hygienic procedures when preparing it to prevent cross-contamination. A red chopping board should be used for raw meat.

Meat varies in its fat content; the fat is found on the outside of the meat and throughout. The visible fat is saturated fat so can be trimmed off with a small knife before cooking as a healthier option.

Figure 1.2.11 Fillet and loin of beef

Figure 1.2.12 Lamb loin chops

In the case of bacon and gammon, the outside skin (**rind**) should be removed before cooking; this can be done with a small knife or scissors.

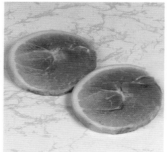

Figure 1.2.13 Gammon and gammon steaks

Fish

Fresh fish is usually sold whole, or cut into steaks or fillets. Fish sometimes carries food poisoning bacteria; so it is important to follow the same hygienic procedures as when using raw meat. A blue chopping board should be used.

Research activity

Watch the clip on how to fillet a round fish.

A **fish fillet** is a cut of fish that is free from bone. You can get two fillets from a round fish such as salmon, and four fillets from a flat fish such as Dover sole.

To fillet a round fish:

1   Using a filleting knife cut the flesh along the line of the backbone and raise the fillet from the middle of the back to the sides, working from head to tail.
2   Then reverse the fish and remove the second fillet from tail to head.

Key word

Fish fillet is a cut of fish that is free from bones.

Figure 1.2.14 Filleting a round fish

Fish can also be cut into:
- steaks, which are thick slices of fish off the bone
- goujons, filleted fish that has been cut into strips.

Figure 1.2.15 Tuna steak

Figure 1.2.16 Goujons

Fish pie

450 g fresh white fish

100 g shellfish, such as prawns, mussels (optional)

Can of sweetcorn (optional)

2 hard-boiled eggs, chopped up (optional)

100 g frozen peas, defrosted (optional)

500 ml milk

50 g butter or low-fat spread

50 g plain flour

Salt and pepper

Topping

300 g potatoes

50 ml milk and 25 g butter to mash potatoes

Method

1 Preheat the oven to 180°C.
2 Peel and cut potatoes for the topping into quarters. Cover with cold water, bring to the boil and simmer until soft for approximately 20 minutes. Mash and leave to cool a little before piping.
3 Skin white fish, cut into chunks and place in a shallow casserole dish.
4 Add any other optional ingredients. Season well.
5 Place the milk, margarine and flour into a saucepan. Over a medium heat, whisk the ingredients together until they come to the boil and thicken.
6 Pour over the fish.
7 Pipe mashed potato on the top. Bake for 35–45 minutes until the sauce is bubbling and the top golden brown.

Extension activities

- Pipe the mashed potato on top of the pie.
- Make your own pastry to place on top of the pie instead of potato.
- Make a roux, béchamel sauce instead of an all-in-one.
- Fillet the fish you are using yourself.
- Serve some steamed vegetables as an accompaniment.

Alternatives

As an alternative to meat and fish, you may also wish to try the following:

Tofu

Tofu is an alternative protein food. It is sold as a curd, usually from the chiller cabinet. It can be cut into cubes and grilled or stir-fried and is often marinated to add extra flavour.

Figure 1.2.17 Tofu

Figure 1.2.18 Crispy deep-fried tofu

Paneer

Paneer is an unsalted, white cheese. It has a dense, crumbly texture that goes well with strong flavours. It is often used in Asian cuisine.

Halloumi

Halloumi originates from the Middle East and is traditionally made from ewes' milk, or sometimes goats' milk. It is a robust cheese with a deep savoury flavour, and keeps very well. It is a cooking cheese, which can be cubed or sliced (it cannot be crumbled) and then grilled, barbecued or fried. When cooked, the outside rapidly becomes crisp and golden brown, while the centre melts. The cheese does not lose its shape when cooked.

Figure 1.2.19 Halloumi

SKILL 3 PREPARING FRUIT AND VEGETABLES

Fruit and vegetables are edible plants, which can be eaten raw or cooked. These days, there is a huge variety of fresh fruit and vegetables available throughout the year; they add a wide variety of colours, flavours and textures to a meal, as well as providing essential nutrients.

Figure 1.3.1 Stuffed peppers

Key terms in the preparation of fruit and vegetables

Figure 1.3.2 A ricer

Key term	Description
Mash	To reduce to a soft mass by using a masher or ricer. For example, using a masher to make mashed potato.
Shred	To slice in long, thin strips. For example, cabbage shredded to make coleslaw.
Scissor snip	To cut food with a pair of scissors instead of a knife, for example using scissors for snipping herbs into small pieces.
Scoop	A hollow-shaped spoon attached to a handle used for picking up a quantity of food, such as ice cream, or an ingredient such as flour.
Crush	To crush into tiny pieces with another implement. For example, soft fruit can be crushed to make a textured sauce or decoration or biscuits for a dessert base.
Grate	To make coarse or fine threads by repeatedly rubbing over one of the sides of a grater. A grater has small sharp-edged holes of different sizes and shapes. For example, grating carrots, onions for a salad, grating the zest of a lemon into finer fragments.
Peel	To remove thinly the skin of fruit and vegetables using a peeler. For example, taking the skin off potatoes.
Segment	To peel and divide into pieces. For example, an orange or a grapefruit.

Table 1.3.1 Key terms in the preparation of fruit and vegetables

AQA GCSE Food Preparation and Nutrition

De-skin	To remove the skin by either putting the fruit or vegetable into boiling water, or placing a pepper on direct heat to remove the skin. Tomatoes are often de-skinned, de-seeded and then chopped.
De-seed	To remove seeds before using. For example, de-seeding a red pepper.
Blanch	Blanching means to cook quickly in boiling water and then cool immediately. This retains colour of e.g. fruits and vegetables. This process stops enzyme action and can be carried out if freezing vegetables such as runner beans.
Shape	Using a knife to create a shape. For example, a tomato waterlily.

Table 1.3.1 continued

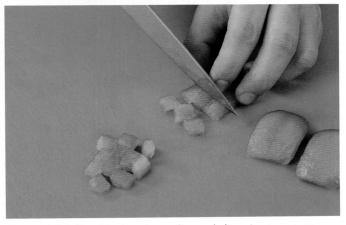

Figure 1.3.3 De-skinning, de-seeding and chopping tomatoes

Research activity

Visit the website and look at all the clips on how to prepare a range of fruit and vegetables.

http://www.jamieshomecookingskills.com/skills-specific.php?skill=howto-videos

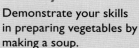
Mixed vegetable soup

400 g mixed vegetables, such as carrot, onion, leek, parsnip, swede, potato

25 g butter (this can be omitted and a small amount of oil, or spray oil can be used)

750 ml boiling water and a vegetable stock cube

Salt and pepper

Method

1 Wash, peel and dice vegetables.
2 Melt butter in a large saucepan and sauté vegetables until they are shiny, approximately 5–7 minutes.
3 Add water, stock cube and seasoning.
4 Bring to the boil and simmer until the vegetables are soft, about 15–20 minutes.

Extension activity

Prepare a blended soup using an unusual vegetable.

Figure 1.3.4 Duchesse potatoes

- **Pipe** – to press a soft food, such as mashed potato, through a piping bag fitted with a shaped nozzle, to form the food into an interesting shape and make the finished dish look attractive. An example is piped potato on the top of a fish pie, or Duchesse potatoes.
- **Blend** – to mix two or more ingredients together. This can be done by hand, by using a hand blender (liquidiser) or a food processor.
- **Juice** – to extract the juice from fruit or vegetables. For example, using a lemon squeezer to juice a lemon.

Figure 1.3.5 A blender

Figure 1.3.6 Garnishes

Preparing garnishes

Adding a food on a finished dish can improve the aesthetic appearance. Decorations on savoury food dishes are called **garnishes**. Decorations on sweet foods are simply called **decorations**.

Some examples of garnishes include:

Garnish name	Description
Fanning	A strawberry can be cut into slices with a knife leaving the top of the strawberry intact which creates a fan effect.
'Waterlily' effect	Using a knife, a V shape is cut out around the middle to create a toothed effect. Tomatoes and melon can be prepared in this way.
Scoring with a fork	Score down with a sharp knife or fork to give ridged effect. Cucumber and lemons can be prepared in this way.
Twists	Slice, then cut from the edge to just past the centre. Cucumber, oranges and lemons can be prepared in this way.
Ribbons	Courgettes or cucumbers can be peeled along their length to produce ribbons which can be arranged in different ways, e.g. making a spiral, folding or wrapping round another food.
Curls	Placing cut vegetable in ice-cold water can be very effective. Radishes can be cut through almost to the base; they will open out in iced water. Spring onions: the green leaves can be cut through into small strips while still attached to the root; they will curl if left in iced water.

Table 1.3.2 Garnishes

Key words

Mash means to reduce to a soft mass by using a masher.

Shred means to slice in long, thin strips.

Scissor means to cut food with a pair of scissors instead of a knife.

Snip means to cut, usually with a pair of scissors, with a small, quick stroke.

Scoop is a hollow-shaped spoon with a handle.

Crush means to crush into tiny pieces with another implement.

Grate means to make coarse or fine threads by repeatedly rubbing over one of the sides of a grater.

Peel means to remove thinly the skin of fruit and vegetables using a peeler.

Segment means to peel and pull apart, for example an orange.

De-skin means to remove the skin by either putting the fruit or vegetable into boiling water or, for peppers, placing on direct heat.

De-seed means to remove seeds before using.

Blanch means to put fruits or vegetables in boiling water for a few seconds, then cool quickly.

Shape means using a knife to create a shape.

Spoilage and preventing food poisoning when preparing fruit and vegetables

When buying fruit and vegetables, it is important to note that, to avoid the food spoiling too quickly, you should only buy fruit and vegetables if they are:

- in packaging that has not been damaged
- within their 'best before' date if you are buying packaged fruit and vegetables
- not bruised, mouldy, soft or wilted
- firm to the touch.

Figure 1.3.7 Fruit and vegetable spoilage

Fruit should be eaten as quickly as possible after buying, because it continues to ripen after it has been picked. In order to keep vegetables fresh and avoid spoilage, they should be kept in a cool, dark environment, or in a refrigerator. Always keep bananas at room temperature.

When preparing fruit and vegetables, wash to remove any soil, dust, insects and pesticide sprays. This can prevent the risk of food poisoning. Remove any blemishes and outer leaves. Peel if necessary. It is essential that, when fruit and vegetables are washed, they should be dried, especially if they are going to be used in cooking, so as to avoid adding excess liquid to the dish. A good way of doing this is to pat the fruit dry with absorbent kitchen roll.

Some fruit and vegetables will go brown once they are peeled and cut, such as apples, potatoes and pears. This is called **enzymic browning**.

You will learn about enzymic browning in Topic 4.1 Food spoilage and contamination.

You can prevent enzymic browning when using fruit and vegetables by:

- sealing all the cut surfaces – by using an acid, pickled onions, dipping fruit in lemon juice or by covering in cling film.
- blanching – putting them in boiling water for a few seconds then cool them quickly, for example blanching runner beans before freezing them.
- cooking the vegetables or fruit as soon as they have been prepared – for example, in a tarte tatin.
- sugary syrup – for example, fruit can be covered in a sugary syrup.

Apple tarte tatin

50 g butter

50 g caster sugar

2.5 g ($\frac{1}{2}$ tsp) ground cinnamon

6 eating apples

1 x pack ready-rolled puff pastry

Method

1 Preheat the oven to 200°C.
2 Peel, quarter and core the apples. Melt the butter in a tarte tatin tin, then stir in the sugar, heat until caramelising and add the cinnamon and apples. Cook over a medium heat for about 10 minutes, stirring occasionally.
3 Unroll the pastry and use a fork to prick it all over. Place the pastry over the apples, tucking the edges into the tin.
4 Bake for 20–30 minutes until golden.
5 When the tart is cooked, leave to settle in the tin for 5 minutes or so before running the blade of a knife round the edge to dislodge any pastry that has stuck. Invert a plate over the top and turn out the tart, with any juices left in the tin.
6 Extension opportunity: The student could make their own puff pastry instead of using bought.

Figure 1.3.7 Making apple tarte tatin

SKILL 4 USE OF THE COOKER

Using the grill

Grilling is a dry method of cooking food by applying heat to the surface of the food.

The scientific principles behind grilling are covered in Topic 3.1 Cooking of food and heat transfer. See page 196. This section will cover how to grill and the most appropriate foods to select for grilling.

Grilling is a really useful method of cooking because it is quick. It is also healthy because it does not need fat, and if the food being grilled contains fat some of it drains away as it is cooked.

Grilled food has a distinctive appearance and flavour. The food being grilled is visible during cooking, which makes it easier to check whether it is cooked or not.

Methods of grilling

There are three different ways in which you can grill food:
- grilling under heat
- using a char grill
- barbecuing.

Figure 1.4.1 An electric cooker

AQA GCSE Food Preparation and Nutrition

Grilling under heat

This is achieved by using the grill section of a conventional cooker. Grills have a variable control so you can select the heat you require according to your recipe. They also have multi-position shelves, and the shelves are also often reversible with a higher and lower position to get the right distance between the grill and the food.

Most cookers come with a grill pan and a handle, which is often detachable. This means the pan can be pulled out from under the grill, the food checked and turned, and the pan slid back under.

Some manufacturers recommend grilling with the door open, others with the door closed – it's important to follow their instructions for safety reasons.

Grilling over heat

This is achieved by using a char grill, where grill bars are heated from underneath; the heat comes from either gas, electric or charcoal.

It can also be achieved by cooking with a griddle pan, which has raised ribs to mark the food. The griddle lines are called quadrilage; they give the food an attractive griddled effect.

Figure 1.4.2 Using a char grill to cook burgers

Figure 1.4.3 Using a griddle pan

Barbecuing

Barbecuing is a very popular method of cooking, which many people use for cooking outdoors in good weather. To **barbecue** is to cook food over a grill over burning charcoal.

Figure 1.4.4 Barbecuing

Tips for grilling

- Always preheat the grill before use to ensure it is at the correct temperature.
- Place the food directly under the grill.
- Smaller, thinner items will cook very quickly.
- Thicker food, which takes longer, is better cooked on the lower shelf of the grill to avoid the outside being overcooked and the inside being undercooked. It is best not to grill food that is over 3.5 cm thick.
- Food should be turned often to ensure even cooking.
- It is a good idea to use tongs to turn food over, or slices for delicate food such as fish.
- Foods may need brushing with a marinade, oil or butter to stop them from drying out during cooking.

The range of foods suitable for grilling

- **Meat** – best-quality tender meat such as steak, lamb and pork chops, chicken breast, burgers and sausages.
- **Vegetables** – tomatoes, mushrooms, thick slices of onion.
- **Fish** – fish fingers, cod steaks, tuna steaks.
- **Halloumi** – this cheese works very well when griddled, as it holds its shape.
- **Seeds and nuts** – many seeds and nuts can be toasted under the grill, such as hazelnuts, almonds, coconuts and sesame seeds. They cook extremely quickly, and will need watching carefully. They will also need moving around to ensure even cooking.
- **Breads** – croissants, brioche and bread slices can be toasted on each side using a grill to crisp and brown the outside. Naan bread can be cooked by grilling the prepared and shaped dough.

Figure 1.4.5 Griddled halloumi

Dishes can be finished off under the grill after they have been cooked through. The surface can be sprinkled with breadcrumbs or cheese and breadcrumbs – this is called **au gratin**.

Naan bread

450 g strong bread flour, plus extra to roll out

2 level teaspoons fast-action yeast

10 g (2 tsp) salt

350 ml warm water

18 m (1 tbsp) olive oil

Method

1. Mix the flour in a bowl with the yeast and salt. Add the water and oil and mix to a dough. Leave to sit for 5 minutes as it is.
2. Flour the work surface and hands, then knead the dough for 1–2 minutes until smooth and springy.
3. Leave to stand for 10 minutes in a warm place.
4. Cut the dough into eight even pieces and roll each one out into a thin circle.
5. Heat the grill to high. Dust a baking sheet with flour, then grill the breads for $1\frac{1}{2}$–2 minutes on each side until puffed and golden. You'll need to do this in batches.

Using the oven

It is important to know how to use the oven to avoid dishes being spoiled that have been prepared correctly.

Use the checklist below when preparing dishes using the oven.

- ☑ Read the recipe correctly.
- ☑ Select the correct oven temperature.
- ☑ Make sure the oven has reached the correct temperature before placing dishes in the oven (electric ovens have a light on the control panel which comes on when the oven is put on, and goes out when the oven reaches the correct temperature). However, some foods may be put into a cold oven and benefit from the heat of the oven as it warms, e.g. bread rolls which need to prove before baking.
- ☑ If you are using a fan-assisted oven it doesn't matter where the items are placed in the oven, as fans circulate the air, distributing the heat evenly. Check the recipe carefully because the temperature may need to be set lower, and the cooking time may be reduced.
- ☑ —Try not to open the oven door more than necessary while cooking (If you open the oven, heat is lost and the oven will need time to recover).
- ☑ Give food in the oven plenty of space. If food is too close together, some parts may not cook evenly.
- ☑ Select the correct height of shelf (if the oven being used is not fan assisted, the top of your oven is hotter than the bottom as heat rises).
- ☑ Check the position of the shelf above if the dish you are making is going to rise considerably.

The scientific principles behind baking, roasting, casseroles/tagines and braising are covered in Topic 3.1 Cooking of food and heat transfer. See page 196. This section will cover how to use the oven, and the most appropriate foods to select for baking, roasting, casseroles/tagines and braising.

Baking

Baking is cooking food in a hot oven without extra fat being added during the cooking process. When baking, it is important that the oven is preheated as baked food needs to be placed in a hot oven.

If a baking tin is being used, it is important to check it fits in the oven. It should not touch the sides of the oven as it may prevent the hot air from circulating round.

A range of foods can be baked: cakes, biscuits, scones, pastry, vegetables, fruit and pre-prepared products.

Figure 1.4.6 Scones

Roasting

Roasting is cooking and browning with the aid of fat. Roasted foods have a good flavour and an attractive crisp appearance. Meat is roasted by sealing it first to keep the juices in, then cooking it, basting it with hot fat regularly throughout the cooking process.

A range of food can be roasted: beef, lamb, pork and chicken, vegetables such as potatoes, or mixed vegetables such as peppers, onions and tomatoes.

Figure 1.4.7 Roast potatoes

Roasted vegetables

1 red onion

1 red pepper

1 yellow pepper

1 courgette

Sea salt

1–2 tbsp olive oil, or some spray oil

Method

1 Preheat the oven to 180°C.
2 Deseed the peppers and cut them into chunks.
3 Peel onion and cut into chunks
4 Slice courgette thickly.
5 Spread evenly on a non-stick tray.
6 Drizzle with oil and season.
7 Place in the preheated oven and roast until vegetables are tender, about 30–40 minutes.

Casseroles and tagines

Casseroling is a slow, gentle, moist method of cooking where the food is completely covered in liquid and cooked in the oven. The end result is called a **casserole**. The oven does not need to be preheated for casseroles and tagines because they are going to be in the oven for a long time, usually on a low heat.

A range of foods can be casseroled: meat, chicken and vegetables.

> **Key words**
>
> **Barbecue** means to cook food on a grill over burning charcoal.
>
> **Au gratin** refers to a dish sprinkled with breadcrumbs or cheese and breadcrumbs, and browned under the grill.
>
> **Casserole** refers to food that is completely covered in liquid, then cooked in the oven.

Spicy lentil and vegetable casserole

2 carrots

1 parsnip (optional)

2 medium-sized sweet potatoes

1 medium-sized potato

18 ml (1 tbsp) oil

1 onion, chopped

1 garlic clove, crushed

18 ml (1 tbsp) korma curry paste

550 ml stock (2 stock cubes and 550 ml boiling water)

50 g red lentils

Salt and pepper

Figure I.4.8

Method

1 Peel and thickly slice the carrots and parsnip.
2 Peel and chop the potato and sweet potatoes into chunks.
3 Heat the oil in a large pan and cook the onion and garlic over a medium heat for 3–4 minutes until softened, stirring occasionally. Add the potatoes, carrots and parsnip, and cook for 6–7 minutes, stirring, until all the vegetables are golden.
4 Add the lentils and stir in the curry paste. Pour over the stock and then bring to the boil.
5 The casserole can then be cooked in the oven on a low heat until the vegetables are tender and the lentils have absorbed the liquid.
6 Alternatively, to speed up cooking if this is being done in lesson time of an hour, you can cook it on the hob. Once the casserole has come to the boil, reduce the heat and simmer until the lentils and vegetables are tender and the sauce has thickened.

Tagine is the Moroccan word for a glazed earthenware pot with a distinctive lid. It is also used to describe the food cooked in it.

Cooking in a tagine is done in the same way as cooking a casserole. The shape of the lid also creates circulation within the dish, infusing the food with spices and flavours.

Most Moroccan tagine recipes require initial browning of the meat and vegetables before the liquid is added and simmered.

Chicken tagine

350 g skinless chicken breasts sliced thinly.

18 ml (1 tbsp) olive oil

1 onion, thinly sliced

1 garlic clove, crushed or finely chopped

75 g dried apricots, chopped

400 g tin chopped tomatoes

1 yellow, red or green pepper, de-seeded and chopped

400 ml stock made with boiling water and 1 vegetable stock cube.

400 g tin chickpeas, drained

Seasoning

2.5 g ($\frac{1}{2}$ tsp) ground cumin

14 ml (1 tbsp) of harissa

Optional ingredient

Fresh coriander chopped to garnish.

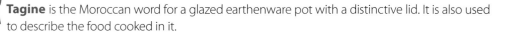

Figure 1.4.9

Method

1 Heat the oil in a non-stick pan and cook the onion and chicken for 5 to 7 minutes or until the chicken is white and the onion has softened.
2 Add the garlic, cumin and harissa and cook for a one minute.
3 Add the apricots, chick peas, tomatoes, peppers, water, stock cube, seasoning. Stir well and bring to the boil. Simmer until the vegetables are tender, and the chicken is cooked through – approximately 15 to 20 minutes.

Extension activity

Make an accompaniment to go with the tagine, for example couscous.
200 g couscous
Pinch of salt
250 ml boiling water

Method

Place couscous into a bowl, add 200 ml of boiling water, stir and then set aside for the grains to slowly absorb the liquid.
Fluff the couscous with a fork once all of the liquid has been absorbed.

Braising

Braising is a moist method of cooking used for cooking larger pieces of food, where the food is only half covered with a liquid. The food is cooked slowly in a pan, usually with a tight-fitting lid, on a very low temperature. The food can be braised either on the hob or in the oven.

A range of foods can be braised: meat, vegetables and rice. Rice works very well when braised and is called pilaf.

Figure 1.4.10 Braised lamb shanks

Braised rice

25 g butter

1 small brown onion, finely chopped

100 g long grain rice

200 ml vegetable stock

Salt and pepper

Method

1   Preheat the oven to 200°C.
2   Fry the onion in the butter for 2–3 minutes until soft.
3   Add the rice and continue cooking for 2–3 minutes.
4   Add the stock, season and bring to the boil.
5   Transfer to an ovenproof dish and braise for approximately 15 minutes.
6   Test to see if it is cooked – the rice should be soft in the centre, and all the liquid should have been absorbed.

Using a blender

Types of blender	
Blender	A piece of equipment which has sharp blades that rotate at the bottom of a goblet to cut up food and reduce it to a pulp. Some blenders are free-standing and some fit onto a food mixer or processor.
Liquidiser	Pulverises ingredients almost to a liquid.
Smoothie maker	Pulverises fruits and vegetables to produce healthy drinks.
Hand blender	Food is blended in a separate jug.
Soup maker	Make soups from start to finish, including blending.

Table 1.5.1 Types of blender

- **Blenders** save time when crushing fruit, vegetables and soups.
- Families with babies or very young children may find this appliance useful to blend nourishing homemade meals into purées, and freeze them in batches. It makes them less reliant on commercial baby foods.
- Families may also find it useful to make fruit smoothies, because they can appeal to children who may eat them more readily than fresh fruit.

Figure 1.5.1 Blender

Figure 1.5.2 Hand blender

Dishes that can be prepared using a blender

Blenders are useful for puréeing baby food, soups, fruit, fruit coulis, fruit shakes, slushes, protein drinks and smoothies.

Figure 1.5.3 A blended soup

Tropical fruit smoothie

$\frac{1}{2}$ small melon

1 pear

1 peach

1 banana

1 small pot of pineapple yoghurt

Method

1 Peel, deseed and chop melon into chunks.
2 Core the pear and cut into chunks.
3 Remove the stone from the peach and cut into chunks.
4 Peel the banana and cut into slices.

Using a food processor

Figure 1.5.4 A food processor

A **food processor** is a powerful piece of equipment with various attachments that can prepare a variety of foods. It is particularly useful for cutting and shredding large quantities of vegetables. It is very quick, and can save time in food preparation.

The main uses of a food processor are to chop, liquidise, purée, grate and slice. Exactly how things are cut and sliced depends on the blades that are fitted to the machine. It also has a blade that can be used for flour mixtures.

Dishes that can be prepared using a food processor

Food processors can:

- shred cabbage to make coleslaw
- grate carrots and cheese
- chop vegetables finely, such as onions
- rub fat into flour
- make pastry
- make purée mixtures
- make breadcrumbs.

① Cut the cabbage into four pieces and remove the stalk. Cut the cabbage and carrot into julienne strips.

② Mix the cabbage and carrot in a bowl

③ Stir in the mayonnaise and seasoning

Figure 1.5.5 Coleslaw

Lemon cheesecake

150 g digestive biscuits

75 g butter

1 lemon

250 ml double cream

225 g mascarpone cheese

50 g icing sugar

Fruit, to decorate

Method

1 Put the biscuits into a food processor and process until they are fine crumbs.
2 Melt the butter in a pan and stir in the biscuit crumbs. Use this to line the base of a flan case or shallow dish.
3 Finely grate the zest of the lemon and squeeze out the juice.
4 Whisk the cream, mascarpone cheese and sieved icing sugar together until thick.
5 Fold in the lemon zest and lemon juice.
6 Spread three-quarters of the mixture over the crumbs.
7 Use the remaining mixture and pipe on top.
8 Decorate with fruit and chill in the refrigerator until ready to serve.

Extension activities

Demonstrate the use of a food processor to:
● slice fruits for a topping
● prepare a fruit purée topping
● prepare a cheesecake that includes gelatine.

Practical activity

Make a dessert which uses a mixer or a processor.

Teacher's note – This is a simple cheesecake recipe which can be used.

Carrot and raisin salad

6 large carrots

1 tbsp parsley

2 tbsp olive oil

1 tbsp orange juice

75 g raisins

25 g sesame seeds

Method

1 Grate the carrots in the food processor and put in a large serving bowl.
2 Chop the parsley in the food processor.
3 Whisk together the oil and orange juice to make the dressing.
4 Stir the raisins, parsley and dressing into the carrots.
5 Garnish with sesame seeds.

Figure 1.5.6 Hand-held mixer

Using a mixer

There are a huge variety of **mixers** available in the shops – they are either hand-held mixers or table-top machines.

Type of mixer	Description
Hand-held mixers	Designed to mix, whisk, knead or beat small quantities of food.
Table-top mixers	More powerful and are designed to deal with larger quantities of food.

Table 1.5.2 Mixers

Dishes that can be prepared using a mixer

Mixers are used successfully to whisk cream, or to whisk egg white to make meringue. They can be used to beat mixtures such as cakes. Some mixers have a dough hook for kneading bread dough.

With the addition of other attachments, which can be added to the machine, more specialised functions can be achieved, such as potato peeling, meat mincing or fruit squeezing.

Many food processors today are multi-task machines that incorporate both processing and mixing into one machine; these take up less space in the kitchen.

Figure 1.5.7 Table-top mixer

Figure 1.5.8 Piping meringues

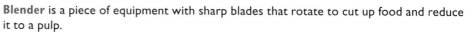

Key words

Blender is a piece of equipment with sharp blades that rotate to cut up food and reduce it to a pulp.

Food processor is a piece of equipment with various attachments that can prepare a variety of foods, such as slice and grate vegetables.

Mixer is a machine that primarily whisks and beats.

AQA GCSE Food Preparation and Nutrition

Mini pavlovas

3 egg whites
150 g caster sugar
5 g (1 tsp) cornflour
6 ml (1 tsp) lemon juice
200 g raspberries and/or strawberries, to decorate
250 ml double or whipping cream, to decorate

Method

1 Preheat the oven to 140°C.
2 Whisk the egg whites until they are stiff and dry.
3 Whisk in half of the sugar mixture until stiff and shiny.
4 Fold in the remaining sugar, cornflour and lemon juice.
5 Spoon or pipe onto a baking sheet lined with parchment.
6 Bake in the oven until firm and crispy on the outside and slightly gooey in the middle – about 30–40 minutes.
7 Cool the meringues.
8 Decorate with fruit and whipped cream.

Safe use of food mixers and food processors

- It is important to make sure that the plug and plug socket are kept away from water. Electrical equipment must not be used with wet hands.
- Follow manufacturer instructions and make sure any locks are in place.
- Only use electrical equipment on stable surfaces, i.e. not on the edge of a table.
- Take care if the equipment has cutting and grating blades – these are extremely sharp.
- Don't overfill the bowl or container – the contents may spill out, and if it is hot soup or other hot liquid being puréed then it can scald. Overfilling may also mean it takes longer to blend and may overwork the motor.
- Make sure the machine is switched off when not in use.

Using a pasta machine

Pasta machines make easy work of rolling and cutting pasta dough. There are both electric pasta makers and compact hand-turned ones. Both types of machine come with different rollers and attachments for cutting and shaping pasta.

The machine works by feeding the pasta dough through the rollers on the widest setting first; this is done several times to ensure the dough is both smooth and of an even thickness. The dough is passed through the rollers again, narrowing the roller setting each time.

Once you have a long thin strip of dough it needs to be dried over a pasta dryer or a wooden pole before cutting or shaping it. If cutting the pasta by machine, the correct cutters need to be fitted. The shapes can also be cut out by hand.

Figure 1.5.9 Using a pasta machine

Figure 1.5.10 Ravioli

Dishes that can be prepared using a pasta machine

A huge variety of shapes can be made out of pasta dough using a pasta machine. The pasta can then be used in a range of dishes, such as spaghetti carbonara, spaghetti Bolognese, lasagne, ravioli and cannelloni.

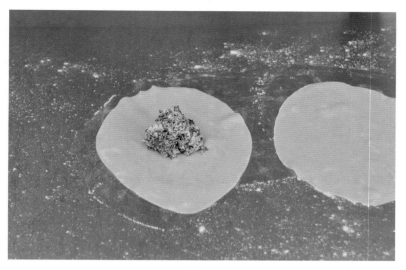

Figure 1.5.11 Making giant ravioli

Pasta dough

225 g double 00 flour

7.5 g ($\frac{1}{2}$ tsp) salt or dried herbs

18 ml (1 tbsp) oil

2 eggs

18-35 ml (1–2 tbsp) water

Method

1 Place the flour and salt on the worktop and mix in the rest of the ingredients using your hands.
2 Knead the dough until it is smooth (about 5 minutes).
3 If time, leave to rest for 30 minutes.
4 Use a pasta machine to roll your dough, then cut it into the desired shape.
5 Cook the pasta designs in a pan half-full of boiling water for 3–5 minutes or until it is al dente. Drain and serve with a little passata and grated cheese.

Using a microwave oven

Microwave ovens are useful pieces of equipment, which are used for:
- heating food
- cooking food
- defrosting food
- cooking frozen or fresh ready meals.

They are available in different categories from A to E based on the power output, which is measured in watts – the higher the wattage the more powerful the microwave is and the quicker it can cook food.

Advantages of using a microwave oven

Microwaves:
- save time and energy because they cook food much more quickly than conventional methods, for example a baked jacket potato. A short standing time is part of the cooking process.
- can save on washing up if foods are cooked and served in the same dish.
- are also easy to clean and usually just need a wipe over.
- retain the flavour and colour of foods, particularly vegetables. This is generally better than with other methods of cooking due to the quick cooking times.
- cook vegetables with a small amount of liquid successfully.
- can be used to reheat a meal easily and quickly without losing its quality, which can be useful if a member of a household has missed a meal earlier.
- cook fish quickly and retain its moisture.
- cook sponge puddings well with no colour change.
- reheat ready meals successfully and quickly.
- defrost foods such as chicken portions quickly.

Figure 1.5.12 A microwave

Disadvantages of using a microwave oven

- Food can easily be overcooked and foods like fish can break up. Timing of cooking is therefore critical.
- A microwave oven does not brown or crisp foods so some foods are unsuitable for microwaving; for example, pastry dishes and biscuits do not work well cooked by this method.
- Foods with a high fat or sugar content are best not cooked in a microwave because the temperatures involved can cause combustion.
- Tomatoes and poached eggs, if cooked in a microwave, must have the skins pierced or they will burst.
- Cold spots may occur if food is not stirred regularly.
- Metal cannot be used in the microwave, nor can some plastics.

Figure 1.5.13 A ready meal

It is possible to cook a main dish in the microwave.

Ratatouille – in the microwave

Cooking time about 15 minutes, microwave settings maximum.

Figure 1.5.14

Ingredients

- 100 g mushrooms sliced
- 1 medium aubergine sliced
- 1 tin of chopped tomatoes
- 1 red or green pepper finely sliced
- 1 medium onion, peeled and sliced
- 18 ml (1 tsp) tomato puree
- 2 garlic cloves peeled and crushed
- 18 ml (1 tsp) olive oil
- 6 ml (1 tsp) dried mixed herbs
- Freshly ground black pepper

Method

1 Place all ingredients in a large bowl. Cover with cling film, pierce cling film, and cook on full power for 5 minutes.
2 Stir, then cook for 5 minutes. Stir again and cook for a further 5 minutes.
3 Taste and adjust the seasoning. Cook for a further 5 minutes if necessary.

SKILL 6 COOKING METHODS

Water-based methods using the hob

When cooking on the hob, it is important that you make sure you are familiar with your hob, and get used to how much heat each setting gives. Temperature regulation is crucial when using a water-based method of cooking on the hob.

Care needs to be taken with hot, boiling water and steam to avoid accidents and scalds – lower food carefully into the water to avoid splashes and spills.

You will learn more about the different cooking methods in Topic 3.1 Cooking of food and heat transfer. See page 196.

Boiling

Boiling is a method of cooking where foods are cooked in boiling water or other liquid, which makes them tender. Water boils at 100°C, and when it is boiling you can see bubbles and the water moves. There are other liquids as well as water that food can be boiled in. The most commonly used liquids in which to boil food are:

- water
- milk
- stock
- infusions.

Figure 1.6.1 A halogen hob

There are two methods of boiling:
1 Water should be placed in a saucepan on the highest heat, until it boils. Add the food when the water is boiling. Cover the pan with a tightly-fitting lid to keep the heat in and time the food. The heat can then be reduced slightly.
2 Cover the food with cold water, heat it up to boiling point, then reduce the heat slightly once boiling.

Care needs to be taken because the food may disintegrate if boiled for too long. As some of the water-soluble nutrients are lost in the cooking liquid, it is a good idea to use the liquid too – it can be used to make stock or a sauce.

Figure 1.6.2 Spaghetti boiling

It is a healthy method of cooking because no fat is used.

All food being boiled should be of the same size to ensure it all cooks at the same rate.

The amount of water used varies – a general rule is that it should cover the food completely, but use the minimum possible for vegetables. The opposite is true for pasta where there should be more water so the pasta can move around.

Older, tougher and therefore cheaper cuts of meat can be gently boiled to make them more tasty and tender.

Foods suitable for boiling include whole eggs, gammon, jam, rice, pasta and stock.

AQA GCSE Food Preparation and Nutrition

Steaming

Steaming is a method of cooking where food is cooked from the steam coming off boiling water. The water is brought to the boil in the steamer or saucepan and the food is then placed in a steaming compartment above the water, or wrapped tightly and placed in the water. Other liquids may be used to add flavour and moisture, such as stock and **infused liquids** (liquids with seasoning, spice, herbs or wine added).

It is very difficult to overcook steamed food; it remains soft and will not become crispy. Because no water comes into direct contact with the food there is very little nutrient loss. No fat is used either, so it is a healthy method of cooking especially for vegetables. Sponge puddings can be steamed and due to the steam they are much lighter in texture than baked sponges.

When opening a steamer take care to let some steam escape before you look at or lift out the food.

There are different ways in which you can steam food:

- **The plate method** – putting the food between two plates on top of a pan of boiling water.
- **The saucepan method** – placing food in a container/bowl into a saucepan of boiling water. The water must come halfway up the dish.
- **Tiered steamer** – using a tiered steamer pan on top of a saucepan containing boiling water.
- **Using an electric steamer** – works like a tiered steamer but electricity is used to heat the water in the bottom layer rather than a saucepan on the hob.

Whichever method is used, it is important not to let the water boil dry. Check it and top it up when necessary.

Foods suitable for steaming include vegetables, fish, suet puddings and sponge puddings.

Steamed jam pudding

This is a recipe for a traditional steamed suet pudding. It will take 2 hours to steam, and the saucepan method is used.

50 g shredded suet

100 g self-raising flour

Pinch of salt

1 egg

A little milk to mix

50 g jam

Method

1. Mix the suet into the flour and add a pinch of salt.
2. Beat the egg, add it to the flour and suet mixture, and add enough milk to make a soft dropping consistency.
3. Grease a small heatproof bowl and put the jam in the bottom.
4. Place the mixture into the greased bowl. Cover with foil, folded in the middle to allow the mixture to expand while being steamed. Tie the foil securely in place.
5. Place carefully in a saucepan with some water boiling in the bottom.
6. Steam until cooked – about $1\frac{1}{2}$ –2 hours.

Figure 1.6.3 Different methods of steaming

Steamed salmon

2 skinned salmon fillets
1 red onion, sliced
$\frac{1}{2}$ lemon
Salt and pepper

Method

1 On top of each salmon fillet, place some sliced onion and a ¼ lemon. Season with salt and pepper.
2 Wrap each salmon fillet up into a foil parcel. The foil should leave space around the salmon and have a hole in the top for the steam to escape.
3 Place in a tiered steamer or an electric steamer, and steam for 20–25 minutes, or until the salmon is cooked through.
4 Optional: If your steamer is tiered you could steam some potatoes and vegetables as an accompaniment.

Poaching

Poaching is a method of cooking where food is cooked in a liquid that is just below boiling point. The poaching liquid is heated until not quite boiling, so the occasional bubble is visible. The food is then slowly lowered into the liquid and cooked very gently. It is necessary to control the heat carefully, so that the liquid is not too cool but it doesn't boil.

Poaching makes food very tender, and the flavour is enhanced in the cooking process because it is gentle. It is a healthy method of cooking because few nutrients are lost and no fat is used.

The liquids that can be used for poaching are the same liquids that can be used for boiling, but fruit can also be poached in wine, for example pears in red wine, and a syrup.

A saucepan or poaching pan are used along with a slotted spoon to lift the poached food carefully out of the liquid.

Figure 1.6.4 Poached eggs

Foods suitable for poaching are chicken, fish such as salmon, eggs and fruit such as pears.

① Half fill a small pan with water and bring to simmering point, add one tablespoon of vinegar

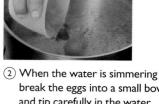

② When the water is simmering break the eggs into a small bowl and tip carefully in the water

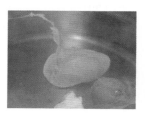

③ The egg will then form a ball shape

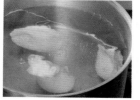

④ Cook the egg for 3 to 4 minutes until lightly set

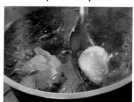

⑤ Remove from the water with a slotted spoon

Figure 1.6.5 How to make poached eggs

Simmering

Simmering is where foods are cooked in water or another liquid that is just below boiling point. The liquid can be heated quickly until it boils, then turned down to a gentler heat to allow the food to cook. The same liquids used for boiling foods can be used for simmering.

Foods suitable for simmering include vegetables and fruit. Curries are often simmered to develop the flavour fully.

Practical activity

Make a dish which illustrates simmering.

Teacher's notes – This is a curry recipe where the students make the paste themselves. For students with additional needs the paste from a jar can be used.

Students could also use mycoprotein or just vegetables to make the dish suitable for a vegetarian.

Green Thai chicken curry

2–3 green chillies

1 onion, roughly chopped

12 cm piece of ginger

18 ml (1 tbsp) mango chutney

1 handful of fresh coriander

Juice of 1 lime

4 skinless chicken fillets

1 tin coconut milk

Few drops fish sauce

Salt and pepper

Figure I.6.6

2 × 100 g packets of any of the following: baby sweetcorn, mange tout, sugar snap peas, asparagus tips or green beans

Method

1 Blend chillies, onion, ginger, mango chutney, coriander and lime juice in a blender until they form a smooth paste.
2 Cut the chicken into chunks.
3 Massage the paste into the chicken and let it soak in.
4 Meanwhile fry the chicken fillets in the pan for 5–7 minutes.
5 Add the tin of coconut milk, fish sauce, salt and pepper.
6 Add the chosen vegetables, bring to the boil and simmer for approximately 20 minutes.

Blanching

Blanching is a method of cooking where food is cooked very quickly in boiling water for a short period of time and then quickly cooked to stop the cooking process. It is also used to remove the skin from fruit and vegetables, for example peaches or tomatoes. Chips can be blanched and then fried later making them fluffy inside and crisp outside.

Chefs often blanch vegetables and then plunge them into cold water to stop the cooking process. These vegetables can then be reheated very quickly when needed without losing their colour or shape. Vegetables and fruits are also blanched before freezing to help maintain their colour and to destroy enzymes which would otherwise spoil them.

Figure 1.6.7 Blanched vegetables

How to blanch vegetables

1 Wash, peel, trim and cut the vegetables into the same size and shape.
2 Bring enough water to cover the vegetables to the boil.
3 Add the vegetables to the water.
4 Cook the vegetables until they are the required texture – 1 or 2 minutes is usually enough.
5 Drain the vegetables.
6 Place the vegetables in cold water to stop the cooking process.

The vegetables can then be used in a variety of ways, such as:
- shallow-fried, for example sauté potatoes
- in a sauce, for example a vegetable bake, vegetables in a white sauce
- griddled, for example asparagus.

Key words

Boiling is a method of cooking where foods are cooked in boiling water.

Steaming is a method of cooking where food is cooked in the steam coming from boiling water.

Infused liquids are liquids with seasoning, spice, herbs or wine added.

Poaching is a method of cooking where food is cooked in a liquid that is just below boiling point.

Simmering refers to water that is heated to just below boiling point.

Blanching is a method of cooking where food is cooked very quickly in boiling water for a short period of time.

Dry heat and fat-based methods using the hob

When you fry foods the temperature is much higher than the temperature when cooking in water, so timing is crucial. When frying, always dry food thoroughly first to avoid it spitting. Make sure the heat is not too low, otherwise the fat will be absorbed into the food, making it greasy and more difficult to crisp. For this reason, do not fry too much food at the same time.

There are safety rules that need to be followed when frying:
- Don't leave a frying pan unattended when cooking.
- Do not overheat the fat.
- Keep the handle turned inwards to prevent it being knocked and spilled.
- If the fat starts to smoke, turn off the heat immediately as this means it is near to its flash point and could ignite.

Figure 1.6.8 Spray used when dry-frying

Dry-frying

Dry-frying is heating food on a low heat without any fat or oil. Foods suitable for dry-frying are foods that naturally contain fat: the fat melts and cooks the food. For example, minced beef can be dry-fried when making a Bolognese sauce. Other foods suitable for dry-frying include bacon and sausages.

It is a healthier way of frying because the fat within the food is used rather than adding extra fat. It is also advisable to dry-fry in a non-stick frying pan to avoid the food sticking to the pan. It is possible to buy a spray, which sprays a very thin coating of oil onto a frying pan.

Shallow frying

Shallow frying is a quick method of cooking where a small amount of fat is used to cook food in a frying pan. The fat should only come about halfway up the food. The food is in direct contact with the fat so it cooks very quickly. This method of cooking adds flavour and moisture to the food and stops it from sticking to the frying pan.
- Oil can be used for shallow frying, as it can be heated successfully to a high temperature.
- Butter can be used for shallow frying, but care needs to be taken because it burns easily.
- If a mixture of butter and oil is used, you get the flavour of butter but the oil will prevent the butter from burning.

It is important that the fat is heated before the food needing to be fried is added. Shallow-fried food has a distinctive flavour, is crispy and browned on the outside. All foods need to be turned so it is cooked and browned on both sides.

Figure 1.6.9 Fried eggs

Foods suitable for shallow frying include eggs, burgers, fish cakes and pancakes.

Stir-frying

Stir-frying is a really quick method of cooking. Small pieces of food are fast-fried in a small amount of oil in a wok. A **wok** is a rounded frying pan. The wok and the oil must be hot before adding the food. All the food should be chopped and sliced finely to ensure that it is cooked evenly and quickly. The food should be moved around when cooking to ensure the heat is equally distributed, so the food cooks evenly. It is a good idea to stir-fry the meat first to ensure it is cooked thoroughly before you add the vegetables.

Foods suitable for stir-frying are steak, pork tenderloin, chicken breast, vegetables and noodles.

Figure 1.6.10 Stir-frying

Chicken chow mein

1 pack of noodles

2 skinless chicken breasts or Quorn™ fillets

1 garlic clove

Small chunk of ginger

1 onion

50 g mushrooms

1 red or green pepper

1 carrot

18–36 ml (1–2 tbsp) oil

100 g beansprouts

Sauce

50 ml soy sauce

100 ml oyster sauce

100 ml tomato purée

Method

1 Half-fill a saucepan with water and bring to the boil. Add noodles and boil for 3–5 minutes until soft. Drain and place on your serving dish.
2 Slice chicken or Quorn into thin strips.
3 Finely chop garlic and ginger.
4 Cut the vegetables into julienne strips.
5 Heat the oil in a wok. Stir-fry the chicken until it is cooked through. (If using Quorn this can be stir-fried with the vegetables.)
6 Add the vegetables and cook for 5–7 minutes until shiny and al dente.
7 Mix all the sauce ingredients together and add, along with the beansprouts, and simmer for a further 2 minutes.
8 Arrange carefully on top of the noodles.

Key words

Dry-frying refers to heating food on a low heat without any fat or oil.
Shallow frying is a quick method of cooking where a small amount of fat is used to cook food in a frying pan.
Stir-frying is a quick method of cooking where small pieces of food are fast-fried in a small amount of oil in a wok.
Wok is a rounded frying pan.

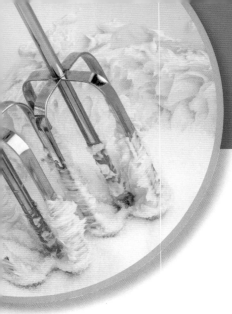

SKILL 7 PREPARING, COMBINING AND SHAPING

Roll

To **roll** is to spread out or flatten.

There are various ingredients that can be rolled to create dishes.

Rolling pastry

- Shortcrust pastry is rolled before using. When rolling the pastry, use a rolling pin and roll with firm, even strokes.
- Pastry should be rolled in one direction so as not to distort the pastry shape, and the pastry should be moved a few degrees regularly as you roll.
- Pastry is rolled on a lightly floured surface to stop it from sticking.

Other ingredients such as bread dough, biscuit dough can be rolled, filled and then rolled into a sausage and cut into slices to makepinwheel shapes.

A Swiss roll is a whisked cake which can be spread with jam and rolled. It is essential to work quickly when making a Swiss roll because the cake will roll when it is still warm but it may crack if the cake cools. Roulades are another example of a rolled dish.

Figure 1.7.1 Rolled pastry

Figure 1.7.2 Bread pinwheels

Savoury palmiers

375 g pack ready-rolled puff pastry

35 ml (2 tbsp) sun-dried tomato purée, or red or green pesto

100 g grated Cheddar (or similar hard) cheese

1 egg, beaten

1 tsp dried oregano or mixed herbs

Method

1. Preheat oven to 200°C.
2. Line a baking sheet with parchment.
3. Unroll the pastry and spread a layer of tomato purée/pesto over it, leaving a 1 cm border around the edges.
4. Scatter the grated cheese over the top.
5. With the shortest end towards you, take both long edges of the pastry and roll them towards each other to meet in the middle.
6. Brush a little egg down the centre to stick the two halves together.
7. Cut the roll into 12 equal slices, laying them cut-side up on the baking sheet.
8. Brush each palmier with beaten egg and sprinkle with the herbs.
9. Bake for 12–15 minutes until puffed and golden.

Swiss roll

3 eggs

75 g caster sugar

75 g self-raising flour

35-53 ml (2–3 tbsp) jam

Extra caster sugar (25 g) for rolling up

Method

1 Light the oven to gas 6 or 200° C.
2 Place the eggs and sugar in a bowl. Whisk until very thick and creamy.
3 Fold in the flour carefully.
4 Sieve the flour onto the egg and sugar mixture and fold in with a metal tablespoon.
5 Pour into a tin, and bake in the oven for 10 to 12 minutes.
6 Place a piece of parchment on the table, sprinkle with extra sugar.
7 Turn out the Swiss roll onto the parchment paper.
8 Trim the edges with a sharp knife.
9 Spread with warmed jam and bake in oven.
10 Roll up into a roll.

Wrap

Wraps are fillings that are wrapped in soft flat breads such as tortillas or pittas. A wide variety of fillings can be used. There are different ways of folding and rolling the wraps to keep the filling secure.

Skewer

A **skewer** is a long metal or wooden pin used to secure food on during cooking. To **skewer** is to hold pieces of food together using a metal or wooden pin.

Meat and vegetables can be threaded on skewers and cooked. Skewered meat and vegetables are called kebabs, which are often marinated before grilling or cooking on a barbecue.

● For kebabs, flat metal skewers are good, particularly for meats as they conduct the heat well.
● Bamboo and wooden skewers are less expensive but they should be soaked in water before use each time to stop them from burning.

Figure 1.7.3 Wraps

Figure 1.7.4 Kebabs

Mix

To **mix** is the process of combining two or more ingredients to become one. For example, when making a Victoria sandwhich cake the butter and sugar are mixed together (or creamed) with a wooden spoon or electric hand which to combine them.

Most recipes require you to combine or mix the ingredients in some way so that they blend together. Combining is similar to mixing; for example, 'combine all the ingredients' – this instruction may also specify 'thoroughly' or 'gently', depending on what is required in the end result.

Equipment used to mix includes spoons, spatulas, whisks, processors and blenders.

Figure 1.7.5 Mixing

Coat

To **coat** is to add another ingredient to create an attractive finish. You can coat the sides of a cake with butter icing, then roll the cake in chocolate sprinkles.

Also, to coat is to create another protective layer when cooking. Two protective coatings are usually used:

- Flour – for example, meat can be coated in flour when shallow-fried to help seal in the flavour.
- Egg and breadcrumbs – for example, fish cakes are made, shaped and dipped in egg and then breadcrumbs to make a crispy coating. The coating helps to seal them and prevents the fish from overcooking.

Fish cakes

Figure I.7.6

500 g mashed potato

Can of fish, such as tuna or salmon

15 g (1 tbsp) chopped fresh parsley

1 egg

Golden/fresh breadcrumbs

Salt and pepper

Method

1 Preheat the oven to 200°C.
2 Place the mashed potato in a bowl.
3 Drain the canned fish and flake it into the mashed potato.
4 Add the chopped parsley, season and mix together.
5 Shape into four or six equal-sized cakes.
6 Beat the egg and put it in a small bowl. Place the breadcrumbs in a small bowl.
7 Dip each cake in the egg, then the breadcrumbs.
8 Bake in the oven on a non-stick baking tray at for about 20–30 minutes.
9 Alternately, they can be shallow fried on a medium heat for 15 minutes.

A recipe which demonstrates mixing, rolling, shaping and coating is fish cakes (see recipe on page 59).

① Mix the potatoes and fish, add seasoning

② Lightly flour the work surface and roll mixture into a log shape

③ Divide the mixture into portions

④ Roll each portion into a ball, and flatten into a disc

⑤ Coat the fish cake into egg and breadcrumbs

⑥ Using a palette knife neaten the edges of the fish cake

Figure 1.7.10 How to make fish cakes

Trifle

Base

1 pack of sponge fingers/Swiss roll/trifle sponges

1 tin of fruit, or 250–350 g of fresh fruit such as raspberries, strawberries

(If you use fresh fruit, you will need about 100 ml liquid, e.g. fruit juice, to soak into the sponges.)

Crème patisserie

1 egg plus 1 extra egg yolk

50 g caster sugar

25 g plain flour

300 ml milk

1 ml ($\frac{1}{4}$ tsp) vanilla essence

Figure I.7.8

Topping

250–300 ml whipping cream or double cream

Extra fruit for decoration

A see-through serving dish

Method

1 First make the crème patisserie. Whisk the eggs and sugar until they are nearly white. Gradually stir in the flour and then the milk.
2 Pour into a saucepan and bring to the boil slowly on a medium heat. Simmer for 2–3 minutes. Add the vanilla essence. Leave to cool; stir every now and again to prevent a skin forming.
3 Place a sponge layer at the bottom of your serving dish. Add enough fruit juice (drained from the can or from a carton) to moisten the sponge.
4 Put your fruit on top of the sponge.
5 Spread the crème patisserie on top of the fruit.
6 Whisk the cream until it holds its shape and spread three-quarters over the crème patisserie.
7 Pipe the remaining cream on the top, and decorate.

Shape and bind wet mixtures

Key words

Layer means to make up a dish with differing ingredients one on top of another.

Bind means to bring the ingredients in a mixture together using a binding ingredient.

To **bind** is to bring the ingredients in a mixture together using a binding ingredient. Some ingredients need binding together so that they do not fall apart, such as beef burgers and meatballs. Water and eggs are binding ingredients. When making meatballs or burgers, an egg is used to bind the ingredients together so that they do not fall apart when they are shaped and cooked.

When shaping raw meat mixtures, it is essential to follow food hygiene rules in order to prevent cross-contamination. Using the correct colour chopping board is crucial. Make sure your hands are washed thoroughly.

In recipes such as falafel the ingredients are blended together using a food processor, which binds the ingredients together sufficiently so they can be shaped into patties and then shallow fried or baked.

Baked falafels

35 ml (2 tbsp) olive oil

1 onion, finely chopped

1 garlic clove, crushed

1 x 400 g can of chickpeas

10 g (2 tsp) ground cumin

Zest of 1 lemon

Salt and pepper

1 egg, beaten

Figure 1.7.9

Method

1. Preheat the oven to 200°C.
2. Put 1 tablespoon of oil and the onion in a small pan and fry until soft. Add the garlic and cook for 2 more minutes and put into a bowl.
3. Add the drained chickpeas and mash well using a food processor.
4. Add the cumin, lemon zest, salt and pepper and mix well. Add the egg and mix together.
5. Divide the mixture into eight balls and place on a baking tray.
6. Drizzle with 1 tablespoon of oil and bake for 25 minutes, until golden.

Layer

To **layer** is to make up a dish with differing ingredients, one on top of another.

● An example of a layered dish is lasagne, which is made from layers of pasta, cheese sauce and a tomato-based sauce (either including vegetables or meat) placed on top of one another.

● Trifle is an English dessert made from layers of thick custard, fruit, sponge cake, fruit juice or jelly, and whipped cream.

Lasagne

Figure 1.7.7 Lasagne

Meat sauce

500 g minced beef

1 onion

50 g mushrooms

1 small pepper

1 garlic clove, crushed

400 g tin of chopped tomatoes

18 ml (1 tbsp) tomato purée

5 g (1 tsp) mixed herbs

Cheese sauce

50 g butter or low-fat spread

50 g flour

550 ml milk

75 g Cheddar cheese, grated

250 g lasagne sheets

Optional ingredients

Red/green/yellow pepper

1 courgette

1 carrot

Method

1 Preheat the oven to 180°C.
2 Dry-fry the mince in a saucepan until brown, stirring occasionally.
3 While mince is dry-frying, dice all vegetables.
4 Add vegetables and all other ingredients.
5 Bring to the boil and simmer for 10–15 minutes.
6 Melt butter or spread in a saucepan. Add flour and stir to make a roux, cooking for 1 minute. Then gradually add milk, beating well after each addition and ensuring it comes to the boil.
7 Take off the heat and put on a pan stand. Stir in three-quarters of the grated cheese.
8 To assemble the lasagne, layer up meat sauce, lasagne sheets, cheese sauce, meat sauce, lasagne sheets, cheese sauce. Sprinkle with the remaining cheese.
9 Bake for 35–40 minutes until golden brown and the sauce is bubbling. This can be baked at home, if it is prepared in the lesson.

SKILL 8 SAUCE-MAKING

A **sauce** is a well-flavoured liquid which has been thickened. The properties and characteristics of a sauce are influenced by the way in which it is made and the proportion of ingredients used.

There are many reasons why sauces are added to food. They:

- add colour
- add flavour
- add texture
- bind different ingredients together
- make the dish look more appetising and attractive
- add nutrients
- balance the richness of some foods.

Figure 1.8.1 A white sauce

Figure 1.8.2 Tomato and cucumber salsa

Starch-based sauces

The science of starch-based sauce-making

Starch has a very useful property which is to thicken mixtures. When liquids and starch are mixed together and heated, the mixture will thicken.

Starches can be used to make sauces, custards, gravies, batters and glazes.

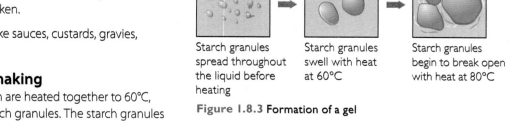

Starch granules spread throughout the liquid before heating

Starch granules swell with heat at 60°C

Starch granules begin to break open with heat at 80°C

Figure 1.8.3 Formation of a gel

The stages in sauce making
- When a liquid and starch are heated together to 60°C, the liquid enters the starch granules. The starch granules will begin to swell.
- At 80°C the granules will burst. The starch thickens the mixture forming a gel with the liquid. This process is known as **gelatinisation**.
- At 100°C the process of gelatinisation is complete.
- On cooling, the gel sets and the **sauce** will become thicker. The thickness or consistency of the sauce is known as its **viscosity**.

You will leave move about gelatinisation in the section on Carbohydrates in Topic 2.1 macronutrients. See page 109.

Starch-based sauce-making

Starch-based sauces are usually thickened with one of these ingredients:
- flour, which has a high proportion of starch
- cornflour, which is a pure starch
- arrowroot, which is a pure starch.

Starch-based sauces can be made by the roux method, the all-in-one method and the blended method.

Roux method	All-in-one method	Blended
The roux method is the traditional way in which to make a basic white sauce.	The all-in-one method is a quick and simple way in which to make a white sauce.	Blended sauces are usually sweet and made with cornflour or arrowroot or custard powder.
1 Melt the fat in a saucepan over gentle heat (make sure the butter does not brown).	1 Place all the ingredients in the saucepan.	1 Mix the arrowroot or cornflour with a small amount of the liquid to make a thin smooth paste.
2 Add the flour and stir it in using a wooden spoon. Cook the roux gently for 1–2 minutes, stirring all the time to prevent browning.	2 Heat gently, whisking all of the time to avoid any lumps forming, until the mixture comes to the boil.	2 Bring the remainder of the liquid to the boil in a small saucepan. Pour over the paste stirring well.
3 Remove the pan from heat. Gradually add the milk to the roux, beating all the time to avoid any lumps.	3 Turn down the heat and simmer for three minutes to allow the sauce to become glossy.	3 Return the mixture to the pan, bring to the boil and stir all the time.
4 Return pan to the heat. Bring the sauce to the boil, stirring all the time. Once the sauce has boiled turn the heat down and simmer for two minutes to allow the sauce to become glossy.	4 Remove from the heat, add seasoning and any other chosen ingredients (e.g. cheese).	4 When the sauce has thickened take off the heat.
5 Remove from the heat. Add seasoning and any other chosen ingredients (e.g. cheese).		

Table 1.8.1 The three methods of making sauces

Figure 1.8.4 Making a roux

The viscosity of the sauce (i.e. its thickness or consistency) is determined by the ratio or proportion of starch to liquid. The higher the ratio of starch to liquid, the thicker the sauce. Starch-based sauces can be classified into three main consistencies:

- pouring
- coating
- binding.

The consistency of sauces differs depending on what they are being used for. For example, custard is designed to be poured onto a dessert such as apple pie. A coating sauce has to coat food such as pasta, and a really thick sauce would be needed to bind the ingredients together to make fish cakes.

Care needs to be taken when making starch-based sauces as faults can occur.

Type of sauce	Ratio of ingredients	Description of sauce	Example of dish
Pouring	500 ml milk 30 g fat 30 g flour	A pouring sauce, at boiling point, should just thinly coat the back of a spoon, and should pour freely.	Custard
Coating	500 ml milk 50 g fat 50 g flour	A coating sauce, at boiling point, should coat the back of a spoon.	Macaroni cheese
Binding/panada	500 ml milk 100 g fat 100 g flour	A binding sauce or panada should be thick enough to bind dry ingredients together.	Fish cakes

Table 1.8.2 Different types of sauce for different uses

Figure 1.8.5 Custard

Figure 1.8.6 Macaroni cheese

Figure 1.8.7 Fish cakes

SECTION 1 FOOD PREPARATION SKILLS

Variations

Other ingredients can be added to starch-based sauces to change their flavour and use – for example, béchamel sauce and infused velouté sauce. Béchamel and velouté sauces are often used as the filling for vol au vents.

Béchamel sauce

To make béchamel sauce place 1 small piece of carrot, a small onion, 6 whole peppercorns and 1 bay leaf into the milk, bring to the boil very slowly and leave to **infuse** for about 20 minutes. Strain the milk, and make the sauce following the roux method.

The ingredients used to infuse the milk can be altered, for instance an onion studded with cloves may be used.

Figure 1.8.8 Infusing milk

Velouté sauce

Velouté sauce is a white sauce made with stock instead of milk. It is also made by the roux method but is often simmered for a longer time to allow the flavours to infuse.

Practical activity

Make a sweet dish and a savoury dish which each use a starch-based sauce.

Reduction sauces

Reduction sauces are made when liquid is simmered over the heat so that the water content evaporates resulting in a concentrated sauce. This process thickens and intensifies the flavour of the sauce.

Reduction sauces can be made from the cooking liquid in which meat, fish or vegetables have been cooked, or by **deglazing** the brown sediment from the bottom of pan with water, stock or wine following pan frying. Reduction sauces take time; some can take up to an hour. The time does depend on how much liquid has been used. Reduction sauces include red and white wine sauces, pan sauces and many cream sauces. Using a sauté pan which is wider and shallower than a conventional saucepan allows the sauce to heat and evaporate more quickly.

Practical activity

Make a dish which incorporates a sauce that has been made by the reduction method – for example, curry sauce to be served with Quorn™ or chicken, or a tomato-based sauce made with minced beef or TVP (see definition on page 102).

Figure 1.8.9 Tomato sauce is a reduction sauce

Key words

Infuse is to flavour a liquid with an ingredient by slowly heating to boiling point and then allowing to cool.

Reduction is the process of simmering a liquid over heat until it thickens. It is also the name of the concentrated liquid that forms during this process.

Deglazing is to loosen the browned juices on the bottom of the pan by adding a liquid to the hot pan and stirring while the liquid is boiling.

Emulsion sauces

Sauces such as mayonnaise and hollandaise are emulsified sauces. The sauce is an **emulsion**. An emulsion is formed when two **immiscible** liquids (liquids which would not normally mix) are mixed together. They are made by forming a suspension of tiny droplets of fat, such as oil or melted butter in a liquid, such as water, or vinegar. The emulsified sauce can be stable or unstable.

Stable emulsions

Sauces such as mayonnaise and hollandaise sauce are stable emulsions. They are stable because an egg yolk has been added. Egg yolk contains an emulsifying agent called lecithin which has the ability to combine with both oil and water and stops the sauce from separating. Immiscible liquids which are shaken together will eventually separate into layers. Oil and water are immiscible.

Figure 1.8.10 A jar of mayonnaise

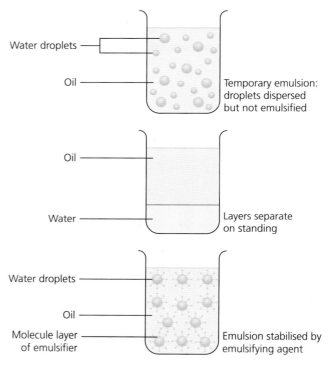

Figure 1.8.11 Emulsification

Unstable emulsions

Salad dressings such as vinaigrette are an unstable emulsion because they only consist of oil and vinegar with flavourings. They do not include an emulsifying ingredient such as egg yolk so they separate very quickly after they have been made. Dressings are therefore often made to be used immediately, or are shaken before they are used.

Figure 1.8.12 Emulsified sauces

You will learn more about the functional and chemical properties of emulsions in the section on Fats in Topic 2.1 Macronutrients. See page 104.

Key words

Emulsion refers to the tiny drops of one liquid spread evenly through a second liquid.

Emulsification is the process of using an emulsifier (such as egg yolk) to stabilise an insoluble mixture.

Immiscible means not able to be mixed or blended together.

Check your knowledge and understanding

1 Explain the process of gelatinisation.
2 List five reasons why you would add sauce to a dish.
3 Why is the thickness of the sauce important?
4 What are the three starches that can be used to make a sauce? Give an example of a dish in which each of them would be used.
5 How can a sauce be thickened without starch?
6 Describe what happens to the ingredients used to make a white sauce when they are heated.
7 Why is it important to stir a sauce when cooking?
8 What is an infused sauce?
9 How does simmering a sauce affect its consistency and flavour?
10 Name an unstable emulsion sauce and a stable emulsion sauce. What is the difference between them?

SKILL 9 TENDERISING AND MARINATING

Tenderising and marinating are ways in which we can make food more tender, moist and flavoursome.

Marinating is to soak foods such as fish, meat, poultry and vegetables in a marinade to help develop the flavour, tenderise and in some instances colour the food before it is cooked

A **marinade** is highly seasoned liquid which is used to give flavour, keep food moist, and assist in tenderising foods. The liquid can be acidic, alkaline or a salt solution.

Meat poultry, fish and vegetables can all be marinated.

Figure 1.9.1 Some meat in a marinade

Tenderising meat and poultry

Tenderising meat is a process by which the tough muscle fibres are broken down in order to make the meat more tender to eat.

Meat can be tenderised in three different ways:
● by cooking it at a low temperature for a long time (see in Topic 3.1 Cooking of food and heat transfer, Selecting appropriate cooking methods)
● by mechanical action – physically breaking down the muscle fibres by pounding them with a hammer, mincing or cutting larger pieces of meat into chunks
● chemically by marinating.

Tenderising meat and poultry by mechanical action

Tougher cuts of meat can be tenderised by hammering the meat using a meat mallet. The hammering action flattens the meat and breaks up some of the fibres and connective tissues, making the meat more tender. It is a good idea to do this between some waxed paper.

Tenderising meat and poultry by marinating

Meat is marinated to give it flavour and to soften its texture. If an acidic marinade is used such as a citrus marinade shown in the recipe below, the acidic ingredients (in this case the citric acid in the lemon juice) denatures the protein in the

Figure 1.9.2 Tenderising meat by hammering it with a meat mallet

meat. **Denaturation** is where there is a change in shape of the protein molecules. The acid marinade softens the proteins on the surface of the meat making the meat more tender. The marinated meat is then usually cooked by barbecuing, grilling or roasting. When grilling, barbecuing or roasting the marinade can also be basted on the food, or it can be cooked separately in a saucepan to make an accompanying sauce.

Citrus marinade

Grated zest and juice of one lemon

53 ml (3 tbsp) of vegetable oil

35 ml (2 tbsp) of honey

17 ml (1 tbsp) soy sauce

6 ml (1 tsp) Dijon mustard

Ground black pepper

It is also possible to use fruit as a meat tenderiser. Kiwi, pineapple and papaya all contain **proteolytic enzymes** that break down the muscle fibres in meat making it much more tender.

Natural yoghurt can also used as a tenderiser because it contains enzymes which tenderise the food as well as adding flavour, for example chicken tikka.

Yoghurt marinade

50 ml natural yoghurt

1 small onion finely chopped

1 crushed garlic clove

3 g ($\frac{1}{2}$ tsp) of coriander, cumin and turmeric

Tenderising fish by marinating

Fish can be marinated to add flavour and moisture. It can also be 'cooked' by marinating it in acid. The acid in the juice denatures the proteins in the fish. The fish will then alter its texture and colour by changing from translucent to opaque and the texture becomes firm. An example of this is ceviche.

Figure 1.9.3 Ceviche

Key words

Marinating is to soak foods such as fish, meat, poultry and vegetables in a marinade to help develop the flavour, tenderise and in some instances colour the food before it is cooked.

Marinade is a highly flavoured liquid, which is used to give flavour, keep food moist and assist in tenderising foods. The liquid can be acidic or a salty solution.

Tenderising meat is a process by which the tough muscle fibres are broken down in order to make the meat more tender to eat.

Denaturation is where there is change in shape of the protein molecule.

Proteolytic enzymes are enzymes that break down the muscle fibres in meat, making it much more tender.

Marinating vegetables and alternatives

Marinades are easy to prepare and will add zest and flavour to fruit, vegetables and alternatives such as tofu and Quorn™.

Marinades suitable for vegetables and alternatives can be made of a variety of ingredients such as oil, wine, vinegar, soy sauce, garlic, herbs and spices. The marinades will not only add flavour to the food but they will add moisture when the liquid is absorbed. Tofu and Quorn™ readily absorb flavours from other ingredients. Fruit can also be marinated.

Figure 1.9.4 Marinated tofu

Marinated peaches

4 peaches

35 ml (2 tbsp) of clear honey

35 ml (2 tbsp) of orange juice

A squeeze of lemon juice

Check your knowledge and understanding

1   What is marinating?
2   What is a marinade?
3   Why is food marinated?
4   How is meat tenderised by mechanical action?
5   What does an acidic ingredient do to the structure of meat?
6   Which fruits contain proteolytic enzymes?
7   Why are tofu and Quorn™ such good ingredients to marinate?

SKILL 10 DOUGH

A **dough** is a mixture of dry ingredients, such as flour, and a liquid, such as water, that is mixed, kneaded, shaped and then baked.

Pastry

Pastry is a combination of flour, fat and liquid, which is made into a dough. The dough is then shaped and baked. Pastry is often used to support or cover other ingredients.

The variety and texture of the pastry depends on the proportion of these ingredients and the way they are mixed and on the method of cooking.

Figure 1.10.1 Pastry dough

Shortcrust pastry

The ingredients used for making shortcrust pastry are shown in the table below:

Ingredient	Function
Plain flour	Used because it does not rise. It has a low gluten content which produces a short, crumb texture.
Fat (a mixture of white fat and low-fat spread or butter are used)	The fat coats the flour granules to prevent gluten formation – this process is called **shortening**. The white fat makes the pastry short in texture, and the low-fat spread or butter add colour and flavour.
Water	Binds the ingredients together.
Salt	Added to enhance the flavour.

Table 1.10.1 Ingredients for shortcrust pastry

The proportion or ratio of ingredients to use is:

- **half fat to flour** (for example, with 200 g flour use 100 g total fat)
- 1 teaspoonful (5 ml) of water for each 25 g flour.

Shortcrust pastry

200 g plain flour

50 g hard margarine or butter

50 g lard or white fat such as Trex

Cold water to mix

Method

1 Weigh the ingredients carefully.
2 Rub the fat into the flour and salt until the mixture resembles golden breadcrumbs.

Figure 1.10.2

3 Mix in the water using a palette knife until the mixture comes together.
4 Knead lightly.
5 Rest the pastry.
6 Roll the pastry to the required thickness and shape (see Rolling pastry section in Section 1 Skill 7 Preparing, combining and shaping, page 56).
7 Bake the pastry in a hot oven at 200°C.

Quiche Lorraine

200 g shortcrust pastry

150 g bacon, chopped

3 eggs

250 ml milk

50 g Cheddar (or similar hard) cheese, grated

Salt and pepper

Optional ingredients:

1 onion

50 g mushrooms

1 red/green/yellow pepper

1 small can of sweetcorn

Method

1 Make pastry. Chill for about 30 minutes, if time.
2 Preheat the oven to 200°C.
3 Roll out and line a 20 cm quiche tin. Bake blind for 10 minutes in the oven.
4 Fry the bacon and place in the pastry case.
5 Beat the eggs and milk lightly. Pour over the bacon.
6 Sprinkle with cheese and season.
7 Bake for 25–30 minutes at 180°C.
8 Remove from the oven and leave to rest for 10 minutes, cut and serve.
9 Alternatively, leave until completely cold before cutting.

These are common faults when making shortcrust pastry:

- Insufficient air incorporated – this gives a heavy texture.
- Too much liquid is added – this makes the pastry tough.
- Too much handling when rolling out – this causes hard, badly risen pastry.
- No time allowed for 'relaxing' – this causes pastry to shrink when cooked.
- Stretching pastry when rolling – this also causes pastry to shrink when cooked.
- Oven too cool – this causes ill-risen, greasy pastry; or pastry that is hard on the outside and soggy inside.

Shaping: using shortcrust pastry to line a flan ring

A traditional savoury flan tin has straight sides. A fluted tin is often used for sweet dishes to add to the overall finish of the dish. Most come with removable bases to make it easy to remove the flan without disturbing the base of it.

A traditional flan ring has no base and is a ring with straight or fluted sides, which is put directly onto a baking sheet.

How to line a flan ring with pastry:

1 Roll out the pastry so that it is 5 cm larger than the flan ring.
2 Lightly grease the flan ring and baking sheet, and place the flan ring on the baking sheet.
3 Place the rolling pin in the centre of the pastry and fold one side back over the rolling pin.
4 Lift the pastry into the ring and press firmly against the bottom (the baking sheet) and sides.
5 Use the rolling pin to remove any excess pastry from the top of the ring.

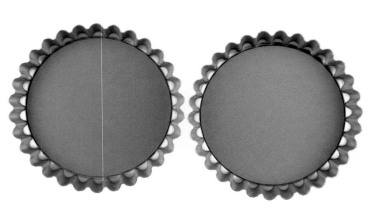

Figure 1.10.3 Flan rings

Figure 1.10.4 Lining a flan ring

AQA GCSE Food Preparation and Nutrition

Baking blind

Many pastry flans need to be baked before the filling goes in. This is called baking blind.

To bake blind:

1 Place a large circle of greaseproof paper over the pastry in the flan ring. Some recipes recommend pricking the surface of the pastry with a fork to stop it from rising.
2 Add baking beans to weigh the pastry down and to stop it from rising.
3 Bake in a hot oven for around 15 minutes.
4 Remove the greaseproof paper and beans and place the flan back in the oven for 5 minutes to ensure the pastry is fully dried out.

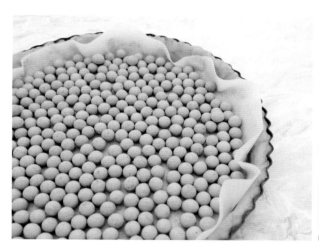

Figure 1.10.5 Baking pastry blind

Figure 1.10.6 Fruit tartlets

Puff pastry

The ingredients used to make puff pastry are shown in the table below:

Ingredient	Function
Strong plain flour	Has a high gluten content to produce flaky crispy layers.
Fat (butter or low-fat spread)	Adds colour and flavour.
Water	Binds the ingredients together and also combines with the gluten to form stretchy elastic dough.
Salt	Helps develop the flavour and also strengthen the gluten.
Lemon juice	Softens the gluten so that the pastry is crisp and tender.

Table 1.10.2 Ingredients for puff pastry

The proportion or ratio of ingredients to use is:
- **equal fat to flour** (for example, with 200 g flour use 200 g of fat)
- 1 tablespoonful (15 ml) of water for each 25 g flour, plus 5 ml lemon juice.

Puff pastry

200 g strong plain flour

Pinch of salt

200 g chilled butter

15 ml lemon juice

150 ml water

Method

1 Sieve the flour and salt into a bowl.
2 Rub in 25 g of the butter.
3 Place the rest of the butter between two sheets of cling film and gently beat it with a rolling pin until it is a flat square.
4 Add the lemon juice and enough water to the flour mixture to make a soft dough.
5 Turn out onto a lightly floured table and knead lightly until smooth.
6 Roll the dough into a 25 cm square.
7 Place the butter in the centre of the dough diagonally so that it looks like a diamond shape. Fold in each corner of the dough to enclose the butter completely.
8 Roll out the dough into a rectangle. Fold up the bottom third and fold down the top third, seal the edges by pressing down with a rolling pin and chill the pastry for at least 15 minutes, depending on time available.
9 Allow the pastry to relax/rest in the fridge before rolling, folding and chilling three to five more times.

It is a long process making puff pastry, and as ready-made and ready-rolled puff pastry is easily available, this is often used in recipes as a shortcut. However, ready-made/ready-rolled pastry can be costly and will increase the cost of the recipe.

Puff pastry is light, crisp and buttery in flavour. It is the richest and yet the lightest of all pastries. Air is trapped between the layers of the dough and this, together with the steam created from the water, means the pastry rises up into many layers when it is baked.

Shaping puff pastry

Puff pastry can be rolled and shaped in many different ways.

Palmiers (see recipe on page 57) are made from puff pastry. The pastry is rolled out, coated with sugar, and then the two sides are rolled up so that they meet together in the middle, making a roll that is then cut into about 0.5 cm slices and baked.

(see recipe on page 57)

Figure 1.10.7 Palmiers

Finishing methods for pastry

The finish to any pastry product is important for a number of reasons. All the pastry products made should be the same size, finish and shape. Decorations should be delicate and balanced, piping should be neat and tidy.

The three basic techniques for finishing pastry are:
- **Dusting:** You can dust with icing sugar, icing sugar with cocoa, or icing sugar with cinnamon. Dusting should be light and delicate, just enough to decorate the top of the product. A fine sieve is usually used to dust sweet pastry products.
- **Piping:** Cream, chocolate or custard can be piped inside pastry products or used as decoration.
- **Filling**: It is important to use the correct amount of filling inside a pastry product. Too little filling and the product may lose its shape when cooked, too much and it will spill over and spoil the appearance.

A fork can also be used to add interest to the edges of a pie.

Glazing

A **glaze** is a coating of a shiny, often sweet, sometimes savoury, substance applied to food usually by dipping, drizzling or brushing. Two glazes frequently used for pastries are:
- Apricot glaze – this is made from apricot jam and a little water.
- Eggwash – an egg yolk or whole egg can be beaten and brushed on the top of the pastry.

Pasta

Pasta is a mixture of flour, salt and water; sometimes egg is added to make richer pasta. The word pasta literally means 'dough' or 'paste'.

The ingredients used to make pasta dough are shown in the table below:

Ingredient	Function
Durum wheat flour (sometimes called dopio zero flour – 00)	It is suitable for making pasta because the durum wheat is rich in gluten and holds its shape during cooking, and makes a stretchy dough.
Salt	For flavour.
Eggs	Make the dough elastic, and soft.
Water and oil	Make the dough possible to shape. During the drying process most water is removed.

Table 1.10.3 Ingredients for pasta

How to make pasta dough

1 Place the flour and salt in a bowl and mix in the rest of the ingredients using your hands. A food processor can be used to save time.
2 Knead the dough until it is smooth (about 5 minutes).
3 If time, leave to rest for 30 minutes.
4 Roll the dough using a pasta machine, and cut into the desired shape.

It is possible to roll pasta on a well-floured surface to a thickness of about 0.5 mm if a pasta machine is not available.

Figure 1.10.8 Making pasta

Bread

Bread is a combination of flour, yeast, salt and liquid, which is made into a dough. The dough is then mixed, **kneaded**, left to rise, **knocked back**, **shaped**, **proved** and baked.

The variety and texture of the bread depends on the proportion of these ingredients and the way they are mixed, as well as on the method of cooking. For example, a strong flour such as wholemeal can be used which often requires more water – changing the proportion of the recipe. There are many different types of bread available, and many cultures have their own bread recipes. (You may wish to explore the breads found in different cuisines in Topic 5.2 British and international cuisines.)

Other ingredients such as sugar, fat, eggs can also be added to produce different types of bread.

You will learn more about bread-making and the properties of the ingredients used to make bread in Topic 3.2 Functional and chemical properties of food.

The ingredients used to make bread are shown in the table below:

Ingredient	Function
Strong plain flour	Has a high gluten content which with water will form an elastic stretch dough.
Yeast (the most common type of yeast is easy blend or fast action dried yeast)	The raising agent.
Water (lukewarm)	Provides warm conditions and moisture for the yeast **fermentation**. Fermentation is the process by which yeast produces carbon dioxide and alcohol when provided with food, warmth and moisture.
Salt	Helps develop the flavour and also strengthen the gluten.
Sugar	A small amount may be added as the food for the yeast but the yeast can also feed on the natural sugars in the flour.
Fat/oil	Helps the bread stay fresh for longer.

Table 1.10.4 Ingredients for bread

How to make bread dough

1 Place flour, salt, yeast and sugar into a mixing bowl.
2 Rub fat into the dry ingredients.
3 Add water gradually until the dough is soft.
4 Knead dough on a lightly floured table until it is smooth and elastic.
5 Leave the dough to prove in a warm place for about an hour.
6 Knock back the dough, shape.

Bread rolls

500 g strong plain flour

10 g (2 tsp) salt

10 g (2 tsp) caster sugar

1 sachet of fast-action yeast

50 g butter or low-fat spread

300 ml hand-hot water

Figure 1.10.9

Method

1 Measure flour, salt, sugar and yeast into a mixing bowl.
2 Rub butter or low-fat spread into the dry ingredients.
3 Add water gradually until the dough is soft and pliable (not sticky).
4 Knead dough on a lightly floured surface until it is smooth and elastic.
5 Shape into rolls and place on a baking sheet lined with baking parchment.
6 Leave to prove until doubled in size.
7 Preheat the oven to 200°C.
8 Bake for 15–20 minutes until risen and golden brown. When tapped on the bottom, rolls should sound hollow.

Shaping bread

Bread dough can be shaped into rolls or a loaf. It can also be rolled out into a rectangle, spread with a filling and then rolled up and cut.

Roly poly bread

Basic Bread Mixture

400 g strong plain flour

2.5 g ($\frac{1}{2}$ tsp) salt

1 sachet of easy blend yeast

25 g caster sugar if a sweet filling is chosen, 5 g (1 tsp) if a savoury filling is chosen

200 ml of warmed milk

25 g melted butter

Filling ideas

Cinnamon whirls: 50 g caster sugar, 100 g raisins, 10 g (2 tsp) cinnamon.
Sultana and spice: 50 g brown sugar, 100 g sultanas, 5 g (1 tsp) mixed spice.
Spiced cranberry: 85 g cranberries, 50 g sultanas, finely grated zest of an orange,5 g (1 tsp) of mixed spice.
Pesto parmesan: 53 ml (3 tbsp) of pesto sauce, 40 g grated fresh parmesan cheese.
Ham and spinach: 17 ml (1 tbsp) of Dijon mustard, 75 g ham chopped into small squares, 25 g shredded fresh baby spinach leaves, 75 g Gruyère cheese grated.
Bacon and Stilton: 100 g cooked bacon cut into small pieces, 10 g Stilton cheese crumbled.

Method

1 Sieve the flour, sugar, and salt into a large bowl, then stir in the yeast.
2 Make a well in the centre and add enough milk to make soft dough.
3 Turn out on to a lightly floured surface and knead until smooth and elastic.
4 Roll out the dough into a rectangle approximately 40x20 cm.
5 Melt the butter and spread all over the dough.
6 Sprinkle the remaining ingredients onto the dough leaving a 1 cm border around the edges.
7 Starting from a long side roll up the dough fairly tightly like a Swiss roll. Cut into approximately 10 even slices around 4 cm thick.
8 Place the pinwheels on a lined baking sheet and, if possible, leave to rise for 20 to 30 minutes.
9 Bake in the oven for 20 to 25 minutes or until well risen and golden brown.

① Mix the fruit, spice and sugar together.

② Melt butter and spread all over the dough. Sprinkle the remaining ingredients onto the dough leaving a 1 cm border around the edges.

③ Starting from a long side, roll up the dough fairly tightly like a swiss roll.

Figure 1.10.10 Chelsea buns

④ Cut into approximately 10 even slices around 4 cm thick.

The dough can be rolled into a circle to make a pizza.

Figure 1.10.11 Pizza

Pizza

Pizza base

250 g plain flour

5 g (1 tsp) salt

5 g (1 tsp) sugar

25 g margarine, butter or low-fat spread

3.5 g (half a sachet) fast-action yeast

150 ml of hand-hot water

Toppings

2 level tbsp tomato purée

100 g mozzarella or Cheddar cheese

1 tsp herbs, oregano or basil

50 g sliced/diced vegetables or meat (pepperoni, ham or chorizo)

Method

1 Preheat the oven to 200°C.
2 Measure flour, yeast, salt and sugar into a mixing bowl.
3 Add oil to the dry ingredients.
4 Add water gradually until the dough is soft and pliable (not sticky).
5 Knead dough on a lightly floured surface until it is smooth and elastic.
6 Roll out to a 0.5 cm thick circle and place on a baking sheet lined with baking parchment.
7 Spread tomato purée onto the pizza base.
8 Add toppings and sprinkle herbs on top.
9 Leave to prove if you have time.
10 Bake for 15–20 minutes until risen and golden brown.
11 The pizza can then be baked or folded in half to make a calzone.
12 The pizza could have a stuffed crust.

Figure 1.10.12 Calzone

Figure 1.10.13 Naan bread

Before baking, the pizza can be folded in half to make a calzone, and then baked.

Bread dough can also be used to make flat bread such as naan bread.

Finishing methods for bread

Various ingredients can be used for topping or finishing bread before it is baked.

● Bread can be sprinkled with seeds, cracked wheat, rolled oats, salt flakes, grated cheese or herbs.

● Sweet breads can be dusted with icing sugar or sprinkled with crushed sugar cubes, nuts or flaked almonds.

A sharp knife can be used to make lines across the bread – and when the bread rises in the oven the lines will open and look attractive.

Glazing bread

Brushing bread with a glaze before baking will enhance the colour of the bread, as well as giving flavour to the crust. Glazes give an attractive finish, add moisture and allow decorations or garnishes to be stuck onto the surface of the dough.

The most common ingredients used to glaze bread are water, milk or beaten egg. Other ingredients such as warmed honey, thin glacé icing, melted butter and oil can also be used.

Figure 1.10.14 Tiger bread

> **Key words**
>
> **Bread** is a combination of flour, yeast, sugar, salt and liquid, which is made into a dough.
>
> **Knead** means to manipulate dough by pushing it across a work surface and pulling it back. This is essential to develop the gluten.
>
> **Knock back** means to knead out the carbon dioxide in risen dough to remove large air pockets to ensure an even texture.
>
> **Shape** means to give a prepared dough its final shape before proving.
>
> **Proving** is the last rising of the bread dough in its final shape before it is baked.
>
> **Fermentation** is the process by which yeast produces carbon dioxide and alcohol when provided with food, warmth and moisture.

SKILL 11 RAISING AGENTS

Raising agents are added to a wide variety of sweet and savoury mixtures, such as cakes, scones and breads, to make them rise. They also contribute to the lightness and sponginess of mixtures. The lightness is based upon the principle that gases expand when heated. The gases used to make mixtures rise are:

- air – which is a mixture of gases
- carbon dioxide gas
- steam – which is water as a gas.

Egg whites or whole eggs can be whisked together trapping air, and are used when making meringues and whisked sponges.

Self-raising flour, baking powder and bicarbonate of soda are chemical raising agents, which produce the gas carbon dioxide, which makes mixtures rise, such as for cakes and scones.

The liquid used in batters or choux pastry turns to steam while these are being cooked, and that also helps with rising.

You will learn about raising agents in Topic 3.2 Functional and chemical properties of food. See page 212.

> ### Key word
> **Raising agent** is something added to sweet or savoury mixtures, such as cakes, scones and breads, to make them rise.

Eggs as a raising agent

- When an egg yolk is whisked, only a tiny amount of air is trapped.
- When a whole egg is whisked, it will trap a certain amount of air but the foam produced soon rises to the top of the liquid and some escapes. If sugar is whisked with the eggs, a more stable foam is produced. This is the method used to make a Swiss roll.
- When an egg white is whisked, it easily traps air to form a stiff foam, which is more stable than a whole egg foam. This is the method used to make meringues.
- Egg whites are also whisked when making soufflés and roulades.

Figure 1.11.1 Swiss roll

Spinach and cream cheese roulade

Figure 1.11.2

400 g spinach

5 large eggs, separated

45 g (3 tbsp) self-raising flour

Salt and pepper

200 g fromage frais

150 g cream cheese

Parmesan cheese, finely grated

Method

1 Preheat the oven to 170°C and line a rectangular tin with baking paper.
2 Wilt the spinach in 2 tablespoons of water, then when cool squeeze out as much excess liquid as you can.
3 Put the spinach into a food processor and add the egg yolks, flour and salt and pepper.
4 Blend thoroughly.
5 Whisk the egg whites until stiff, then fold into the spinach. Spread in the tin and bake for 12–15 minutes until firm.
6 Beat the fromage frais into the cream cheese until soft and creamy.
7 Place some baking paper on the worktop, sprinkled with Parmesan.
8 Turn the spinach roulade out onto the cheese and carefully remove the paper from the back.
9 Spread with the cream cheese mix.
10 Using the paper to help, roll the roulade up from the shortest end.

Self-raising flour as a raising agent

Self-raising flour is plain white or wholemeal flour to which raising agents have been added. It is possible to make self-raising flour from plain flour by adding 4 teaspoons of baking powder to 250 g of plain flour. The raising agent is usually baking powder. The self-raising flour reacts with the liquid in the mixture to produce carbon dioxide gas, which raises the mixture. It is mostly used in cakes and baked products.

Figure 1.11.3 Self-raising flour

Savoury scone round

225 g self-raising flour

50 g butter

75 g extra ingredients: 2 or 3 of your choice of chopped ham, chopped cooked bacon, grated cheese, sun-dried tomatoes, sweetcorn:

125 ml milk

Sprinkling mixed herbs, such as chives, rosemary, mixed herbs

Method

1 Preheat the oven to 180°C.
2 Line a baking sheet with parchment paper.
3 Place the flour in a large mixing bowl.
4 Rub the butter into the flour using fingertips, until the mixture looks like breadcrumbs.
5 Add the extra ingredients.
6 Add the milk a little at a time, until the mixture becomes a soft but not sticky dough.
7 Roll out into a round and mark out six triangles.
8 Bake in the oven for 20 minutes or until firm and golden.

Bicarbonate of soda as a raising agent

Bicarbonate of soda is a white powder which, when mixed with acidic ingredients such as buttermilk, yoghurt, cream of tartar or soured cream, produces carbon dioxide. The amount of bicarbonate of soda used needs to be measured carefully because too much can leave an unpleasant taste, and a yellowish crumb, so it is often used in strongly flavoured cakes such as gingerbread.

Irish soda bread

Figure 1.11.4 Bicarbonate of soda

Figure 1.11.5

200 g plain white flour

200 g plain wholemeal flour

15g (1 tsp) salt

30 g (2 tsp) bicarbonate of soda

25 g butter, cut into cubes

300 ml buttermilk

Method

1 Preheat the oven to 200°C.
2 Place the flours, salt and bicarbonate of soda in a bowl.
3 Rub in the butter.
4 Add enough buttermilk to make a soft dough.
5 Knead lightly and shape into a round.
6 Mark the round with a sharp knife into six or eight segments.
7 Bake in the oven for 30–40 minutes until cooked.

Baking powder as a raising agent

Baking powder is a white powder that is usually a mixture of bicarbonate of soda, an acid (such as cream of tartar) and a filler such as cornflour to keep the mixture dry. When mixed with liquid, it produces carbon dioxide gas, which raises the mixture. This reaction happens very quickly so mixtures using baking powder need to be mixed quickly and placed in the oven quickly. A good example would be muffins, which are mixed very quickly. When using baking powder, prepare baking cases or tins before making the mixture so that time is not wasted and the raising agent is not activated too early. Baking powder is often added to cake recipes along with self-raising flour to assist in the raising process, making cakes light and fluffy in texture.

Figure 1.11.6 Baking powder

Yeast as a raising agent

Yeast is a living tiny-celled plant which, when supplied with warmth, moisture and food (sugar or starch), breaks down the food into carbon dioxide and alcohol. This process is called fermentation. Yeast is the raising agent used in bread-making.

Steam as a raising agent

In mixtures that contain a lot of water, such as batters and choux pastry, the water evaporates as steam in the hot oven pushing the mixture up, and then it sets on cooking. Water changes to steam at 100°C boiling point. Steam has a volume about 1,600 times larger than the original volume of the water.

Batters

A **batter** is a mixture of flour, liquid and usually an egg. The mixture is beaten well and in the process, some air is incorporated but the main raising agent in a batter is steam.

Batters are used to:
- make pancakes and crêpes
- coat food that is then fried, such as fish and chicken
- make fritters – slices of fruit and vegetables coated in batter and fried
- make baked foods, such as Yorkshire puddings or toad in the hole.

American-style pancakes

Figure 1.11.7

Ingredients

100 g self-raising flour

1 tsp baking powder

15 g (1 tbsp) caster sugar

1 egg

100 ml milk

53-7 ml (3–4 tbsp) oil

Making it different

100 g blueberries

100 g ready-to eat dried fruit, such as chopped apricots and sour cherries or cranberries

Small carton of natural or Greek yoghurt

sliced banana

Method

1 Place flour, baking powder and sugar in a bowl.
2 Beat the eggs and milk together.
3 Add gradually to the flour, whisking thoroughly.
4 Heat the frying pan with a little oil.
5 Spoon in the batter about 1 tablespoon at a time.
6 When bubbles appear on the top, turn the pancake over.
7 Cook until brown on the second side, then keep warm while you cook all the mixture.

Extension activity

Make a sauce, for example a fruit coulis or a citrus sauce to go with the pancakes.

Choux pastry

Choux pastry is a light, crisp, hollow pastry used to make profiteroles, eclairs and gougeres. Choux pastry is baked in a hot oven so that the incorporated water quickly turns to steam, which allows the mixture to rise.

Figure 1.11.8 Chocolate eclairs

> ## Key words
>
> **Batter** is a mixture of flour, milk or water, and usually an egg.
>
> **Choux pastry** is a light, crisp, hollow pastry used to make profiteroles, eclairs and gougeres.

Gougeres

55 g butter, diced	Pinch of salt
150 ml cold water	2 eggs, lightly beaten
75 g strong white bread flour	100 g grated cheese

Method

1 Preheat the oven to 180°C.
2 Grease or line a baking sheet.
3 Put the butter and water in a pan and bring to the boil.
4 Remove from the heat and tip the flour and salt into the pan. Reduce the heat to low and return the pan to the hob.
5 Beat the mix with a wooden spoon over a low heat, until it comes away easily from the sides.
6 Leave to cool for 10 minutes.
7 Beat in the eggs a little at a time, mixing until smooth yet strong enough to stand in peaks. You may not need all the egg.
8 Fold in the grated cheese.
9 Pipe the choux into rounds on a baking tray, leaving a space between each. Bake for 20–25 minutes, until lightly golden and crisp to the touch.

Profiteroles

150 ml water	2 eggs
50 g butter, cut into cubes	100 g chocolate
75 g strong plain flour	250 ml cream – double or whipping

Method

1 Line a baking sheet with parchment.
2 Put butter and water in a saucepan, heat until boiling.
3 Add flour, beat well, place back on heat to cook roux until it leaves the sides of the pan.
4 Leave to cool for a few minutes and add the eggs a little at a time, and beat well.
5 Put spoonfuls of the mixture on a baking sheet – or pipe.
6 Place in oven at 200°C for approximately 25 minutes. When they are puffed and golden take out of the oven, make a hole in them to allow the steam to escape, and place back in the oven for about 5 more minutes to fully dry out in the centre.
7 Melt the chocolate.
8 Whip the cream, then split open the profiterole and fill with cream. Alternatively the cream can be piped in.
9 Dip each one in the melted chocolate.

AQA GCSE Food Preparation and Nutrition

① Put butter and water in a saucepan, heat until boiling.

② Add flour.

③ Beat well, place back on heat to cook roux until it leaves the sides of the pan.

④ Leave to cool for a few minutes and add the eggs a little at a time. Beat well.

⑤ Pipe mixture into required shape.

Figure 1.11.9 Making choux pastry

SKILL 12 SETTING MIXTURES

Removal of heat

Starches such as cornflour, when heated with a liquid, will thicken a mixture. This process is called **gelatinisation**.

You will learn about gelatinisation in Topic 3.2 Functional and chemical properties of food. See page 212. See also Section 1 Skill 8 Sauce-making, page 64.

This mixture can then be chilled and it will set. This process is called **gelation**.

Figure 1.12.1 Custard

> ### Key words
>
> **Gelatinisation** is when starch granules are mixed with a liquid and heated, which makes them swell and break open, causing the liquid to thicken.
>
> **Gelation** is when a mixture is thickened by starch, and sets on chilling.

Examples of the gelation process are:
- When commercially-bought custard powder is mixed with milk and heated. The custard thickens and will set on chilling and can be used as one of the layers to make the dessert trifle.
- When making the traditional dessert blancmange.

AQA GCSE Food Preparation and Nutrition

Teacher demonstration

Figure 1.12.2

Fruit blancmange

71 g (4 tbsp) of cornflour

55 g caster sugar

550 ml skimmed milk

500 g of soft fruit, for example
strawberries, raspberries,
blackberries (optional 25 to 50 g
icing sugar to sweeten)

Method

1 Using a food processor or blender, blend the soft fruit until it is a purée. If you
  don't want seeds in your puree then sieve the purée to remove the seeds.
2 Blend cornflour and sugar in a bowl with two tablespoons of the milk.
3 Heat the remaining milk in a saucepan until almost boiling.
4 Pour the hot milk on to the cornflour mixture, stirring well.
5 Return the mixture to the saucepan and heat gently until the mixture thickens.
6 Pour mixture into a mould and chill in the refrigerator until set.

Use of protein

The texture of foods that contain protein, such as eggs, can be altered by heat. When protein
is heated, there is a change in its chemical structure, which is called **denaturation**, and this
then leads to **coagulation**, which is the setting of proteins.

You will learn about denaturation and coagulation in Topic 3.2 Functional and chemical
properties of food. See page 212.

Figure 1.12.3 Quiche
Lorraine

Examples of proteins being used to set a mixture are:
- making an egg custard
- making a cheese flan or quiche (see page 77)
- making a bread and butter pudding.

Baked egg custard

2 eggs

250 ml milk

30 g caster sugar

1 drop vanilla essence

A sprinkle of nutmeg

Method

1. Beat eggs and sugar together.
2. Heat the milk until warm.
3. Add the milk to beaten eggs and sugar, stir in the vanilla essence.
4. Strain into a greased ovenproof dish and sprinkle with grated nutmeg.
5. Place the ovenproof dish in a roasting tin of boiling water.
6. Bake in oven at 180°C for 30 to 40 minutes or until set.

Extension activity

Make some shortcrust pastry and make individual custard tarts.

Figure 1.12.4 Bread and butter pudding

> ### Key words
>
> **Denaturation** occurs when there is a change in shape of the protein molecules.
>
> **Coagulation** is the setting of proteins during heating.

Bread and butter pudding.

3 slices of white or brown bread

25 g butter or spread, a little extra for greasing the ovenproof dish

50 g dried fruit

25 g sugar

350 ml milk

2 eggs

Method

1. Lightly grease an ovenproof dish.
2. Spread the bread with the butter and cut each slice into four triangles.
3. Place a layer of the bread in the dish, sprinkle with fruit and sugar, repeat this and end with a layer of bread.
4. Beat the eggs and the milk together.
5. Pour over the bread through a sieve. Leave for ten minutes to stand, if time.
6. Bake for 30 to 40 minutes or until set and golden brown.

Extension activity

Make a healthier version of the traditional bread and butter pudding.

Make a different version of bread and butter pudding, for example using brioche or croissants.

AQA GCSE Food Preparation and Nutrition

SECTION 2
Food, Nutrition and Health

This section includes the following topics:

2.1 Macronutrients

2.2 Micronutrients (and water)

2.3 Nutritional needs and health

Section 2 practice questions

TOPIC 2.1 MACRONUTRIENTS

Protein

Learning objectives

In this section you will learn about:
- the **function** of protein in the body
- the terms low and high **biological value** protein and **protein complementation**
- the main **sources** of protein and **protein alternatives**
- the **amount of protein** required each day to remain healthy, called the Dietary Reference Value (DRV)
- the effects of a deficiency and excess of protein.

Key words

Amino acids are the basic components of all proteins.

Essential amino acids are amino acids that cannot be made by the body, they must come from food.

Non-essential amino acids are amino acids that can be made by the body and are always available.

High biological value protein is protein that contains all ten essential amino acids.

Low biological value protein is protein that lacks one or more essential amino acid.

The functions of protein

Protein is present throughout the human body. Protein is responsible for many functions in your body, including building every cell and tissue.

Protein is needed for:
- the growth of all body cells and tissue
- the repair and maintenance of all body tissue
- providing an energy source; if the body doesn't receive enough energy from carbohydrates or fat then 1 g of protein will provide 4 kcals of energy
- making hormones, enzymes and antibodies.

The biological value of protein

Proteins are big molecules and form long chains. The chains are made up of building blocks called **amino acids**. There are about 20 different amino acids found in plants and animals, each one having a specific function in the body. Amino acids combine in different ways to make all the proteins in your body.

Figure 2.1.1 An amino acid chain

When you eat protein, it is broken down into amino acids. These are rearranged into new proteins that your body needs. Most amino acids can be made by the body (**non-essential amino acids**) but some can only be obtained from food; these are called **essential amino acids**. There are eight essential amino acids needed by adults and children, and some extra ones needed just by children because they are growing.

Different foods contain different amounts of amino acids. Foods which contain all the essential amino acids are called **high biological value (HBV)**. Generally, the HBV proteins come from animal products, such as meat, fish, dairy produce and eggs. The only plants that contain all the essential amino acids are soya beans and soya products, and a grain called quinoa.

Foods which lack one of more of the essential amino acids are called **low biological value (LBV)**. LBV proteins include beans, pulses, nuts and seeds and cereals.

Figure 2.1.2 LBV protein foods

Protein complementation

When protein foods are mixed together the biological value will increase. The approach of combining LBV proteins foods to form a HBV protein meal is known as **protein complementation**. Beans, peas and lentils, for example, are a good source of the amino acid lysine but grains such as wheat, rice and oats, are low in lysine. By combining both groups of foods a complete mix of essential amino acids is achieved and a high biological outcome.

Other examples of protein complementation include:
- lentil dhal with chapatis
- peas and rice
- baked beans on toast
- houmous (chickpeas) with pitta bread.

Protein complementation is needed to ensure that vegetarians get all the essential amino acids. Protein complementation can save money because LBV tend to be cheaper than HBV proteins.

Key words

Protein complementation is combining LBV protein foods to form a HBV protein meal.

Extension activity

Plan and make a lunch which demonstrates protein complementation.

Explain how the combination of different proteins complement each other in the lunch.

The sources of protein

Proteins are available from animal and plant sources. In the UK most of our protein comes from animal sources.

High biological value sources	Low biological value sources
Meat and meat products, e.g. beef, lamb, chicken, pork, bacon, sausages, Fish and seafood, e.g. tuna, prawns Milk, yoghurts, cheese Eggs Soya beans and soya products Quinoa Quorn™	Cereals, e.g. wheat, rice, oats, barley Cereal products, e.g. bread, pasta, chapatis Sweetcorn Peas, beans, lentils Nuts and nut products, e.g. peanut butter Seeds

Table 2.1.1 Protein sources

Practical activity

Prepare and make a high protein snack. Identify the main sources of protein in your snack.

Figure 2.1.3 High protein snack: Chicken salad

Activity

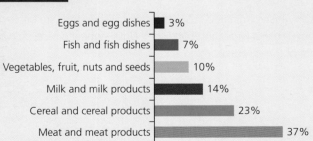

Eggs and egg dishes — 3%
Fish and fish dishes — 7%
Vegetables, fruit, nuts and seeds — 10%
Milk and milk products — 14%
Cereal and cereal products — 23%
Meat and meat products — 37%

Figure 2.1.4 Sources of protein in the diet of UK adults

Use the graph to answer the following questions.
1 Which food group provides the largest source of protein in the diet?
2 Which food group provides 3 per cent of protein in the diet?
3 What percentage of protein comes from cereals and cereal products?
4 Which foods would be found in the milk and milk products group?
5 What advice might be given to a vegetarian to meet their dietary needs for protein?

Protein alternatives

Food manufacturers have developed products which can be used in food preparation as an alternative to animal protein.

There are three main **protein alternatives**: soya, mycoprotein and quinoa.

Soya

Figure 2.1.5 Soya beans

Soya beans are consumed as an alternative to meat or other animal products. Soya beans are known as **edamame beans**, when eaten fresh. Soya is used in many products which include:

- **Textured Vegetable Protein** (TVP) in the form of mince and chunks has been developed from the soya bean. TVP is added to recipes to replace meat or used to make burgers, sausages and ready meals.
- **Tofu** is bean curd made from soya milk. The proteins set producing a cheese-like product. Tofu can be soft, hard, smoked and marinated.
- **Soya milk** is made from soaking soya beans in water. Soya cheese, yoghurts, shakes and cream are available.
- **Tempeh** is a mass of soya beans made by cooking and dehulling the beans to form a solid 'cake' which can be sliced.
- **Miso** is a fermented paste made from soya beans, rice or barley grains, salt and water.

Mycoprotein

The product Quorn™ is made from mycoprotein. Mycoprotein is a type of fungus which is grown under special conditions similar to that used for growing yeast in bread. It can be made into a wide range of products but is not suitable for very strict vegetarians (vegans) because egg white is used during the production.

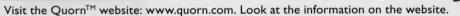

Research activity

Visit the Quorn™ website: www.quorn.com. Look at the information on the website.

True or false – do you agree with these statements about Quorn™?
- It can be bought in different forms.
- It has a very strong flavour.
- It has vitamins and minerals added.
- It is high in fat.
- It easy to store.
- It is more expensive than meat or fish.
- It can be cooked in many different ways.
- It is a HBV protein.

Quinoa

Quinoa are tiny, bead-shaped seeds which originated in South America. The seeds are cooked in the same way as rice and can be used in a wide range of dishes. Unlike wheat or rice, quinoa is a HBV protein containing all eight of the essential amino acids.

Dietary reference value for protein

The table shows the amounts of protein needed each day by different groups of people.

Age	Males	Females
11–14 years	42.1 g	41.2 g
15–18 years	55.2 g	45 g
19–49 years	55.5 g	45 g
50 years+	53.3 g	46.5 g

Reference Nutrient Intakes from Department of Health, Dietary Reference Values for Food Energy and Nutrients for the United Kingdom, HMSO, 1991.

Table 2.1.2 The different requirements for protein (grams per day)

Key points about protein intake:
- Men require more protein than women due to the fact they are usually bigger than women.
- Babies and children require a lot of protein (relative to their size) because they are growing.
- Teenagers need more protein to support their rapid growth spurt.

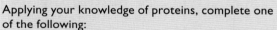

Key words

Protein alternatives are products which have been developed for use in food preparation as an alternative to animal protein.

Kwashiorkor is a type of malnutrition linked to a lack of protein and energy.

Deficiency and excess of protein

Protein deficiency is very rare in the developed world. Most people eat a wide range of foods that contain protein so even if you are a vegetarian, you are likely to be getting all the amino acids your body needs.

Protein deficiency can occur in the developing world. **Kwashiorkor** is a deficiency of protein and energy. It usually occurs in children in developing countries where there is famine or an unstable food supply. Children suffering from kwashiorkor have poor growth rates, retain water in their body tissues, and suffer hair loss and persistent infections.

Too much protein in the diet can be harmful to the kidneys and liver because they have to break the protein down. If we don't use the extra protein we consume for energy it will be stored as fat leading to weight gain.

Practical activity

Applying your knowledge of proteins, complete one of the following:
1. A two-course meal for a teenager aged 15–18 years. Show how this meal provides about 18 g of protein – about one third of their daily needs. Prepare and make one dish from the meal.
2. An investigation into different protein foods to find out which supplies the best source of protein. Plan and make a dish using one of the best sources.
3. An investigation into snacks, which can be eaten on the go. Find out which supplies the most protein.

Check your knowledge and understanding

1. State **three** reasons why the body needs protein.
2. How much energy (kcals) does 1 g of protein provide?
3. Give the definition of an essential amino acid?
4. Identify **three** high biological value proteins.
5. Identify **three** low biological value proteins.
6. Explain the difference between high biological value proteins and low biological value proteins.
7. Explain the effect of having too much protein in your diet.
8. Describe what is meant by protein complementation.
9. Evaluate the use of protein alternatives in the diet.
10. Discuss the protein requirements of males and females.

Fats

Learning objectives

In this section you will learn about:
- the **function** of fat in the body
- the main **sources** of fat in the diet
- the terms **saturated** and **unsaturated** fat
- the **amount of fat** required each day to remain healthy, called the Dietary Reference Value (DRV)
- the effects of a **deficiency** and **excess** of fat.

Functions of fats

Eating fat is essential for a balanced diet. The term fats includes both fats and oils. Fats tend to be solid at room temperature while oils are liquid. The functions of fats and oils in the body are basically the same.

Fats are needed for:
- providing us with a concentrated source of energy as 1 g of fat provides 9 kcals of energy
- making all body cells
- keeping the body warm, it forms **adipose tissue** under the skin
- protecting vital organs such as the kidneys
- providing the fat soluble vitamins A, D, E and K
- providing the essential fatty acids.

In addition, fats and oils have an important role in improving the flavour, texture and smell of the food we eat. They make food crispy, crumbly and moist.

Fats and oils slow down the stomach from emptying and take longer to digest. This can make you feel satisfied and full for a longer period of time after eating foods rich in fat.

Sources of fats

Fats can be **visible** in some foods such as a fat layer on the outside of lamb or pork. Sometimes you can see the fat inside meat as a white marbling. Visible fat is the butter on a slice of bread.

Some fats are **invisible** and cannot be seen easily because they have been used to make the product. Crisps, biscuits and cakes contain invisible fat. Some liquid food, such as milk, egg yolks, mayonnaise and gravies contain fat droplets which are difficult to see. When fat droplets are distributed in water we call this an **emulsion**.

Extension activity

Find out about emulsions. How do fat droplets behave in water and water droplets behave in fat? Find examples of each in food.

Animal fat sources	Vegetable fat sources
Butter, ghee, lard, goose fat, suet, dripping	Vegetable and plant oils, e.g. olive, sunflower, rapeseed.
Meat, e.g. beef, lamb, chicken, pork, duck, bacon	Avocados and olives
Meat products, e.g. sausages, chorizo, burgers	Nuts and nut products, e.g. peanut butter
Oily fish, e.g. tuna, salmon	Seeds, e.g. sesame seeds
Full-fat Greek yoghurts, hard cheese, cream	Fat spreads
Eggs	
Chocolate, pastries, biscuits, cakes	

Table 2.1.3 Sources of fat

Hydrogenation is the chemical process when vegetable oils are 'hardened', to make them solid at room temperature.

Partially hydrogenated vegetable oils may contain **trans fats**. These are thought to cause health problems such as heart disease. Food manufacturers are being encouraged to reduce the amount of hydrogenated fat in our food. Only 2 per cent of our daily energy should come from trans fats, this is no more than about 5 g of fat a day.

Key words

Hydrogenation is the process in which vegetable oils are 'hardened' to make them solid at room temperature.

Invisible fat is fat that is not clearly seen in food.

Visible fat is fat that can be clearly seen in food.

Trans fats are formed when oil goes through a process called hydrogenation, which makes the oil solid.

Figure 2.1.6 Visible fat

Figure 2.1.7 Invisible fat

Types of fats and oils

The chemical name for a fat is a **triglyceride**. A triglyceride molecule is made of three **fatty acids** parts attached to one **glycerol** part.

The fatty acids are the most important part of the molecule. They can either be **saturated** (full up) or **unsaturated** (not full up) with hydrogen atoms.

Saturated fats

Saturated fats have single bonds between all of the carbon atoms in the carbon chain. All of the bonds are saturated with hydrogen.

Saturated fats are solid at room temperature. Generally they are found in animal products such as red meat, butter, ghee, cream, hard cheese and eggs. Saturated fats are also found in meat products such as sausages, pies, chocolate, biscuits, cakes and pastries. Some vegetables and plants oil are saturated, for example coconut oil and palm oil.

Saturated fats are have been linked to heart disease. Foods that are high in saturated fat will contain cholesterol. A combination of saturated fat and cholesterol can lead to a build up of fatty deposits in and around the heart. Most people in the UK eat too much saturated fat.

The British Dietetic Association estimate we eat 20 per cent more than the recommended maximum.
- The average man should eat no more than 30 g of saturated fat a day.
- The average woman should eat no more than 20 g of saturated fat a day.

Group work

Discuss the differences between saturated and unsaturated fats.

Unsaturated fats

Sometimes the chain of carbon atoms has some hydrogen atoms missing. This creates an unsaturated molecule and results in a 'double bond' between two of the carbon atoms in the chain. The double bond puts a bend or curve in the carbon chain and this allows movement. **Unsaturated fats** are liquids at room temperature, for example sunflower oil, olive oil.

Eating unsaturated fats instead of saturated is recommended. Unsaturated fats are found in:
1. oily fish such as salmon, sardines and mackerel
2. nuts and seeds
3. sunflower and olive oils.

Research suggests that unsaturated fats are healthier than saturated fats. They may lower blood cholesterol levels and reduce the risk of heart disease.

There are two types of unsaturated fats:
- **Monounsaturated fatty acids** have one double bond. The prefix 'mono' means one. Avocados, cashews and peanuts are good sources of monounsaturated fatty acids.
- **Polyunsaturated fatty acids** have two or more double bonds in the carbon chains. The prefix 'poly' means two or more. Corn, soya and sunflower oils are good sources of polyunsaturated fatty acids.

Teacher's tip

LDL also stands for '*Lousy* density lipoprotein' which might help students to remember that it is bad!

Essential fatty acids

Omega 3 and omega 6 are two polyunsaturated fatty acids that are very important for heath. They are called essential fatty acids. **Essential fatty acids** must be eaten in the diet as the body cannot make them. They are vital for the proper functioning of the brain and heart and for the development of our nervous system.
- Omega 3 is found in oily fish, seeds and green leafy vegetables.
- Omega 6 is found in vegetables, grains, seeds and chicken.

Cholesterol

Cholesterol is a fatty substance which is needed for the normal functioning of the body. Cholesterol is an essential part of cell membranes and helps with the digestion of fats. Cholesterol is made by the body but it is also found in fatty foods. Eating foods that are high in saturated fat will raise cholesterol levels in the blood.

Cholesterol is carried around the body by proteins called **lipoproteins**. There are two types of lipoprotein:

- low density lipoprotein (LDL) called **'bad cholesterol'**
- high density lipoprotein (HDL) called **'good cholesterol'**.

Too much bad cholesterol and saturated fat in the body can build up in arteries and cause heart disease. Good cholesterol may actually help to protect against heart disease.

Key words

Triglyceride is the chemical name for a fat molecule.

Saturated fatty acids have single bonds on the carbon chain.

Saturated fats contain saturated fatty acids, are usually from animal sources and can be harmful to health.

Unsaturated fatty acids have a double bond on one or more carbon atoms.

Unsaturated fats contain unsaturated fatty acids and are thought to be better for health.

Essential fatty acids are required for development and cannot be made by the body.

Cholesterol is a fatty substance found in the blood; it is essential for humans but can be harmful.

Dietary reference value for fat

Fat should provide no more than 35 per cent of food energy. However, it is estimated that around 42 per cent of energy in the typical British diet comes from fat. This figure needs to be reduced.

Too much fat we eat comes from animal sources (saturated fats). Only 11 per cent of our energy intake should come from saturated fat. The goal for essential fatty acids is about 1–2 per cent of total energy intake.

Activity

There are several simple ways to reduce fat intake. Produce a flyer or a customer information guide telling the consumer of ways in which they can reduce their fat intake during the purchase, preparation and cooking of food.

Figure 2.1.11 Obesity

Deficiencies and excess of fat

We all need some fat in our diet. However, in more economically developed countries there is concern that people are eating too much fat, in particular eating too much saturated fat. Saturated fat can raise our 'bad cholesterol' levels in the body, which increases the risk of heart disease. It's important to cut down on fat and choose foods that contain unsaturated fat.

Eating too much fat can make us more likely to put on weight. This is because foods that are high in fat are high in energy too. Obesity develops if you combine eating too many energy rich foods with a lack of exercise. Being overweight raises our risk of serious health problems, such as type 2 diabetes and high blood pressure, as well as heart disease.

A lack of fat in the diet over time will result in weight loss. Omega 3 fatty acids provide protection from heart disease and this would be lost. There could also be deficiencies of the fat soluble vitamins A, D, E and K.

Practical activity

Plan and make a dish to show **one** of the following:
- A savoury main dish where the saturated fats have be changed to unsaturated fats. Explain your changes to reduce the saturated fat content.
- A lasagne or pasta bake which has been adapted to reduce the total fat content. Explain how you have reduced the total fat content of your dish.

Research activity

1 Visit a major food retailer's website and investigate the range of chilled ready meals available.
   Focus on the fat content per 100g and the saturated fat content per 100g of each meal. Include some 'low fat' or 'reduced fat' chilled ready meals too.
   Record your findings in a table like this:

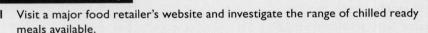

Name of chilled meal	Fat content per 100 g	Saturated fat content per 100 g	Main sources of fat in the meal
Spanish meatballs in tomato sauce	10.1 g	2.6 g	Pork, chorizo

2 Which chilled meals contain the greatest amount of fat? Which contain the least?
3 How do the low fat ready meals compare to the full fat ready meals?

Check your knowledge and understanding

1 Describe **three** functions of fat in the diet.
2 Explain the difference between visible and invisible fat.
3 Name **three** sources of animal fat.
4 Name **three** sources of vegetable fat.
5 Discuss the main differences between unsaturated and saturated fats.

6 What are essential fatty acids?
7 Describe why essential fatty acids are important.
8 Explain why saturated fat is harmful to health.
9 Explain what could happen if too much fat is eaten.
10 Assess the importance of cholesterol in the diet.

Carbohydrates

Learning objectives

In this topic you will learn about:

- the **functions** of carbohydrates in the body
- the main **sources** of carbohydrates
- the different types of carbohydrate including **starch**, **sugar** and **dietary fibre**
- the effects of a **deficiency** and **excess** of carbohydrate
- the **amount of carbohydrate** required each day to remain healthy, called the Dietary Reference Value (DRV).

Carbohydrates are an energy source made by plants during **photosynthesis**. The plant energy provides human energy, if eaten.

The functions of carbohydrate

Carbohydrate is present throughout the body and is required for energy needed for movement, growth and chemical reactions and processes

Carbohydrate is needed for:

- providing energy
- acting as a **'protein sparer'**. If the diet is low in carbohydrate, then protein is used as an energy source. Carbohydrate should stop the use of protein as an energy source so that the protein can continue its primary function for growth and repair.

> **Key words**
>
> **Sugar:** a sweet carbohydrate and source of energy.
> **Starch:** a complex carbohydrate and source of energy.

Sources of carbohydrate

Carbohydrates exist in many forms; they can be divided into three groups: **sugars**, **starches** and **dietary fibre**. Sugars are the simplest form of carbohydrates, starches and dietary fibre are more complex carbohydrates.

Figure 2.1.12 Foods high in carbohydrate

Figure 2.1.13 Sugar

Sugars

Sugars can be divided into **simple sugars** and **double sugars** according to the size of the molecule.

Sugars are easily broken down by the body. They are absorbed quickly into the bloodstream, providing an instant burst of energy.

Sugar group	Sugar name	Sources
Simple sugars The chemical name is **monosaccharides**.	Glucose	Ripe fruits and vegetables
	Fructose	Fruits and honey
Double sugars The chemical name is **disaccharides**.	Sucrose	Granulated sugar, caster sugar, demerara sugar, icing sugar, treacle, golden syrup
	Lactose	Found in milk, yoghurt, cream and cheese
	Maltose	Found in cereals and used to make beer and malt drinks

Table 2.1.4 Types of sugar

Figure 2.1.14 Fruit sugar in a slice of melon

Free and fruit sugars

Another way in which sugar can be classified is according to where it is found in the food.

Sugars that are found naturally inside fruit and vegetable cells are called **fruit sugars**. These are sometimes called 'natural sugars'.

Sugars that are added to food or found outside the cell structure are called **free sugars**. Free sugars are processed sugars such as granulated, caster, demerara, icing sugar, treacle and golden syrup. They also include the sugar found in honey and **unsweetened fruit juices**.

A diet high in free sugars can lead to tooth decay and obesity. Sugar provides energy but contains no other nutrients. Artificial sweeteners are sometimes added to food products e.g. sugar-free diet drinks. They add sweetness to the flavour of the food without increasing the energy content.

Key words

Fruit sugar: sugar found inside fruit (fresh, stewed, canned and dried) and vegetable cells.

Free sugar: sugar which is added to food.

Simple sugars or **monosaccharides:** single sugar units (e.g. glucose and fructose).

Double sugars or **disaccharides:** two single units of sugar joined together (e.g. sucrose).

Figure 2.1.15 Free sugar used in a biscuit making

Sources of sugar in the diet

Many foods and drinks contain fruit sugars such as fruits and vegetables.

Processed foods such as breakfast cereals, biscuits, cakes, pastries, jams, marmalade, chocolate, confectionary and sweetened soft drinks also contain free sugar. It is recommended that only 5 per cent of the energy we require should come from free sugars.

Hidden sugars

The sugar we add to our food accounts for a tiny fraction of the sugar we eat. Many processed foods contain hidden sugar. Hidden sugars can be found in foods that you wouldn't expect sugar to be found including savoury foods like salad dressings, bread, sauces and soups. You need to look carefully at food labels to identify hidden sugars. Here are some of the hidden sugars found on food labels:

- corn sugar
- dextrose
- fructose
- glucose
- maltose
- molasses
- invert sugar.

Research activities

1 Many foods contain hidden sugars. Look at the list below: which foods contain the most sugar? Indicate the top five.
   - Tomato ketchup
   - Stir-in sweet and sour sauce
   - Salad cream
   - Low-fat fruit yoghurt
   - Choc ice
   - Frosted corn flakes
   - Regular cola
   - Baked beans
   - Sweetened fruit juice
   - Chocolate spread
   - Fruit pastilles
2 From a display of different food products (suggestions above) find out from the label the sugar content in grams of **one serving** of each the foods. Make a table to show the results.
3 Considering that 1 level teaspoon of sugar weighs 5 g, which foods contain the most teaspoons of sugar? How does this compare to the initial top five above?

Starches

Starches are complex carbohydrates. They are also known as **polysaccharides**. Polysaccharides are made up of many simple sugars (glucose) joined together.

The most important starches are:

- **Starch** is the main food store in plants. It is made up of many molecules of glucose. Starch exists in granules of a size and shape distinctive to each plant.
- **Pectin** is found naturally in some fruits. It forms gels in water and helps jams to set. It is not fibrous but it is thought to help to reduce the amount of cholesterol in the blood.
- **Glycogen** is made from glucose by humans. Small amounts are stored in the liver and muscles as an energy reserve.

Sources of starch in the diet

Good sources of **starchy foods** include:

- root vegetables (for examples, potatoes, carrots)
- cereals and cereal products (for examples, bread, pasta rice, lentils, beans, breakfast cereals, biscuits, pastries).

Starches account for almost 60 per cent of the total carbohydrate intake in the average British diet. They should form the main part of the meals we eat every day and supply most of our energy.

> ### Key words
>
> **Polysaccharide:**
>
> **Glucose:** the simplest form of sugar.
>
> **Glycogen:** a store of glucose in humans.

Figure 2.1.16 Root vegetables such as potatoes, are a good source of starch

Excess and deficiency of sugars and starches

Eating too much sugar is bad for us. A diet rich in sugar will cause tooth decay and a gain in weight. Research suggests that people eat more sugar than they should.

More information on the effects of eating sugar and starch can be found in the diet, nutrition and health section in Topic 2.3 Nutritional needs and health (page 178).

A lack of carbohydrate in the diet is unusual. Some people choose to follow diets that reduce the amount of carbohydrates they eat. The aim of a low sugar diet may be to lose weight and reduce the effects of too much sugar.

Dietary reference values for sugars and starches

High intakes of free sugars have been linked to tooth decay and obesity. Free sugars need to be reduced in the diet and should be restricted to providing 5 per cent of daily energy (calorie) requirements. This is about 30 g of sugar a day for those aged 11 and over.

Currently, all population groups exceed this recommendation. Teenagers' intakes are the highest of all groups and they consume 50 per cent more sugar on average than is currently recommended.

| Carbohydrate | 50% of total food energy from carbohydrates | 45% from starchy carbohydrate, milk sugar and **fruit sugar** |
| | | no more than 5% from **free sugars** |

Table 2.1.5 Recommended energy sources for carbohydrates (percentage energy)

Extension activity

Discuss ways in which a teenager right reduce the amount of sugar in their daily diet.

Figure 2.1.17 Teenagers consume more sugar on average than currently recommended

Dietary fibre

Dietary fibre is a polysaccharide found in the cell walls of vegetables, fruits, pulses and cereal grains. The dietary fibre cannot be broken down by the digestive system so passes through the intestine, absorbing water and increasing in bulk. The process helps to strengthen the muscles of the intestine and push out undigested foods.

Figure 2.1.18 Bran flakes are a good source of dietary fibre

The functions of dietary fibre

Dietary fibre is needed for:

- allowing the digestive system to remain healthy and function properly
- helping weight control as high fibre foods release energy slowly leaving us feeling fuller for longer
- preventing some bowel diseases, for example constipation, diverticulitis and bowel cancer
- providing soluble fibre which can help to reduce cholesterol levels.

Sources of dietary fibre

There are two types of dietary fibre – insoluble and soluble.

- **Insoluble fibre** passes through the body mostly unchanged as it is undigested. It absorbs water and swells, resulting in a bulkier stool.
- **Soluble fibre** slows down the digestion and absorption of carbohydrates, so it helps to control blood sugar levels, which helps to stop you feeling hungry. Some research suggests that soluble fibre can reduce the blood cholesterol levels.

Soluble fibre	Insoluble fibre
<ul><li>Oats</li><li>Nuts</li><li>Legumes (e.g. peas, beans and lentils)</li><li>Fruits such as prunes, bananas, apples, pears, plums</li><li>Vegetables such as potatoes, sweet potatoes, broccoli and carrots</li></ul>	<ul><li>Wholegrain foods (e.g. wholegrain bread, breakfast cereals and pasta)</li><li>Brown rice</li><li>Wheat bran</li><li>Fruit and vegetables peel and skins</li><li>Nuts and seeds</li></ul>

Table 2.1.6 The sources of dietary fibre

Figure 2.1.19 Lentil soup contains soluble fibre

Excess and deficiency of dietary fibre

A diet rich in cereals can reduce the body's ability to absorb iron and calcium. The cereal can bind with the minerals making them less likely to be absorbed in the intestines.

A deficiency of dietary fibre can contribute towards constipation and this could lead to an increased risk of bowel cancer.

Dietary reference values for fibre

SACN (Scientific Advisory Committee on Nutrition) recommends that the Dietary Reference Value (DRV) for dietary fibre is **30 g** for adults.

Children should eat less because of their small body size. Very young children should avoid too many fibre-rich foods as being full up with fibre can it make it difficult for them meet their other nutritional needs.

> ### Key words
>
> **Milk sugar:** lactose in milk, yoghurt, cheese and cream.
>
> **Dietary fibre:** a polysaccharide found in the cell walls of vegetables, fruits, pulses and cereal grains.
>
> **Insoluble fibre:** dietary fibre which helps to prevent constipation.
>
> **Soluble fibre:** dietary fibre which helps to reduce cholesterol.

Activity

Using the items below plan a breakfast for yourself that would provide **6 g of fibre**.

Breakfast items	Serving size	Fibre content of 1 serving
Wholemeal bread	1 slice	1.8 g
White bread	1 slice	0.7 g
Brown bread	1 slice	1.2 g
All-bran cereal		9.6 g
Bran flakes		3.9 g
Cornflakes	a small bowl	0.3 g
Fruit 'n' Fibre cereal		2.1 g
Muesli		2.6 g
Weetabix		3.9 g
Dried apricots	8 apricots	5.4 g
Prunes	8 prunes	1.9 g
Apples	1 medium	1.8 g
Banana	1 medium	1.1 g
Raspberries	a small handful	1.5 g
Grapes	a small handful	1.0 g
Grapefruit	$\frac{1}{2}$ grapefruit	1.0 g
Melon	1 medium slice	1.5 g
Mango	2 slices	3.1 g
Orange	1 medium	2.7 g
Pear	1 medium	3.7 g
Pineapple	1 slice	1.4 g
Egg	1 egg	none
Yoghurt	125 g	none
Milk	150 ml	none
Bacon	2 slices	none
Strawberry jam	10 g	none
Fat spread/butter	10 g	none

Practical activity

Find a recipe for a cake, dessert or muffin that you could adapt to increase the fibre content. Explain all the adaptions you have made.

Calculate the fibre content of the dish before and after the changes. Use the British Nutrition Foundation website to calculate the content: http://explorefood.foodafactoflife.org.uk/

Check your knowledge and understanding

1. Give **one** reason why the body needs carbohydrate.
2. Explain why carbohydrates are a 'protein sparer'.
3. Explain what is meant by the term 'free sugar'.
4. Explain the term 'hidden sugar'.
5. Identify **three** starchy foods.
6. Describe **two** functions of dietary fibre.
7. Explain the difference between soluble and insoluble fibre.
8. How much fibre should an adult eat each day?
9. Discuss how fibre intake can be increased in the diet.
10. Assess the value of carbohydrates in the diet of teenagers.

TOPIC 2.2 MICRONUTRIENTS

The **micronutrients** are vitamins and minerals. They are required in very small amounts in the diet. The units used to measure how much you need each day are either **micrograms** or milligrams. The microgram is the very smallest amount.

1 milligram (mg) = 1,000 micrograms (mcg)

Vitamins: fat-soluble vitamins

Vitamins A, D, E and K are fat-soluble vitamins. Fat-soluble vitamins can be stored in the body for months and even years.

Learning objectives

In this section you will learn about:
- the **function** of fat-soluble vitamins in the body
- the main **sources** of fat-soluble vitamins in the diet
- the effects of a **deficiency** and **excess** of fat-soluble vitamins
- the **amount of fat-soluble vitamins** required each day to remain healthy, called the Dietary Reference Value (DRV).

Vitamin A

Vitamin A is a **fat-soluble vitamin**. Fat-soluble vitamins are stored in the liver and do not need to be eaten in large amounts.

Key words

Micronutrients are the nutrients needed in small amounts. Vitamins and minerals are micronutrients.

Microgram is the smallest unit of measurement used to measure micronutrients.

Fat-soluble vitamins are vitamins A, D, E and K which dissolve in fat.

Antioxidants are vitamins A, C and E, which protect the cells from harmful substances.

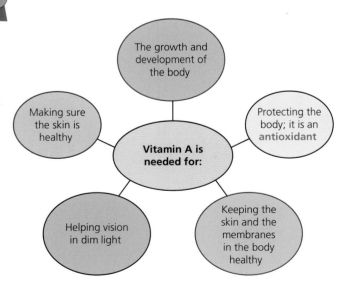

Figure 2.2.1 Functions of vitamin A

AQA GCSE Food Preparation and Nutrition

The sources of vitamin A

There are two types of vitamin A. They are called **retinol** and **betacarotene**.

- **Retinol** is vitamin A from animal sources.
- **Betacarotene** is vitamin A from vegetable sources.

In the UK, about 75 per cent of our vitamin A is supplied in the form of retinol and 25 per cent as betacarotene.

Figure 2.2.2 Foods that contain retinol and beta carotene

Animal sources (retinol)	Vegetable sources (betacarotene)
• Eggs • Oily fish • Liver • Full fat milk • Butter and cheese • Margarines, fat spreads that have been **fortified**	• Yellow, red and green (leafy) vegetables, such as spinach, carrots, sweet potatoes and red peppers • Yellow fruit, such as mangos and apricots

Table 2.2.1 Good sources of vitamin A

Deficiency of vitamin A

A deficiency of vitamin A is very rare in the UK. The deficiency of vitamin A is called **night blindness**. Night blindness is the failure to see well in dim light. If it is not treated, it can lead to blindness. Since carrots are a good source of betacarotene, there is truth in the old saying that carrots help you see better in the dark!

Excess of vitamin A

Retinol can be poisonous if eaten in large amounts. Pregnant women should avoid eating large amounts of foods containing vitamin A because it may harm their developing baby. They should avoid eating liver or liver products (for example, pâté) because they are very high in vitamin A.

Dietary Reference Value for vitamin A

The amount of vitamin A you need each day is very small and is measured in micrograms (mcg).

Age	Males	Females
4 years	500 mcg	500 mcg
10 years	500 mcg	500 mcg
14 years	600 mcg	600 mcg
Adults	700 mcg	600 mcg
Older adults (over 50)	700 mcg	700 mcg

Table 2.2.2 Dietary Reference Values for vitamin A

Key word

Night blindness is caused by a lack of vitamin A, and means you are unable to see well in dim light.

Vitamin D

Vitamin D is stored in the liver and body fat. Vitamin D is produced by the action of sunlight on the skin.

The sources of vitamin D

The main source of vitamin D is sunlight. It is because of this that vitamin D is often called the **sunshine vitamin**. Exposure to sunshine can provide vitamin D but dietary sources are essential too.

Good sources of vitamin D are:
- milk, butter, liver, oily fish and eggs
- fortified breakfast cereals with added vitamin D
- fortified fats (for example, soft spreads).

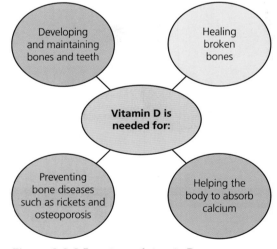

Figure 2.2.3 Functions of vitamin D

Key words

Sunshine vitamin is another name for vitamin D.

Rickets is a condition found in children, where a lack of vitamin D and calcium in the diet cause the bones to soften.

Deficiency of vitamin D

Not enough vitamin D can result in **rickets** in babies and toddlers. Growing bones require vitamin D to harden. Without vitamin D, they will soften and this will cause them to bend and bow.

You will learn more about diet and bone health in Topic 2.3 Nutritional needs and health. See page 148.

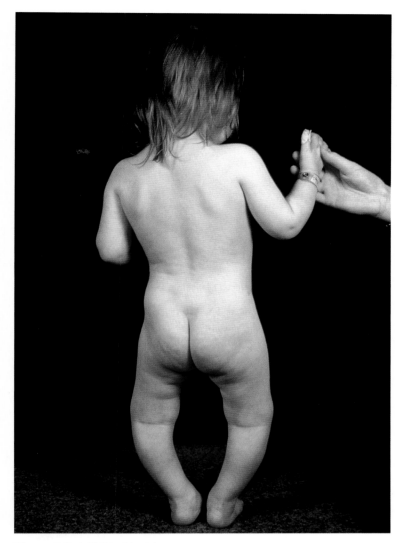

Figure 2.2.4 Child with rickets

Groups at risk of vitamin D deficiency

Some people are more likely to suffer from a lack of vitamin D. They are:

- pregnant and breastfeeding women
- babies and young children under the age of five
- people who are not exposed to much sun, such as people who cover up their skin when outdoors, or those who are inside their home for long periods
- people who have darker skin, such as those of African, African-Caribbean and South Asian origin.

Excess of vitamin D

Too much vitamin D is stored in the body and is unlikely to cause problems.

Dietary Reference Value for vitamin D

The amount of vitamin D you need each day is measured in micrograms (mcg).

The Department of Health recommends that everyone over four years should consume 10 micrograms of vitamin D each day.

Vitamin E

Vitamin E is a fat-soluble vitamin. It is found in every cell in the body and stored in the liver.

Functions of vitamin E

Vitamin E is needed for:
- protecting the body; it is an antioxidant
- forming red blood cells.

Deficiency and excess of vitamin E

A deficiency of vitamin E is rare. Too much vitamin E causes a loss of appetite.

Dietary Reference Value for vitamin E

The amount of vitamin E required each day is measured in **milligrams**. It is:
- 4 milligrams a day for men
- 3 milligrams a day for women.

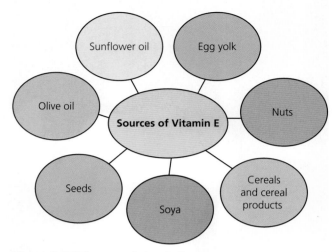

Figure 2.2.5 Sources of vitamin E

Vitamin K

Vitamin K is a fat-soluble vitamin. It can be stored in the liver.

Functions of vitamin K

Vitamin K is needed for:
- making blood clot
- maintaining bone health.

Sources of Vitamin K

- green leafy vegetables, for example green peas and beans, broccoli and spinach
- vegetable oils
- cereals.

Vitamin K is also made by bacteria in the large intestine.

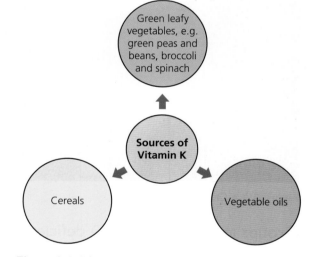

Figure 2.2.6 Sources of vitamin K

Deficiency and excess of vitamin K

Deficiency is rare, as vitamin K is made by the body. Signs of deficiency include easy bruising and bleeding. The blood may take longer to clot in a person suffering vitamin K deficiency.

Newborn babies are at risk of developing a rare condition associated with vitamin K deficiency. The deficiency is almost completely preventable by giving a single dose of vitamin K soon after birth, and such a dose is offered to all UK mothers.

There is not enough evidence to draw conclusions on the possible effects of taking high doses of vitamin K supplements each day.

Dietary Reference Value for vitamin K

The daily requirement for vitamin K is:
- teenagers: 0.045 mg
- males: 0.075 mg
- females: 0.065 mg

Vitamins: water-soluble vitamins

The B group of vitamins and vitamin C are water-soluble. **Water-soluble vitamins** cannot be stored in the body and need to be eaten regularly.

Learning objectives

In this section you will learn about:
- the **function** of water-soluble vitamins in the body
- the main **sources** of water-soluble vitamins in the diet
- the effects of a **deficiency** and **excess** of water-soluble vitamins
- the **amount of water-soluble vitamins** required each day to remain healthy, called the Dietary Reference Value (DRV)
- the ways in which food **preparation** and **cooking** affect the nutritional properties of food.

Figure 2.2.7 Pork contains vitamin B1

Figure 2.2.8 Fish contains vitamin B2

Figure 2.2.9 Broccoli contains folic acid

Water-soluble vitamin	Functions	Sources	Deficiency	Excess
Vitamin B1 (Thiamin)	• Works with other B group vitamins to release energy from food • Helps the nervous system work	• liver • milk • cheese • bread • fortified breakfast cereals • dried fruit • eggs • potatoes • nuts • peas • added to flour	**Beri beri** is a deficiency disease caused by a severe shortage of vitamin B1. It is a muscle wasting disease which is only seen in countries where there are food shortages.	It is very rare for someone to consume too much vitamin B1 unless they are taking supplements.
Vitamin B2 (Riboflavin)	• Helps the body to release energy from the food you eat • Keeps the skin, eyes, the nervous system and mucous membranes healthy	Vitamin B2 is found inside every animal and vegetable cell. Good sources of vitamin B2 are: • chicken • eggs • milk • fish • yoghurt • leafy vegetables • rice • bread • breakfast cereals • soya beans	Vitamin B2 deficiency is rare. However, where there is a serious shortage of food then the symptoms of vitamin B2 deficiency, which include skin problems, dry and cracked lips and poor growth, will be found in children.	No side effects have been reported of eating too much vitamin B2.
Folic acid	• Helps to reduce the risk of nervous system defects in unborn babies • Works with vitamin B12 to form healthy red blood cells	• fortified breakfast cereals • broccoli • Brussels sprouts • liver • chickpeas • spinach • asparagus • peas	Folic acid can reduce the risk of having a baby born with a nervous system defect called **spina bifida**. Spina bifida means 'split spine' and is a defect in the backbone that can occur in unborn babies if not enough folic acid was eaten by the mother during pregnancy. It is estimated that there are between 700 and 900 pregnancies affected by a lack of folic acid each year in the UK.	No harmful side effects have been reported of having too much folic acid.

Table 2.2.3 Water-soluble vitamins

Vitamin B12	<ul><li>Maintains nerve cells</li><li>Makes red blood cells</li><li>Releases energy from the food you eat</li><li>Processes folic acid</li></ul>	<ul><li>meat</li><li>eggs</li><li>milk</li><li>salmon</li><li>fortified breakfast cereals</li><li>cheese</li><li>beef</li><li>cod</li></ul>	If you eat meat, fish or dairy foods you should be able to get enough vitamin B12 from your diet. Vitamin B12 deficiency is known as **pernicious anaemia**. Pernicious anaemia is most likely in **vegans**. Vegans do not eat any animal products. The symptoms of a lack of vitamin B12 are tingling and numbness in the hands and feet and a loss of memory.	There are no known harmful effects of eating too much vitamin B12.
Vitamin C (A limited supply of vitamin C can be stored in the liver and in body tissue. It is commonly referred to as **ascorbic acid**)	<ul><li>Makes and maintains healthy **connective tissue**</li><li>Helps wounds heal and repairs body tissues</li><li>Helps the absorption of iron from the intestines</li><li>Protects the body; it is an antioxidant</li></ul>	<ul><li>oranges and orange juice</li><li>blackcurrants</li><li>broccoli</li><li>potatoes (an average serving of new potatoes will provide 90 per cent of the recommended daily intake of vitamin C)</li><li>red and green peppers</li><li>strawberries</li><li>Brussels sprouts</li><li>tomatoes</li></ul>	A severe deficiency of vitamin C is called **scurvy**. Scurvy is very rare but the symptoms include swollen gums, severe joint pain and new wounds may fail to heal.	Taking large amounts of vitamin C can cause stomach pain and diarrhoea.

Table 2.2.3 Cont.

Figure 2.2.10 Salmon is a good source of vitamin B12

Figure 2.2.11 Sources of vitamin C

Dietary Reference Value for vitamin B1

The amount of vitamin B1 needed is linked to the amount of energy the body needs. More vitamin B1 is needed when the body requires more energy.

People who require more vitamin B1 are:

- pregnant and breastfeeding women, because they are using more energy to carry a baby and produce breast milk
- athletes, because they use up energy during training
- young children and teenagers, because their rapid growth requires more energy.

The amount of vitamin B1 you need each day is measured in milligrams (mg).

Water-soluble vitamins	Vitamin B1		Vitamin B2		Vitamin B3		Folic acid	Vitamin B12	Vitamin C
Ages	Males	Females	Males	Females	Males	Females	Both	Both	Both
4 years	0.7 mg	0.7 mg	11 mg	11 mg	11 mg	11 mg	100 mcg	0.8 mcg	30 mg
10 years	0.7 mg	0.7 mg	12 mg	12 mg	12 mg	12 mg	150 mcg	1.0 mcg	30 mg
14 years	0.9 mg	0.7 mg	15 mg	12 mg	15 mg	12 mg	200 mcg	1.2 mcg	35 mg
Adults	1.0 mg	0.8mg	17 mg	13 mg	17 mg	13 mg	200 mcg	1.5 mcg	40 mg
Older adults (over 50)	0.9 mg	0.8 mg	16 mg	12 mg	16 mg	12 mg	200 mcg	1.5 mcg	40 mg

Table 2.2.4 Dietary Reference Values for water-soluble vitamins

Taking a folic acid supplement may prevent the development of spina bifida in pregnancy. Pregnant women or those thinking of having a baby should take at least 300 micrograms of folic acid each day.

Activity

Copy and complete the following:

Vitamin B1 is also known as .... A deficiency of vitamin B1 is called ....
.... This disease is very rare in developing countries. Good sources of vitamin B1 are
.... , ... and ....

Vitamin B12 deficiency is called .... Vitamin B12 is found in
.... products. A group of vegetarians called .... can find it difficult to eat enough vitamin B12 because it is only found in animal products.

Key words

Thiamin is vitamin B1.

Water-soluble vitamins are the B group of vitamins and vitamin C, which dissolve in water.

Beri beri is a lack of vitamin B1.

Spina bifida is a defect in the backbone that can occur in unborn babies if not enough folic acid was eaten by the mother during pregnancy.

Riboflavin is vitamin B2.

Pernicious anaemia means a lack of vitamin B12.

Pellagra is a lack of vitamin B3.

Vegan is a person who does not eat any animal products.

Connective tissue gives support and structure to body tissues.

Scurvy is a lack of vitamin C.

Research activity

1 Choose a selection of breakfast cereal packages and produce a table showing the amount of vitamins found in a serving of each product.

Here is an example of how the table might look.

Vitamin content	30 g of Crispy Rice served with semi-skimmed milk	30 g of Crunchy Wheat served with semi-skimmed milk
Vitamin D	2.5 ug	1.5 ug
Vitamin C	42 mg	10 mg
Vitamin B1	0.6 mg	0.4 mg
Vitamin B2	1.0 mg	0.7 mg
Vitamin B3	8.2 mg	5.2 mg
Folic acid	108 ug	136 ug

2 Which breakfast cereal is the better source of each vitamin?
3 Which breakfast cereal is the poorer source of each vitamin?

Extension activity

Evaluate each breakfast cereal against the DRVs and consider their suitability for different age groups.

Practical activity

The folic acid found in food is called folate. When completing a nutritional analysis you may see folic acid called folate.
1 Plan and make a dish that will provide an adult with a good supply of folic acid.
2 Calculate the folate (folic acid) content of the dish.

Activity

Deficiency diseases

Match the deficiency disease and symptom to the correct vitamin.

pernicious anaemia	soft bones	vitamin C
scurvy	poor vision	vitamin A
beri beri	swollen gums	vitamin D
night blindness	muscle wasting	vitamin B12
rickets	memory loss	vitamin B1

How preparation and cooking affects the nutritional properties of food

The preparation and cooking of food can affect its nutritional value.

Water-soluble vitamins in the vitamin B group and vitamin C are affected by food preparation and cooking. They are very unstable. They dissolve in water, can be destroyed by contact with sunlight, air and heat and are affected by **enzymes**. Enzymes are chemicals found inside plant cells that control the ripening process but they will destroy vitamins.

You will learn more about the action of enzymes in Topic 4.1 Food spoilage and contamination. See page 248.

Reducing the loss of water-soluble vitamins when preparing and cooking food

You can reduce the loss of water-soluble vitamins (vitamin C and the vitamin B group) by following the principles below.

Buy fruit and vegetables in good condition

Avoid buying bruised or damaged fruit and vegetables. Bruised or damaged fruit and vegetables have broken plant cells, which release enzymes that will start to destroy vitamins.

Choose ripe fruit and vegetables

Choose just-ripened fruit and vegetables as they contain the most vitamins. Ideally, fruit and vegetables should be harvested ripe and eaten shortly afterwards. Unripe or over-ripe fruit and vegetables may have a lower vitamin content than ripe fruit and vegetables.

Store in cool, dark places

Most fruit and vegetables should be stored in the refrigerator. Enzymes are active at room temperature so the cool temperature of a refrigerator will slow down their activity. Sunlight destroys some vitamins too.

Use shortly after buying

Ripening will continue after buying fruit and vegetables, so use them up quickly. Pre-packed bags of salad have a **modified atmosphere** which slows down the ripening process, but once opened the salad will deteriorate quickly and the vitamin loss will be rapid.

Minimise the preparation

Rip or tear fruit and vegetables, when possible, as this reduces cell wall damage. Every time you cut, slice or chop a piece of fruit or vegetable, the cells walls are damaged and enzymes are released that will destroy the vitamins.

Chopping fruit and vegetables into very small pieces is most damaging. Many cell walls are damaged and harmful enzymes released. Using a blunt knife will damage more cell walls; use a sharp vegetable knife because it makes a clean cut.

Key word

Enzymes are biological catalysts found inside plant cells, which control the ripening process.

Key words

Modified atmosphere refers to packaging that uses a combination of gases (nitrogen or carbon dioxide) to increase the shelf life.

Blanching means immersing fruits or vegetables in boiling water for a few minutes and then cooling rapidly. Blanching stops enzyme activity and helps to retain vitamins.

Blanch vegetables

Blanching is immersing the prepared fruits or vegetables in boiling water for a few minutes and then cooling rapidly. Blanching stops enzyme activity and helps to retain vitamins.

Avoid soaking in water

Water-soluble vitamins will leach out of fruit and vegetables if they are placed in water. Soaking them before cooking considerably reduces the vitamin content.

Eat fruit and vegetables raw

Whenever possible, serve fruit and vegetables raw. It has been suggested that as much as 75 per cent of the vitamin C found in green vegetables is lost during cooking.

Cook and eat fruit and vegetables in their skins

Peeling fruit and vegetables before eating or cooking will increase the amount of vitamins lost. The highest concentrations of vitamins are found in the skin. Some fruit, such as oranges and bananas, need to be peeled, but others, such as apples, can be eaten and cooked with the skin on, for example in an apple pie.

Use a small amount of water when cooking fruit and vegetables

The smallest amount of water should be used when cooking vegetables to prevent water-soluble vitamins from dissolving. The more water used, the more water-soluble vitamins will be lost. Choose cooking methods that use small amounts of water (for example microwaving or steaming).

You will learn more about cooking methods that conserve nutrients in Topic 3.1 Cooking of food and heat transfer. See page 196.

Place vegetables in boiling water and cook quickly

When cooking vegetables, it is best to place them into a small amount of boiling water immediately after preparation, as this destroys the enzymes. When vegetables are put in cold water and brought to the boil slowly, the enzymes can destroy the vitamins before the heat from the water destroys the enzymes.

Always cook fruit or vegetables for the minimum amount of time required. Long cooking times will reduce the vitamin content. Use a tightly-fitting lid on the saucepan to speed up the cooking process.

Use the cooking water

Water-soluble vitamins will leach into the cooking water during boiling. Use the cooking water to make gravies, soups and sauces to ensure that the vitamins are eaten.

Figure 2.2.12 Bag of salad with a modified atmosphere

Figure 2.2.13 Steamed broccoli has more vitamin C than boiled

Figure 2.2.14 Stewed fruits served with the cooking liquid that contains the vitamin C

Serve immediately

Cooked vegetables should not be kept warm for long periods before serving. The longer vegetables are kept warm, the greater the water soluble vitamin loss will be. Avoid reheating as this will reduce the vitamin content even more.

Activity

You may need these skills when completing your NEA Task 1. The activity could be presented as an investigation and follow the structure of the NEA.

The table below shows the amount of **vitamin C** found in potatoes that have been prepared and cooked in different ways. Each of the batches of potatoes were prepared as described in the table and the vitamin C content measured.

Potatoes	Vitamin C (per 100g)
Raw, new potatoes (the control)	20 mg
Soaked for 2 hours, plunged into 200 ml boiling water, boiled for 15 minutes	8 mg
Plunged into boiling water, boiled for 15 minutes	10 mg
Plunged into boiling water, boiled for 30 minutes	7 mg
Plunged into boiling water, boiled for 60 minutes	5 mg
Plunged into boiling water, boiled for 15 minutes, kept warm for 30 minutes after cooking	2 mg

Table 2.2.5 Investigating vitamin C in cooked potatoes

1   Describe how the potatoes were prepared and cooked in the batch that contained 10 mg of vitamin C.
2   Which batch contained the lowest amount of vitamin C?
3   Explain the effect of soaking the potatoes on vitamin C.
4   Explain how the length of boiling time affected the vitamin C.

Practical activity

Prepare a **salad** or **vegetable** dish demonstrating the skills required in food preparation and cooking to retain water-soluble vitamins.

Antioxidant functions of vitamins A, C and E

Learning objectives

In this section you will learn about:

● the role of **antioxidants** in protecting body cells from damage and reducing the risk of cancer and heart disease.

What are antioxidants?

All bodily functions and lifestyle habits produce substances called **free radicals** that can attack healthy cells. When free radicals are found in large amounts in the body the healthy cells are weakened, and are more vulnerable to heart disease and certain types of cancer. Antioxidants help to protect healthy cells from the damage caused by free radicals.

Vitamin A, vitamin C and vitamin E are all antioxidants.

Figure 2.2.15 Sources of antioxidants

> **Teacher's tip**
>
> **'ACE'** is a good way to remember the antioxidant vitamins, vitamins A, C and E, which protect the body.

Where are antioxidants found?

Antioxidants are found in foods that contain vitamins A, C and E. There are large amounts of antioxidants in fruits, vegetables, nuts and whole grains and smaller amounts of antioxidants in meat, chicken and fish.

Activities

1 Copy the boxes below and match each group of food sources with the correct antioxidant.

vitamin C	vitamin E	vitamin A
Seeds, nuts, vegetable oil, whole grains	Eggs, oily fish, liver, full-fat milk, butter	Oranges, strawberries, red peppers, tomatoes

2 Berries are an excellent source of antioxidants. How many different types of berry can you name?

Practical activity

1 Find a recipe that includes berries as a main ingredient. Prepare the dish.
2 Complete a nutritional analysis of the micronutrient content of the dish.
3 Compare the findings to the DRVs for children aged 10 years.

Check your knowledge and understanding

1 Give **two** reasons why each of the following vitamins are important in the diet:
   a) Vitamin A
   b) Vitamin D
   c) Vitamin C
2 State **two** good sources of each vitamin:
   a) Vitamin B1
   b) Vitamin B2
   c) Folic acid
   d) Vitamin B12
3 Discuss **three** ways you can make sure vitamin C is retained during **food storage.**
4 Discuss **three** ways you can make sure vitamin C is retained during **food preparation.**
5 Explain why antioxidants are important in the diet.

Minerals

Learning objectives

In this section you will learn about:

- the **function** of calcium, iron, sodium, fluoride, iodine and phosphorus in the body
- the **main sources** of calcium, iron, sodium, fluoride, iodine and phosphorus in the diet
- the effects of a **deficiency** and **excess** of these minerals
- the **amount of calcium**, **iron**, **sodium**, fluoride, iodine and phosphorus required each day to remain healthy
- the importance and functions of water in the body
- the Dietary Reference Value (DRV).

Calcium

There is more calcium in the body than any other mineral.

Functions of calcium

Calcium is needed for:

- helping to build strong bones and teeth
- controlling muscle contractions including the heartbeat
- ensuring that the blood clots normally.

Sources of calcium

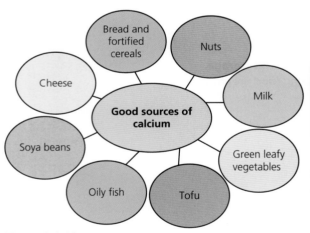

Figure 2.2.16 Sources of calcium

Figure 2.2.17 Foods that contain calcium

Vitamin D helps the absorption of calcium into the body.

Deficiency of calcium

A lack of calcium could lead to a condition called **rickets** in children or **osteoporosis** in adults. Rickets and osteoporosis cause soft and weak bones to develop, which can result in fractures.

You will learn more about bone health in Topic 2.3 Nutritional needs and health. See page 185.

Excess of calcium

Too much calcium could lead to stomach pain and diarrhoea.

Dietary Reference Value for calcium

The amount of calcium you need each day is measured in milligrams (mg).

Age	Males	Females
4 years	450 mg	450 mg
10 years	550 mg	550 mg
14 years	1,000 mg	800 mg
Adults	700 mg	700 mg
Older adults (over 50)	700 mg	700 mg

Table 2.2.6 Dietary Reference Values for calcium

Practical activity

1 Plan and make a dish for a teenager, which includes foods that are **good sources** of calcium and vitamin D.
2 Calculate the calcium content of the dish. Compare it with the recommendation that a teenager should eat about 300 milligrams of calcium in each meal.
3 Explain why the DRVs for calcium are higher for teenagers than for children and adults.

Using the table below and your own research, plan a day's menu for a four-year-old child. The child requires 450 mg of calcium a day.

Calcium in dairy products	Quantity	Calcium (mg)
Milk, all types	200 ml	240
Cheese	Matchbox size 30 g	220
Cheese triangle	15 g	60
Yoghurt	120 g	200
Fromage frais	1 pot – 45 g	60
Hot chocolate	25g serving in 200 ml water	200
Rice pudding	$\frac{1}{2}$ large tin (200 g)	176
Scoop of ice cream	60 g	75
Custard	1 serving (120 ml)	120
Rusk	1 rusk	60
Calcium-enriched orange juice	1 serving 125 ml	150
Calcium-fortified breakfast cereals	30 g serving	137
White bread	1 slice (40 g)	191
Tinned salmon (with bones)	$\frac{1}{2}$ tin (52 g)	47
Scampi in breadcrumbs	6 pieces (90 g)	190
Houmous	100 g	41
Smooth peanut butter	100 g	37
Fish fingers	2 fish fingers	92
Baked beans in tomato sauce	100 g	53
Wholemeal bread	2 large slices (100 g)	54
Pitta bread/chapatti	1 portion (65 g)	60
Orange	1 medium (120 g)	75
Broccoli, boiled	2 spears (85 g)	34
Carrot	50 g – 1 small carrot	17
Green beans	100 g	56
Sausage: low-fat, grilled	2 sausages	130
Cornish pasty	1 serving (100 g)	60
Omelette: cheese	1 serving (100 g)	287
Quiche: cheese & egg	1 serving (100 g)	262
Macaroni cheese	1 serving (100 g)	170
Pizza: cheese & tomato	1 serving (100 g)	210

Iron

Iron is stored in the liver.

Functions of iron

Iron is needed for:

- making red blood cells, which carry oxygen around the body.

Sources of iron

Iron comes from both animal and plant sources.

Figure 2.2.18 Foods that contain iron

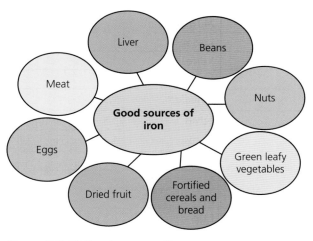

Figure 2.2.19 Good sources of iron

Absorbing iron

- Iron from animal sources is called **haem iron** and can be absorbed into the body easily.
- Iron from vegetables is called **non-haem iron** and is more difficult to absorb.

Certain foods can help the body's ability to absorb iron. To increase the absorption of iron you should eat iron-rich foods with foods and drinks containing vitamin C, for example fresh fruit (especially citrus fruit), fruit juice and vegetables such as peas, tomatoes, broccoli, pepper, cabbage, Brussel sprouts, cauliflower, courgettes and spinach.

> **Key words**
>
> **Haem iron** is iron from animal sources.
>
> **Non-haem iron** is iron from vegetable or plant sources.

Activity

The table shows some foods that contain iron.

Food sources	Portion size	Iron content (mg)
Tinned tuna	100 g	1
Beef, corned beef, duck	100 g	3
Liver pâté	40 g	3
Lamb	100 g	2
Chicken, turkey, pork	100 g	1
Bacon	2 rashers	1
Lentils	4 tbsp, cooked	4.5
Baked beans	$\frac{1}{2}$ tin (210 g)	3
Kidney beans	4 tbsp	3
Soya beans	3 tbsp	3
Houmos	$\frac{1}{2}$ tub (85 g)	1.5
Tofu	100 g	5.4
Chickpeas	100 g (uncooked)	6.2
Quinoa	100 g (uncooked)	4.6
Eggs	1 medium	1
Nuts	1 handful	0.5
Special K, bran flakes fortified with iron	30 g	6.5
Cornflakes, Rice Krispies, Weetabix fortified with iron	30 g	2
Pasta	240 g (cooked)	2
Pitta bread	1 (55 g)	1
Bread (brown/white)	1 slice	1
Canned cherries	90 g	3
Raw onion	$\frac{1}{2}$ medium	1.5
Peas	3 tbsp	1.5
Spinach	$2\frac{1}{2}$ tbsp	1
Raisins	1 tbsp	1
Dried apricots	3	1
Gingernuts	2	1
Cocoa	1 tsp	0.5

Using the table, answer the following questions:

1 Which food contains the most iron? Explain why this is a good source.
2 Identify **four** foods that a vegetarian could choose as a good source of iron.
3 How much iron would these meals provide:
   a) baked beans with 2 slices of toast
   b) bacon (2 rashers), 1 egg, 2 slices of bread
   c) houmos and pitta bread
   d) beef chilli with kidney beans
   e) cereal bar containing dried apricots, raisins, cocoa, nuts and Rice Krispies.
4 Which vitamin is required for the absorption of iron? How could you make sure this vitamin is eaten with iron-rich foods?
5 Identify **three** sources of **haem iron** from the list.

Deficiency of iron

A shortage of iron in the diet is a very common nutritional problem. A lack of iron is called **iron deficiency anaemia**. The symptoms are:

- tiredness
- dizziness
- shortness of breath during exercise
- a pale appearance
- brittle nails and cracked lips.

Women and children are at greatest risk of developing iron deficiency anaemia.

You will learn more about iron deficiency anaemia in Topic 2.3 Nutritional needs and health. See page 188.

Excess of iron

Large quantities of iron can be harmful. The side effects of too much iron are:

- constipation
- feeling sick
- stomach pain.

Dietary Reference Value for iron

The amount of iron you need each day is measured in milligrams (mg).

Age	Males	Females
4 years	6.1 mg	6.1 mg
10 years	8.7 mg	8.7 mg
14 years	11.3 mg	14.8 mg
Adults	8.7 mg	14.8 mg
Older adults (over 50)	8.7 mg	8.7 mg

Table 2.2.7 Dietary Reference Values for iron

Women of child-bearing age and teenage girls should ensure that they have enough iron in their diet to allow for the blood loss during **menstruation**.

Extension activities

Compare the iron intake for males and females.

Outline the nutritional advice you would give to the different groups at risk from anaemia.

Sodium (salt)

The most common form of sodium in the diet is salt (sodium chloride). Government advice is that people of all ages should try to reduce their salt intake. Salt can be hidden in processed foods.

Functions of sodium

Sodium is needed for:

- keeping the level of water in the body balanced.

Sources of sodium

Salt is an important source of sodium. Salt is added to many processed foods.

Figure 2.2.20 Foods that contain sodium

Figure 2.2.21 Good sources of sodium

Excess of sodium

Many people eat too much salt. Salt is linked to an increase in blood pressure, which raises your risk of a stroke or a heart attack.

Deficiency of sodium

Low intakes of sodium result in muscle cramps.

Dietary Reference Value for sodium

The maximum recommended amount of salt is shown in the table below:

Age	Amount per day
Up to 12 months	Less than 1 g
1–3 years	2 g
4–6 years	3 g
7–10 years	5 g
11 years + and adults	6 g

Table 2.2.8 Dietary Reference Value for sodium

Research activity

Investigate salt in the diet

Find out how much salt is found in some popular foods.

- You can use food packaging or the internet to find the information.
- Food manufacturers display nutritional information on the front of pre-packed food. This is very useful when you want to compare different food products.
- Use it to find the amount of salt in the food.

Record your findings in a table.

Figure 2.2.22 A front of pack label

Food	Serving size	Amount of salt per serving
Grilled beef burger	1 burger (94 g)	0.7 g
Back bacon		
Pork sausages		
White bread		
Pot noodle		
Cheddar cheese		
Pork pie		
Onion bhaji		
Egg mayonnaise sandwich		
Baked beans		
Pepperoni pizza		
Potato crisps		

Answer these questions using your research:
1 State which food contains the most salt.
2 You should consume no more than 6 g of salt a day. How much salt is there in:
    a) beans on toast
    b) a cheese sandwich
    c) a sausage sandwich?
3 Describe or explain the harmful effects of eating too much salt.
4 Suggest some ways in which you could reduce the amount of salt you eat. Use these websites to help you: www.losalt.com/uk and www.actiononsalt.org.uk.

Key word

Fluoridation is when fluorine is added to drinking water.

Fluoride

Fluoride is not found in many foods. It is added, in some areas, to the water supply through a process called **fluoridation**.

Functions of fluoride

Fluoride is needed for:

- helping to prevent tooth decay by strengthening the tooth enamel
- supporting bone health.

Sources of fluoride

Drinking water is an important source of fluoride.

Other good sources of fluoride are:
- fish where the bones are eaten, for example sardines
- seafood
- tea.

Excess of fluoride

Very large amounts of fluoride can cause staining and pits to develop on the teeth.

Deficiency of fluoride

Tooth decay is more common if fluoride is not supplied in the diet.

Dietary Reference Values for fluoride

The daily requirement for fluoride is:
- teenagers 2 mg
- males 4 mg
- females 3 mg.

Iodine

Iodine is an essential part of the hormones produced by the thyroid gland in the neck.

Functions of iodine

Iodine is needed for:
- making the hormone thyroxine which maintains a healthy metabolic rate.

Sources of iodine

Iodine is found in many foods.

Good sources of iodine are:
- red meat
- sea fish
- shellfish
- cereals
- grains.

Figure 2.2.23 Shellfish are good sources of iodine

Excess of iodine

Taking high doses of iodine for long periods of time can affect the thyroid gland. This can lead to weight gain.

Deficiency of iodine

Iodine deficiency used to be the main cause of **goitre**. A goitre is a swelling of the **thyroid gland**. Due to improvements in our diet iodine deficiency is now rare in the UK.

Key words

Goitre is caused by a lack of iodine.

Thyroid gland produces hormones that control the metabolic rate.

Dietary Reference Values for iodine

Age	Males	Females
4 years	100 mcg/d	100 mcg/d
10 years	110 mcg/d	110 mcg/d
14 years	130 mcg/d	130 mcg/d
Adults	140 mcg/d	140 mcg/d
Older adults (over 50)	140 mcg/d	140 mcg/d

Table 2.2.9 Dietary Reference Values for iodine

Phosphorus

Phosphorus is present in all body cells. The bones and teeth are where most phosphorus is stored. Our bones and teeth are made from a combination of calcium and phosphorus called **calcium phosphate**.

Functions of phosphorus

Phosphorus is needed for:
- maintaining the bones and teeth
- releasing energy from food.

Sources of phosphorus

Phosphorus is found in many foods.

Good sources of phosphorus are:
- red meat
- dairy foods
- fish
- poultry
- bread
- brown rice
- oats
- beans and lentils

Figure 2.2.24 Sources of phosphorus

Excess of phosphorus

Consuming very large amounts of phosphorus over time can reduce the amount of calcium in the body, which means that bones are more likely to fracture.

Deficiency of phosphorus

Phosphorus is in so many foods that it is unlikely to be deficient in the diet.

Dietary Reference Values for phosphorus

Age	Males	Females
4 years	350 mg	350 mg
10 years	450 mg	450 mg
14 years	775 mg	625 mg
Adults	550 mg	550 mg
Older adults (over 50)	550 mg	550 mg

Table 2.2.10 Dietary Reference Values for phosphorus

Check your knowledge and understanding

1 Name **three** good sources of calcium.
2 Describe **two** functions of calcium in the diet.
3 What is a deficiency of iron known as?
4 Name **two** foods that are a good source of iron.
5 Describe **three** ways you can reduce sodium in your diet.

6 Explain why phosphorous is important in the diet.
7 Discuss the role of minerals in the diet of children.

Water

Water is not a nutrient but is required for life. Your body is about 70 per cent water. Every cell and tissue in the body contains water.

> ## Learning objectives
>
> **In this section you will learn about:**
> - the importance of hydration
> - the functions of water in the diet.

The importance of hydration

The human body can only survive a few days without water. **Hydration** is the supply of water required to maintain the correct amount of fluid in the body. To stay healthy, it is important to replace the water you lose when you breathe, sweat or urinate.

Dehydration occurs when your body loses more water than you take in.

How water is lost from the body

Water is lost from the body through the:
- lungs, because water is lost as vapour when you breathe out
- skin, because water evaporates as you sweat
- kidneys and intestines, because water is lost in your body waste.

The functions of water

Water is needed for:

1. Cooling the body

Sweat evaporation (sweating) is essential for cooling the body. Sweating means that water is lost from the body. This water must be replaced through food or drink to maintain the balance of water in the body.

Body temperature is 37°C. If the temperature of the body increases, just a few degrees, then body cells will be damaged. To prevent body cell damage and overheating, the body will control its temperature by sweating. If the body becomes too hot, glands in the skin will release water or sweat onto the surface of the skin and the body will start to cool down.

You sweat more in hot conditions and when you are exercising. Illness can raise the body temperature and cause sweating too.

Heat stroke is an uncontrolled increase in body temperature. Heat stroke occurs when the body temperature rises but the body lacks water. The body is unable to sweat due to the lack of water and the body temperature rises. A person with heat stroke will have an increased body temperature, rapid heartbeat and can faint.

> ## Key words
>
> **Hydration** is the supply of water required to maintain the correct amount of fluid in the body.
> **Dehydration** is a lack of water.
>
> **Heat stroke** is an uncontrolled increase in body temperature.

2. Removing waste from the body

Water is needed to transport waste products from the body. It prevents constipation and allows waste products to move through the intestines. The kidneys filter the blood and produce urine.

3. Helping the body to use the food you eat

Water is an important part of saliva which you need to be able to swallow food. In the stomach, food mixes with acid and water. These both help to digest food. Nutrients are released from the food and transported around the body by the bloodstream.

The bloodstream is about 90 per cent water.

How much water is needed each day?

How much fluid you need depends on many factors including your age, diet, the amount of physical activity you do and the climate. Most people need about 2 litres of water a day, which is about 8 average size glasses. You will need to drink more than this if you are exercising in hot weather.

Besides water, you can get the fluid you need from low-sugar soft drinks, milk and fruit juices, as well as tea, coffee and other beverages made with hot and cold water.

- Approximately 20–30 per cent of the water you need comes from food.
- 70–80 per cent from drinks and drinking water.

Bottled water has become very popular. In 2014, on average, each person in the UK drank over 40 litres of bottled water.

There are different types of bottled water:

- Natural mineral water must come from an identified and protected source and can be still or sparkling.
- Spring water must originate from an underground source, be bottled at source and be safe without treatment.
- Flavoured water is a soft drink, which can contain minerals, vitamins, flavourings and sweeteners.

Figure 2.2.25 Foods that contain water

Investigate bottled water

Visit a supermarket website (e.g. Tesco's) and complete the table below with ten different bottled waters.

Name of bottled water	Still or sparkling	Type (e.g. spring, mineral or flavoured)	Price per 100 ml (e.g. £0.12/100 ml)

Answer the following questions:

1 What minerals does bottled water contain?
2 Which water was the most expensive?
3 Where is bottled water produced?
4 Explain why the price varies between the different types of water.

A lack of water

When your body does not have enough water you become dehydrated.

One of the first signs of dehydration is feeling thirsty.

The other signs of dehydration are:
- dark urine and not passing much urine when you go to the toilet
- headaches
- lack of energy
- feeling light-headed.

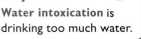

Key word

Water intoxication is drinking too much water.

Too much water

Drinking too much water can be harmful. The condition is called **water intoxication**. Water intoxication is very rare. It can only occur if many litres of water are consumed over a very short period of time.

Check your knowledge and understanding

1 Give **three** functions of water in the diet.
2 Identify **three** ways water is lost from the body.
3 Explain the effect of a lack of water on the body.
4 Discuss the advantages and disadvantages of drinking bottled water.

TOPIC 2.3 NUTRITIONAL NEEDS AND HEALTH

Making informed choices for a varied and balanced diet

Learning objectives

In this section you will learn about:
- the guidelines for a **healthy diet**
- how to consider **portion size** and **cost** when meal planning
- how the nutritional needs of people change and how to plan a balanced diet for different **life stages**
- how to plan a balanced meal for **specific dietary groups**, including:
    - vegetarian and vegan
    - coeliac
    - lactose intolerant
    - high-fibre diets.

The Eatwell Guide

Public Health England has reviewed its dietary recommendations to help improve your health. The Eatwell Guide was developed to promote a balanced diet. It divides food into groups, depending on their nutritional role and shows the proportions of each of the groups needed for a healthy, varied diet. This balance of foods does not need to be eaten for every meal, but for foods eaten over the course of a day or two.

The fruit and vegetables segment is the largest – 40% and this includes the message that at least 5 portions of a variety of fruit and vegetables should be consumed daily. A portion is an 80g serving.

The starchy carbohydrate group is a main group on the Eatwell Guide – 38% and shows a greater emphasis on wholegrains and starchy foods low in salt, fat and sugar. Meals should be based on potatoes, bread, rice, pasta and other starchy carbohydrates.

The protein group is 12% and now emphasises beans and pulses as these are more sustainable sources of protein and have less of an impact on the environment compared to animal proteins. Fish should be eaten twice a week, one of which is oily. Meat and eggs are also included in this segment.

The dairy and alternatives group is 8% and has a greater emphasis on lower fat and lower sugar versions. Dairy alternatives include soy drinks for example.

The smallest segment of the Eatwell Guide is only 1% and just includes unsaturated oils and fat spreads which should be used in small amounts but are included as they provide the important fat soluble vitamins.

Foods high in fat and/or sugar have been removed from the main segments, as these should be eaten less often and in small amounts.

As well as the food groups, extra information is included on hydration with the message that water, lower fat milk, sugar-free drinks including tea and coffee all count for the recommended 6 – 8 cups/glasses of liquid a day, but a reminder that fruit juices and smoothies should be limited to a combined 150ml a day due to their high free sugar content.

A nutrition label has been included to remind you that you should choose foods that are lower in fat, salt and sugars, and so that you are familiar with what this food label looks like when you go shopping.

The average energy needs of men and women have been included – this is to remind you that all foods and drinks contribute to your total energy intake.

It is better to choose a variety of different foods from each segment of the Eatwell Guide to help get the wide range of nutrients the body needs in order to stay healthy.

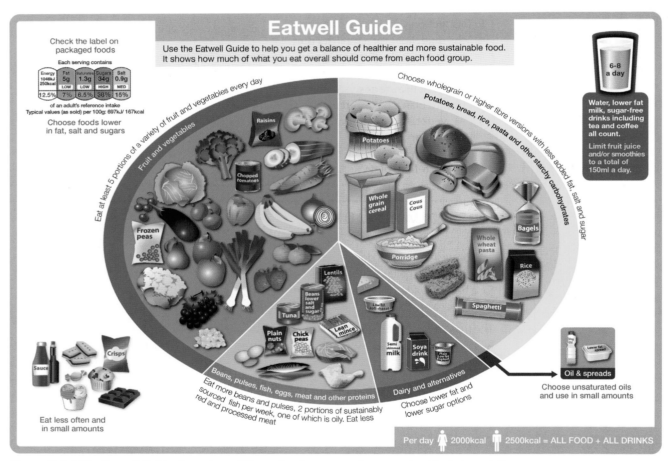

Figure 2.3.1 The Eatwell Guide shows how different foods can contribute to a healthy balanced diet

What are the current guidelines for a healthy diet?

<table>
<tr><td>

Key word

Healthy diet is a balanced diet, low in fat, salt and sugar and high in fibre which meets the current dietary guidelines.

</td></tr>
</table>

To help you to choose a **healthy diet** that is balanced, Public Health England (PHE), which is a government department, has produced eight tips for eating well:

1 Base your meals on starchy foods.
2 Eat lots of fruit and vegetables.
3 Eat more fish, including a portion of oily fish each week.
4 Cut down on saturated fat and sugar.

5 Eat less salt (no more than 6 g a day for adults).
6 Get active and be a healthy weight.
7 Don't get thirsty.
8 Don't skip breakfast.

1 **Base your meals on starchy foods: Starchy foods** include bread, rice, cereals, pasta, potatoes and cassava. Starchy foods should provide most of our energy. As well as energy, they provide calcium, iron and the B group vitamins. Choose **wholegrain** varieties if you can, as these will provide more fibre as well as extra vitamins and minerals.

2 **Eat lots of fruit and vegetables:** We should try to eat at least five portions of fruit and vegetables every day. One portion is 80 g, which is, for example, one apple, banana, orange or pear. Frozen, canned and dried fruits and vegetables all count. A glass of fruit juice counts as a maximum of one portion per day, because fruit juices contain a lot of **free sugars**.

3 **Eat more fish, including a portion of oily fish each week:** We should all aim to eat at least two portions of fish each week. One of these should be **oily fish**; examples of oily fish are: salmon, mackerel, sardines or fresh tuna (tinned tuna does not count as oily fish, as the canning process reduces the fish oils to similar levels to white fish). Oily fish are rich in fats called **omega 3 fatty acids**, which may help to prevent coronary heart disease (CHD). White fish includes cod, haddock, coley and plaice.

4 **Cut down on saturated fat and sugar:** The type of fat we eat is important. We all need some fat in our diet, as it provides the important fat-soluble vitamins, A, D, E and K but if we eat too much saturated fat this raises the amount of cholesterol in the blood, which can lead to heart disease. However, if we eat unsaturated fat, this can help to lower the cholesterol in our blood, therefore reducing the risk of coronary heart disease.

  – Unsaturated fats can be found in vegetable oils such as olive oil, sunflower oil and rapeseed oil. Oily fish, avocados, nuts and seeds are also useful sources.

  – Foods high in saturated fats include hard cheese, meat pies, sausages, pastry, cakes and biscuits. We should try to eat less of these.

Figure 2.3.2 One portion is 80 g

Most of us eat too much sugar. Sugary foods contain free sugars and include sweets, cakes and biscuits as well as fizzy drinks. Too many free sugars can cause tooth decay, especially if they are eaten between meals.

5 **Eat less salt:** For adults, this is no more than 6 g a day. Most people eat too much salt as it is added to many everyday foods we eat, such as breakfast cereals, bread, sauces and ready meals. Eating too much salt can raise your blood pressure and make a stroke or heart disease more likely.

6 **Get healthy and be a healthy weight:** It is not healthy to be either overweight or underweight. Being active every day is important as it helps your muscles to develop and also helps to strengthen your bones. It also helps your digestive system to work properly, which helps to prevent constipation. People who don't exercise very much are more likely to put on weight and develop illnesses as they get older.

7 **Don't get thirsty:** It is recommended that adults drink about 6–8 glasses of water per day, which is about 2 litres. Other fluids such as tea, coffee, milk and fruit juices count towards the daily total, but tap water is the healthiest and easiest choice. We get water from our food as well as our drinks.

8 **Don't skip breakfast:** Breakfast is a very important meal as it comes many hours after your last meal. Breakfast gives you the energy you need to concentrate at school or work and provides important nutrients that you need for good health, for example protein in milk and vitamin C in fresh fruits. Try to choose breakfast cereals without too much sugar and top them with fresh fruit instead.

Figure 2.3.3 You should try to eat fish at least twice a week

Figure 2.3.4 Being active is important

Practical activity

1 Plan a day's meals for an adult based on the Eatwell Guide. Starchy carbohydrates (bread, rice, potatoes and pasta), as well as fruits and vegetables should be the largest parts of the meals. Make sure you also include foods from the meat, fish, eggs and beans group as well as the milk and dairy foods (see the Eatwell Guide, page 148).
2 Make one of the meals in a practical lesson.
3 Carry out sensory and nutritional analysis of the meal.
4 Suggest improvements to the meal based on the sensory and nutritional analysis.

Where can we find advice on good nutrition?

There are many different sources of advice on nutrition. It is important when looking for advice on nutrition that you use reliable sources of information.

Reliable advice on nutrition may come from:

● **The COMA Report** – COMA stands for Committee on Medical Aspects of Food Policy. This is a government report, which sets the Dietary Reference Values (DRVs). The report was written by a committee of scientists and health professionals. They worked out how much of each different nutrient you need to stay healthy and grow properly. The groups are based on age, gender and, for females, whether they are pregnant or breastfeeding.

● **The Scientific Advisory committee on Nutrition** – This group took over from the COMA committee to advise the government on nutrition and health issues. This includes advice on the nutrient content of individual foods, and on the diet as a whole including what a balanced diet is. They also monitor the nutritional status of people in the UK and report on health problems that are diet related, for example: cardiovascular disease, cancer, osteoporosis and obesity (www.gov.uk/government/groups/scientific-advisory-committee-on-nutrition).

● **The Food Standards Agency** – This government department is responsible for food safety and hygiene in England, Wales and Northern Ireland. They give consumers the information they need to make informed choices about where they eat and what they eat. Their aim is to improve public health (www.food.gov.uk).

Figure 2.3.5 The Food Standards Agency helps to ensure the food we eat is safe

- **The National Health Service (NHS)** – The NHS gives advice on nutrition through campaigns such as the '5 a day' campaign. They provide up-to-date and reliable information on many food-related health issues (www.nhs.uk).
- **The British Nutrition Foundation (BNF)** – This charity educates the public in food and nutrition. It provides easy to understand information, based on evidence, and aimed at everyone (www.nutrition.org.uk). Their 'Food a fact of life' website for schools provides up-to-date nutrition advice for children aged 3 to 18 (www.foodafactoflife.org.uk).

Check your knowledge and understanding

1 List the eight tips for eating well.
2 Identify the **two** largest sections on the Eatwell Guide.
3 Give **one** example of a starchy food and plan a two-course lunch for a hungry teenager based on this starchy food.
4 State how many grams is one portion of fruit/vegetables which counts towards your '5 a day'.
5 Explain why oily fish is especially good for you.
6 Discuss why unsaturated fats are better for you than saturated fats.
7 Explain why exercise is an important part of a healthy lifestyle.
8 How much water/fluids should adults drink per day?
9 Suggest reasons why some people say that breakfast is the most important meal of the day.
10 Outline where people can get reliable advice on nutrition. Describe the types of advice these organisations can offer.

Meal planning: portion size and cost

Portion size

When serving up meals, make sure the portion size is adjusted for each person. Remember, everyone has individual nutritional and energy needs. In recent years, plates have become bigger and **portion sizes** can be too large, especially for children. Larger portions encourage you to eat more and can change your opinion of what is a normal amount to eat.

- It is best to serve children's meals on smaller plates to the rest of the family to prevent over-eating.
- Teenagers will need relatively larger portion sizes to provide for their growth spurts and (usually) their increased physical activity.
- Many elderly people are less active and so will need smaller portion sizes than those they ate when younger adults, due to reduced levels of physical activity and their reduced amounts of lean muscle tissue.

Figure 2.3.6 Adjust portion size depending on the age and physical activity level of each person

Practical activity

Plan and make a main meal for a family of four. The meal should contain a source of HBV protein, carbohydrate and at least two to three portions of their '5 a day'. Serve one portion of the meal for a four-year-old child on a plate of the appropriate size. If possible, photograph this meal and include this in your evaluation of the practical session.

Cost of food

The cost of food has increased in recent years and has become a larger part of the **family budget**. This price rise is more difficult for low-income families as they spend a larger proportion of their income on food. It is important that the cost of food is considered when planning meals, especially for those on a limited income, such as students and the elderly.

It is now possible to use online **price comparison sites** to compare the cost of shopping baskets at different shops, which can save money, especially if you are prepared to shop in different stores.

It is usually cheaper to plan meals in advance so that there is less food wasted, and so that the same ingredient may be used for different recipes – for example, a fresh pineapple can be used for a fruit salad for dessert and if covered and refrigerated, the following day as a pizza topping.

Money may be saved when meal planning by finding out about special offers (including 'buy one, get one free') and making a shopping list for the weekly items and only buying items on the list. If you shop at the end of the day, shops often reduce items, but these usually have a short date-mark on them, so they need to be used or frozen (if the food is suitable for home freezing) immediately. It is also best not to shop when you are hungry, as this can lead to impulse-buying of unnecessary foods. Many supermarkets sell value lines, which can also help to save money.

With the increase in internet shopping for food, it can be easier to avoid impulse-buying and **'pester power'** from children. However, there is an increasing amount of advertising on shopping websites, which may also encourage you to buy foods that you don't really need.

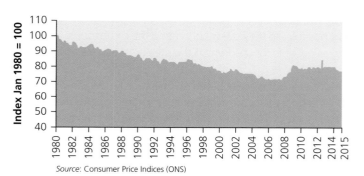

Source: Consumer Price Indices (ONS)

Figure 2.3.7 UK trend in food prices in real terms, January 1980 to January 2015

Key words

Family budget is the family's income and expenditure of money over a specified time.

Price comparison sites are websites that compare supermarket food prices.

Pester power is when children pester adults to buy products.

Check your knowledge and understanding

1 Explain why it is important to adapt the food portion size for individual members of the family.

2 Give **two** reasons why a teenager would require a larger food portion size than an elderly person.

3 Suggest ways money may be saved when meal planning.

4 Describe **two** groups of people who are most likely to be on a low income and who will need to budget carefully when buying food.

5 Suggest **three** pieces of advice for a family trying to save money when:
   a) shopping for food
   b) planning meals.

How people's nutritional needs change and how to plan a balanced diet for different life stages

From birth until old age, your nutritional needs will change.

Young children (aged 1 to 4 years)

Young children go through rapid **growth spurts** as well as usually having a very active lifestyle. As children's stomachs are small, they cannot eat large meals at one time and so they need to eat regular, smaller meals, as well as snacks and drinks throughout the day, to provide sufficient energy and nutrients.

The Eatwell Guide should not be followed for young children (under 2 years), as they benefit from products such as whole milk, which will provide more energy, as well as the important fat-soluble vitamin D, which is needed for the absorption of calcium to strengthen their bones and teeth.

Children aged 2 to 5 years should make gradual changes until they are eating food in the same proportion as the Eatwell Guide in the course of a day or more.

It is important that young children develop good eating habits, so they learn to follow these throughout their lives. These tips will help younger children to eat well:

- Regularly try new foods.
- If children are hungry between meals, give them fresh foods such as fruit and vegetables instead of sweets, biscuits and crisps, which will spoil their appetites.
- Drink water with meals so the taste of the food isn't masked by other flavours and to avoid extra free sugar consumption.
- Let children eat until they are full; don't make children eat everything on their plate.
- Sit as a family to eat meals if possible, so they see others eating the same foods.
- Make mealtimes as relaxing as possible for children, so the mealtime may be enjoyed by all the family.
- Having a small choice of healthier foods may be better, so children can decide what to eat.
- When at nursery/pre-school if school meals are available at lunchtime, opt for these instead of providing a packed lunch as this setting will encourage young children to eat a wider variety of foods with their friends.

Figure 2.3.8 Whole milk supplies vitamin D, which is needed to absorb calcium properly

Practical activity

Young children need to be encouraged to eat healthily and to try different foods. Find a recipe for homemade fish fingers. Make these along with a starchy carbohydrate and some colourful vegetables – in a practical session.

Schoolchildren (aged 5 to 12 years)

Schoolchildren are growing fast and should be physically active every day, which increases the need for more energy (calories) in their diet. Their diet should be varied, again following the principles of the Eatwell Guide, and include the foods they need to provide the nutrients and energy during this time of rapid growth and development.

Because schoolchildren are not as active as they once were, and due to the increase in the consumption of fatty/sugary foods, there are more overweight and obese schoolchildren than in previous years. Over a fifth of 4–5-year-olds and a third of 10–11-year-olds were overweight or obese in 2014/15.

It is important that schoolchildren develop good eating habits so they learn to establish these throughout their lives. These tips will help schoolchildren eat well:

- Encourage schoolchildren to have school meals rather than a packed lunch to increase the variety of the foods they eat. School meals usually have a better nutritional balance than a packed lunch. The School Food Plan sets out standards for all food served in schools and was launched by the Department for Education. It has been the law in all maintained schools, and new academies and free schools since January 2015. Here is a link to find out more: **http://www.schoolfoodplan.com/standards/**.
- Schoolchildren should be encouraged to try new foods, but should never be forced to eat foods they do not want to try.
- Schoolchildren may need to be encouraged to eat a variety of fruit and vegetables; have these as snacks for when children return home from school.
- Make salty, fatty and sugary foods, such as cakes, biscuits, chocolate, sweets and fizzy drinks, a small part of the diet of schoolchildren.
- Drinks such as diluted fruit juices should be consumed at mealtimes rather than between meals, due to the large amount of free sugars they contain; plain tap water is best.
- Encourage schoolchildren to eat proper meals and avoid snacking too much, especially if these snacks are **junk food**.

Teenagers

The body goes through many changes when children become teenagers. They should follow the guidelines of the Eatwell Guide to ensure a good balance of foods and nutrients. Teenagers have rapid growth spurts. However, over a third of teenagers are overweight, so an increase in energy may not be needed by all teenagers depending on their current body weight.

Teenage boys develop new muscle tissue and so their protein requirements are higher than for girls. They are also usually bigger than girls, which increases their calcium requirement.

Teenage girls need more iron than boys due to **menstruation**.

It is important that teenagers continue to eat as healthily as possible; these years are important, especially for some nutrients such as calcium and vitamin D, as the skeleton is being formed. Although the skeleton is not fully formed until the late 20s, most of the minerals required to reach **peak bone mass** are laid down in the teenage years.

These tips will help teenagers to eat well:
- Eat a well-balanced diet following the principles of the Eatwell Guide.
- Eat breakfast; this will help teenagers to concentrate at school.
- Eat regular meals to control **blood sugar levels**.
- Eat **unprocessed foods**, including fruits, vegetables and wholegrain cereals; this will increase the fibre in the teenage diet and contribute to their '5 a day'.
- Avoid fizzy drinks, which are very high in sugar and contain few other nutrients. Some fizzy drinks contain 8 teaspoons of sugar per serving. To reduce the number of high sugar drinks we consume in the UK, a sugar tax will be introduced in 2018, this will be for soft drinks which contain more than 5g of sugar per 100ml. Soft drinks which contain more than 8g of sugar per 100ml will be taxed at a higher rate. Fruit juices and milk based drinks will not be included in this taxing system.

Figure 2.3.9 Many fizzy drinks are high in sugar

Nutrient and energy needs	Reasons why they are important to children and teenagers
Protein	Because of rapid growth. Boys need more protein than girls as they have more muscle tissue.
Calcium and vitamin D	For healthy bone and teeth development. Boys need more calcium than girls as they are usually a bigger build.
Iron and vitamin C	To prevent **iron deficiency anaemia** (see page 139) by keeping the red blood cells healthy. Vitamin C helps the body to absorb the iron. Teenage girls need the most iron as they have periods (menstruation).
Vitamin A	For good eyesight. Boys need more due to their bigger build.
B group vitamins	To release energy from carbohydrates. Boys need more than girls as they are generally more active.
Energy	Energy needs increase as children get older.

Table 2.3.1 Nutrient and energy needs for children and teenagers

Normal amount of red blood cells   Anaemic amount of red blood cells

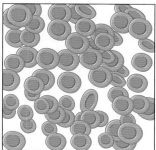 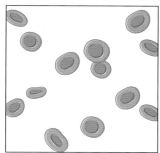

Figure 2.3.10 Teenage girls may suffer from iron deficiency anaemia, when there are fewer red blood cells than needed

Practical activity

1. Teenagers often eat too much free sugar. Modify an existing dessert recipe by lowering the amount of sugar added and/or adding natural sweeteners such as dried fruit that would appeal to teenagers and is a source of iron and vitamin C.
2. Make the dessert in a practical lesson.
3. Carry out sensory analysis to evaluate its acceptability.

Extension activity

Find out which natural ingredients may be used to replace free sugar in recipes. List four of these sugar replacements. Write out the full recipe and method for one of these recipes.

Adults

What adults eat is important because, although they have stopped growing, they still need a well-balanced diet to ensure they have the correct nutrients in the right quantities. The Eatwell Guide should be followed by adults to ensure they achieve this balance. For example, it is important adults eat the correct amount of calories to ensure they stay a healthy weight, and avoid a diet high in free sugars, which can increase the risk of dental decay and are likely to be high in calories, which can lead to weight gain.

A poor diet can lead to conditions such as coronary heart disease (CHD), some cancers and obesity. Many adults eat more food than they need, which is why more than half of adults in the UK are overweight or obese.

Nutrients that are especially important for adults are the mineral calcium and vitamin D. Vitamin D helps the body's absorption of calcium, which ensures that adult bones stay strong. Also, the mineral iron can be low in adult diets, especially adult females who lose iron during the menstrual cycle (their monthly period). Vitamin C helps the body's absorption of iron, which is why the adult diet should contain a high proportion of fruit and vegetables.

> ### Key word
>
> **Haemoglobin** is the part of the red blood cell that carries oxygen around the body.

Nutrients	Reasons why they are important to adults
Calcium and vitamin D	To keep bones and teeth strong, to prevent osteoporosis.
Iron and vitamin C	To keep red blood cells healthy by making **haemoglobin**, which helps to prevent anaemia.

Table 2.3.2 Nutrients which may be deficient in an adult's diet

Figure 2.3.11 The adult diet should have a good supply of calcium and vitamin D to help prevent osteoporosis (weak bones)

Figure 2.3.12 Foods high in vitamin C and iron are important for adults

The elderly (over 65)

As we become elderly (over 65), our nutritional needs change. We still need a well-balanced diet containing all of the nutrients in the correct proportions, but fewer calories (energy) are needed as the bodies of the elderly tend to slow down and become less efficient than they were. Sugary and fatty foods should be avoided as these are **energy dense**, and if eaten too often may lead to storage of too much fat and becoming overweight or obese.

Figure 2.3.13 A healthy diet and regular exercise slow down the effects of ageing

Again, following the Eatwell Guide is important to ensure the correct balance to the diet. Eating at least five portions of fruit and vegetables is helpful to ensure a good supply of the water-soluble vitamins, as well as the antioxidant vitamins A, C and E, which can help to prevent heart disease and some cancers.

Figure 2.3.14 Fruits, vegetables, nuts and seeds supply the antioxidant vitamins A, C and E

As we get older, our bones may become weaker; this is known as **osteoporosis** and can be a problem in old age. As with adults, a diet with good sources of calcium and vitamin D is important.

Exercise also improves the take-up of calcium by the bones so, if an elderly person is inactive, they may need to take a supplement of vitamin D in order to be able to absorb the calcium in their diet.

As the **digestive system** works more slowly as we get older, constipation can be more common in the elderly. It is important that they have enough fibre in their diet (about 30 g per day) and sufficient fluids (about 2 litres per day) to ensure the proper working of the digestive system. As well as constipation, this will help to prevent **diverticular disease** and **cancer of the bowel**.

The elderly may not drink enough fluids, especially if they live alone and have previously been used to regular breaks at work when tea/coffee breaks were a routine part of the day.

Iron deficiency anaemia may be a health issue for the elderly as the body finds it harder to absorb iron as it gets older. Vitamin C is needed to help the body to absorb iron more easily, so these foods should be eaten together. (See Figure 2.3.12 (on page 158) for examples of foods high in iron and vitamin C.)

High blood pressure is more common in the elderly. This may be because they buy more ready meals, which are usually higher in salt than homemade meals. It is the sodium in salt that causes blood pressure to rise. As we get older, our sense of taste weakens, so the elderly are more likely to add extra salt to their food to intensify flavour.

Vitamin B12 is not easily absorbed as our body ages. Some elderly people are deficient in vitamin B12 and may need injections of this vitamin from their doctor. A lack of this vitamin may cause a gradual loss of memory in the elderly.

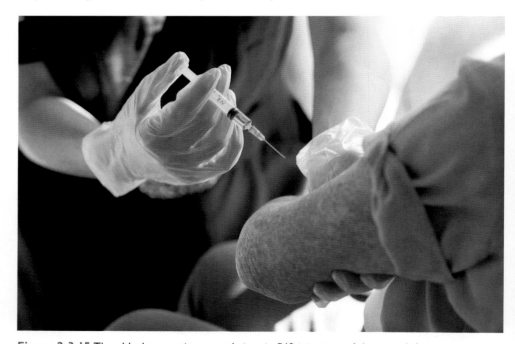

Figure 2.3.15 The elderly sometimes need vitamin B12 injections if they are deficient

Nutrients/other requirements	Reasons why they are important or a problem for the elderly
Vitamins A, C and E (the antioxidant vitamins)	To help prevent heart disease and some cancers.
Calcium and vitamin D	To keep bones strong to prevent osteoporosis.
Fibre and fluids	To prevent constipation, which may lead to diverticular disease and cancer of the bowel.
Vitamin C and iron	To prevent iron deficiency anaemia.
Sodium (salt)	Can cause high blood pressure if too much is eaten.
Vitamin B12	To help prevent memory loss.

Table 2.3.3 Nutritional needs of the elderly

Practical activity

1 Find a main course recipe which is suitable for elderly people. Give your reasons for choosing this recipe and explain why it is particularly suitable for this age group.
2 Make this dish, with a side dish, if appropriate.
3 Calculate the nutritional value to see which of the important nutrients (in Table 2.3.3) it contains.

Figure 2.3.16 Cottage pies are filling, economical and suitable for the elderly

Check your knowledge and understanding

1 Give **two** reasons why young children should not be given large meals.
2 Explain why teenagers have an increased need for protein in their diets.
3 Explain why iron deficiency may be a health problem for young teenage girls.
4 Give **one** reason why boys require more calcium than girls.
5 Identify **two** health problems that adults may develop if they have an unhealthy diet.
6 Name the vitamins needed to help the absorption of:
   a) calcium
   b) iron.
7 Name the deficiency disease which may develop in adults if their diet is low in calcium.
8 Give **two** reasons why the elderly usually need fewer calories than younger adults.
9 Explain why eating too many ready meals can cause high blood pressure.
10 Identify **three** essential nutrients needed by the elderly and explain why they are required by the body.

Planning balanced meals for different dietary groups

Why do people follow special diets?

There are many reasons why people follow special diets:

- It may be a personal choice. For example, you may decide to become a vegetarian because you think it is cruel to kill animals for food when there are other protein foods available.
- It may be essential for your health. For example, you may have been told by your doctor that you have coeliac disease and you must exclude foods containing gluten from your diet.
- It may be part of your religion or culture that you can't eat certain foods, for example if you are Jewish, you can't eat pork.
- It may be due to an allergy or intolerance that you can't eat certain foods, for example if you are allergic or are lactose intolerant to milk you must avoid it and all milk products.

Whatever the reason, you will learn about which foods these diets can and can't contain and how to plan, prepare and cook recipes for these dietary groups.

Vegetarians

There are different types of vegetarians depending on which animal foods are included in the diet.

People may follow a vegetarian diet for different reasons:

- They do not like the thought of eating a dead animal, fish or bird.
- They think it is cruel to kill animals for food.
- Their religion does not allow them to eat meat, fish or poultry.
- They think it is healthier to eat a vegetarian diet than one that includes meat.
- They think it is wasteful to raise animals for food when the same land space could be used more economically to grow crops, which need less care, labour, feeding and water compared with rearing animals.

The three main types of vegetarians are **lacto-vegetarians**, **lacto-ovo vegetarians** and **vegans**.

Lacto-vegetarians

Lacto-vegetarians will not eat animal foods such as meat, poultry and fish, nor products made from animals such as lard and gelatine. They will also not eat eggs, although they will eat dairy products such as milk, butter, cream, cheese and yoghurt.

This type of diet is varied and, although eggs are not included, nutritional deficiencies are unlikely. As egg yolk is a good source of iron, and eggs are not included in this diet, extra care should be taken to ensure an adequate supply of iron along with vitamin C to help its absorption.

Figure 2.3.17 This trademark means the food/product is suitable for vegetarians (lacto-ovo vegetarians)

Figure 2.3.18 This logo means the food is suitable for vegans

Key word

Lacto-vegetarians are vegetarians who eat no fish, meat, meat products or eggs, but eat dairy foods.

Lacto-ovo vegetarians

The **lacto-ovo vegetarian** diet is similar the lacto-vegetarian, but this type of vegetarian eats eggs as well as dairy products. Most UK vegetarians follow this type of diet.

This type of vegetarian diet is varied, and nutritional deficiencies are unlikely if a balanced diet is followed. However, the nutrient that is most likely to be low is, again, the mineral iron as it is more difficult for the body to absorb iron from non-meat foods. The iron in non-meat foods, such as spinach and broccoli, is called **non-haem iron**.

Vegans

A **vegan** diet does not contain any animal foods. This means that no food that involves the slaughter or the use of animals in its production is included in the diet. All foods are plant based so, as well as no meat or eggs, no dairy foods are included in a vegan diet either.

This type of strict vegetarian diet is much more limited, but if planned correctly it can supply all the essential nutrients. Vegan foods need to be selected to ensure they contain adequate supplies of protein, calcium and vitamin D, iron and vitamin C, vitamin A and vitamin B12, which could be lacking in a vegan diet. Most of these nutrients can be found in plant foods, with careful planning. However, Vitamin B12 is not found in vegan foods. A vegan diet should be supplemented with vitamin B12 from **fortified** food products, such as soya milk, almond milk and some breakfast cereals.

Figure 2.3.19 Foods fortified with vitamin B12 and suitable for vegans

The protein foods in a vegan diet are mainly low biological value (LBV, which means lacking one or more of the essential amino acids), and so foods need to be selected that include a balanced mixture of LBV protein foods to ensure all of the essential amino acids are supplied in the diet. Adding together LBV protein foods in this way is called protein complementation (see page 101).

Extension research activity

Using the internet or product leaflets/packaging, investigate vegan foods and which animal foods they are intended to replace.

Include your results in a table similar to the one shown below, including pictures of the vegan alternatives and the nutrients (if any) that the food has been fortified with.

Name of food	Food to replace	Added nutrients (fortified with)	Picture of food packaging
E.g. Soya milk	Cow's milk	Calcium, vitamins B2, B12 and D	

Coeliac disease

People with **coeliac disease** have a sensitivity to gluten. Gluten is a protein found in wheat, rye, barley and sometimes oats. People with coeliac disease react to gluten when it is eaten; their body attacks the healthy tissue in their body by mistake. This can damage the lining of the intestine (part of the digestive system), which stops nutrients from being absorbed.

Why some people develop coeliac disease is not known, but it could be **hereditary** or caused by environmental factors. Some studies have shown that breastfed babies are less likely to develop coeliac disease.

Many different foods contain gluten, so food labels need to be checked to ensure they are **gluten free**. Current food labelling laws mean that gluten needs to be shown as an ingredient.

Gluten is found in many foods, including:

- pasta
- cakes
- biscuits
- breakfast cereals
- most types of bread
- some sauces
- some ready meals.

It is important when preparing, cooking and serving meals for coeliac disease sufferers that different utensils are used to avoid contamination from gluten.

Figure 2.3.20 These bread rolls contain gluten and should be avoided by people with coeliac disease

Group practical activity

Make some gluten free bread rolls and compare these to traditional bread rolls for appearance, flavour and texture.

Figure 2.3.21 Gluten-free flour and pasta are available

Lactose intolerant

Lactose intolerance is fairly common in the UK. It means the body is unable to digest the sugar in milk. The sugar in milk and dairy products is called lactose.

An enzyme in the digestive system called **lactase** is needed to break down lactose. Lactose is a double sugar or disaccharide. Lactase breaks the disaccharide lactose into the two single sugars (monosaccharides) called **glucose** and **galactose**. People with lactose intolerance don't produce enough lactase and so the milk sugar lactose stays in the digestive system, where it ferments and produces gases.

For more about disaccharides and monosaccharides, see Topic 2.1 Macronutrients, page 110.

People with lactose intolerance may develop a bloated stomach and stomach pains as well as flatulence (wind) and diarrhoea.

As dairy foods supply calcium and protein, this food group should not be cut out of your diet unless your doctor has told you that you need to.

Lactose intolerance may be temporary or permanent.

Put simply, this means that if you are lactose intolerant, your body doesn't have the right enzyme to digest milk sugar, so this causes you to have an upset stomach.

Key words

Lactose intolerance means you cannot digest lactose.

Lactase is the enzyme that digests lactose.

Glucose and **galactose** are sugars (single sugars or monosaccharides) found in milk.

Figure 2.3.22 Milk and dairy foods contain lactose which some people cannot digest properly

Research activity

Using the internet, find out about dairy-free alternatives to milk. Make a table to show how dairy foods may be substituted with non-dairy equivalents.

You may find it useful to visit this website to help you: www.alpro.com/uk/foodservice/products.

Practical activity

With a partner, select a dairy product from milk, cheese, yoghurt or cream. Find a recipe using this dairy product and adapt it using a dairy-free alternative to make the recipe suitable for someone with lactose intolerance. Between you make a dairy and non-dairy version of the same recipe. Predict what you think the outcome will be and then carry out sensory analysis to prove or disprove your prediction.

High-fibre diet

Fibre (dietary fibre) is an important part of a healthy diet. It helps to keep the digestive system healthy and regular, and also helps to prevent some diseases that are common in the UK, such as coronary heart disease (CHD), type 2 diabetes and some cancers.

Adults need at least 30 g of fibre a day, but most people get less than this.

Fibre is found in foods that come from plants, such as cereals, fruits and vegetables. Wholegrain varieties of cereals contain more fibre – for example, wholemeal bread, brown rice and brown pasta contain more fibre than the refined white versions.

Figure 2.3.23 Vegetables and wholemeal bread are high in fibre

> **Key words**
>
> **Soluble fibre** is dietary fibre that helps to reduce cholesterol.
>
> **Insoluble fibre** is dietary fibre that helps to prevent constipation.

There are two different types of fibre: **soluble fibre** and **insoluble fibre**. Both are important in a healthy diet.

- Soluble fibre can be digested in your body. It is found in cereals, such as oats, barley and rye, fruits, including apples and bananas, and root vegetables, such as carrots and potatoes. As well as helping to prevent constipation, it can help to reduce cholesterol in the blood. Too much cholesterol can lead to coronary heart disease (e.g. heart attacks).
- Insoluble fibre can't be digested in your body. It helps to keep the digestive system healthy by helping waste food to pass out of the digestive system more easily. It helps to prevent constipation. It is found in wholemeal bread, cereals, nuts and seeds.

High-fibre foods help to fill you up so you are less likely to over-eat and become overweight.

If you need to increase the amount of fibre in your diet, it is better to do this gradually as a sudden increase may cause flatulence (wind) and stomach pains.

It is also important to drink six to eight glasses (approximately 2 litres) of liquid a day (plain water is best, although diluted fruit drinks count, as do tea and coffee) along with fibre as it absorbs water as it moves through the digestive system. Without sufficient liquid, fibre can't do its job properly.

Figure 2.3.24 Drinking plenty of fluids, about 2 litres a day, is important when following a high-fibre diet

Practical activity

1 Find a traditional recipe for **either** spaghetti Bolognese **or** a fruit crumble.
2 Adapt **one** of these recipes to increase both the soluble and insoluble fibre in the recipe.
3 Make one of these recipes in a practical lesson.
4 Use a nutritional analysis programme to compare the amount of fibre before and after the adaptation.

Check your knowledge and understanding

1 Give **three** reasons why people may follow a vegetarian diet.
2 Compare a vegan diet and a lacto-ovo vegetarian diet.
3 Define or give the definition of non-haem iron.
4 Explain why protein complementation is important when planning vegan meals.
5 Name **three** foods that someone with coeliac disease must avoid.
6 Name **two** cereal foods that are gluten free.
7 Describe what lactose intolerant means.
8 Name **two** commercial foods that are available as milk/dairy replacements.
9 Name **two** different types of dietary fibre.
10 Explain why fluids are especially important when following a high-fibre diet.

Energy needs

Why do you need energy?

Your body needs energy for every function and movement that it performs. Even when you are asleep, your body needs energy for breathing, to keep your heart beating, your internal organs working and for digesting food. During the day, you need energy for walking, running, cycling and even sitting down.

You get energy from the foods that you eat. Each food is normally a mixture of different nutrients – for example, bread contains mainly carbohydrate, but also some protein and a small amount of fat.

How is energy measured?

The energy we take into our bodies by consuming food and drinks and the energy we use is measured in **kilocalories (kcal)** or **kilojoules (kj)** (in this book, we will use kilocalories, as this is how food energy is most often measured).

A **kilocalorie** is the amount of heat energy that is needed to raise the temperature of 1 kg of pure water by 1°C.

Sources of energy

The energy in the nutrients is shown below.

1 g of each nutrient	Energy value in kilocalories (kcal)
Protein	4.0
Fat	9.0
Carbohydrate	3.75

Table 2.3.4 Sources of energy

You can see that fat contains more than twice the amount of kilocalories compared with protein and carbohydrate.

Foods may be **energy dense**; this means that for a given weight they contain a lot of kilocalories when compared with the same weight of a food that is not energy dense. The opposite of energy-dense food is low-calorie or **low-energy food**.

Key words

Kilocalorie (kcal) is a unit used to measure the energy in food.

Energy-dense foods are those which contain a high number of calories per gram (e.g. biscuits, chocolate).

Low-energy foods are foods low in energy and high in water.

Some examples of foods that are energy dense are biscuits, nuts, most cheeses, cream, cooking oil, pastries and crisps.

Examples of low-energy foods are most fruit and vegetables.

Figure 2.3.25 High- and low-energy foods

Starchy carbohydrates (for example, bread, rice, pasta, potatoes, chapatis and couscous) should be the main source of your body's energy. Your body first breaks down starch into glucose before it is used as a source of energy.

Fat is found in foods such as butter, cooking oils, cream and oily fish, and provides a concentrated source of energy. Your body has to break fat down into glucose before it can be used as a source of energy. Your body can store fat under your skin and this can be used at a later time for energy.

Protein is found in foods such as meat, fish, eggs, cheese, pulses (peas, beans and lentils) and nuts. Your body will use carbohydrates and fats for energy first, but if there is not enough of these nutrients in your diet, it will change protein into glucose and use this for energy. Protein is sometimes called a **secondary source of energy** for this reason.

The amount of energy you need changes throughout your life because of these main factors:
- **Age** – your energy needs as a teenager will be different from those of a baby or an elderly person. Energy needs increase as children grow older; this peaks in the teenage years and then reduces in adulthood.
- **Activity** – your energy needs will change from day to day depending on the activities you are carrying out.
- **Health** – your own health also affects the amount of energy needed. If you are ill and cannot move around so much, your energy needs will decrease. Sometimes illnesses can increase your need for energy if your body has to repair itself.
- **Gender** – whether you are male or female will affect your energy needs. Normally males need more energy than females. This is because males are usually bigger and have a higher proportion of muscle tissue than females.

Practical activity

Plan and make a pasta-based dish for a male teenager who takes part in a lot of sporting activity. Use a nutritional analysis programme to calculate the energy in one portion of this dish and compare this to the DRV for this target group.

What is basal metabolic rate?

Basal metabolic rate (BMR) is the number of kilocalories you need to stay alive for 24 hours. Different people have different BMRs depending on their age, size, gender and usual levels of physical activity.

To accurately measure the BMR, it needs to be carried out in a laboratory and is calculated from the amount of oxygen your body uses just to function, so the energy needed by the kidneys, lungs, liver, muscles and skin. It should be measured when the body is warm, and at complete rest. You should not eat for 12 hours before having your BMR measured as it should not include the digestion of food. Your BMR does not include other physical activity or exercise, although if you exercise regularly, this will increase your resting BMR.

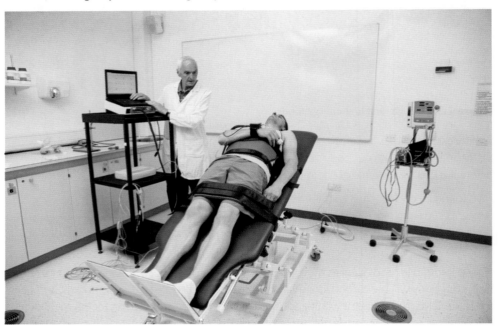

Figure 2.3.26 Basal metabolic rate (BMR) is measured when the body is warm and resting

What is physical activity level (PAL)?

Physical activity level (PAL) is a way of showing your daily physical activity as a number. Your PAL will vary depending on how you spend your time during the day. If you are sedentary (not very active), you will have a lower PAL than someone who moves around a lot in their job (for example, a personal trainer or builder).

It is calculated by the number of activities carried out during the day and how energetic these activities are. This, along with the BMR, can be used to work out how much food energy you need to consume in order to maintain your lifestyle. Most people have a PAL between 1.4 (a very inactive person) and 2.4 (a very active person).

$$\text{Physical Activity Level (PAL)} = \frac{\text{Total energy expenditure (over 24 hours)}}{\text{Basal metabolic rate (over 24 hours)}}$$

Recommended energy sources from nutrients in the UK

Protein	15% of total food energy from proteins	
Fat	No more than 35% of total food energy from fats	No more than 11% from saturated fats
Carbohydrate	50% of total food energy from carbohydrates	45% from fibre-rich starchy carbohydrate and lactose (the sugar in milk) when naturally present in milk and milk products, and sugars contained within the cellular structure of fruits and vegetables
		No more than 5% from free sugars

Table 2.3.5 Recommended energy sources from nutrients in the UK

Experts from the Scientific Advisory Committee on Nutrition (SACN) have published average requirements for energy for children and adults. The tables here show examples of their daily energy requirements for some specific ages and age ranges. These DRVs are estimated average requirements (EARs).

Young children and teenagers need more energy in relation to their size when compared with adults and the elderly. After the age of 18, energy requirements begin to fall. For the elderly (over 65s), energy needs are even lower due to a reduction in their BMR and lower physical activity levels.

Age	Boys (kcal)	Girls (kcal)
4	1,386	1,291
10	2,032	1,936
18	3,155	2,462

Table 2.3.6 Estimated average energy requirements for children and teenagers

Age	Males (kcal)	Females (kcal)
25–34	2,749	2,175
45–54	2,581	2,103
65–74	2,342	1,912

Table 2.3.7 Estimated average energy requirements for adults and the elderly

Health issues linked to over-consumption of some foods

- Eating too much saturated fat can increase your risk of heart disease and stroke.
- Eating too many free sugars may lead to tooth decay, type 2 diabetes (sugar-sweetened drinks have been linked to type 2 diabetes) and obesity.

Teacher's tip
Explain and learn the differences between free sugar, fruit sugar and milk sugar.

Figure 2.3.27 Your age, gender and physical activity level affects how much energy you need per day

Check your knowledge and understanding

1 Describe **three** different reasons your body needs energy.
2 Name the most common unit used to measure energy in food.
3 Identify or name the nutrient which provides the most energy per gram.
4 Name:
   a) **two** energy-dense foods
   b) **two** low-energy foods.
5 Explain which nutrient should provide the most energy in your diet.
6 Describe how energy needs change throughout your life.
7 Explain why it is important to be resting when your BMR is measured.
8 What is the definition of PAL?
9 Draw a pie chart or bar chart to show the percentage of recommended energy sources from protein, fat and carbohydrate.
10 Justify why you should eat less free sugars.

How to carry out nutritional analysis

Learning objectives

In this section you will learn:

- how to plan and modify recipes, meals and diets to reflect the nutritional guidelines for a healthy diet
- how to **analyse** the nutrients in a recipe, meal or diet using **food tables** or computer nutritional analysis software.

Planning and modifying recipes

It is important to eat a wide range of foods to ensure that a good mixture of nutrients is consumed throughout the day. If your diet is limited and you only eat a small number of foods, you are less likely to get all the nutrients you need.

Recipes are the starting point when you are planning a meal. The more varied your recipes are, the more nutrients your meal will provide.

Sometimes you will need to adapt a recipe to improve its nutritional value and to meet the current healthy eating guidelines (see page 147 for further information on these guidelines). To make recipes healthier, generally you will need to adapt recipes to make them lower in sugar, fat and salt and higher in fibre. For example:

- The sugar in most sweet recipes may be reduced by 20 per cent without most people noticing.
- The fat may swapped to include an unsaturated fat (for example, swapping butter for sunflower spread).
- The salt can be removed, reduced or replaced with other flavourings such as herbs, spices and garlic.
- The fibre may be increased by using wholegrain versions of ingredients – for example, wholemeal flour, brown rice and brown pasta to replace their white equivalents.

Activity

Copy and complete this table to show how you can adapt this recipe to follow healthy eating guidelines.

Apple crumble recipe

Topping (traditional recipe)	Topping (adapted recipe)
100 g plain white flour	
75 g butter	
80 g sugar	
1 tsp salt	
Filling (traditional recipe)	**Filling (adapted recipe)**
450 g cooking apples, peeled and sliced	
75 g sugar	
2 tbsp water	

Give some reasons for your **recipe modification**.

Activity

Find a recipe of your own and modify it to reflect the healthy eating guidelines. Include reasons for the changes you have made.

Planning and modifying meals

Meals should be planned following the food groups and proportions on the Eatwell Guide (see page 147) and will depend on the age, weight, height, activity levels and gender of the individual.

Figure 2.3.28 Chicken salad with rice: a balanced meal, following the Eatwell Guide

It would not be practical to make different recipes and meals for everyone in your family, but the correct portion sizes (see page 151) will allow for these differences in nutritional needs. For example, an active teenage girl will need more energy and iron than her five-year-old sister. The nutritional value of meals may be modified by swapping some ingredients and/or including a suitable side dish.

For example, lasagne can be high in fat, but by planning to use lean mince steak (or a meat substitute, such as Quorn™), low-fat Cheddar cheese and serving the lasagne with a side salad, the meal is modified to reduce the overall fat content.

Figure 2.3.29 Lasagne and salad: adding side dishes can improve the nutritional value of a meal

Planning and modifying diets

Your diet consists of all the meals, snacks and drinks you consume over a longer period of time, such as a week or a month. It is your overall diet that is important and this will determine your body weight, growth and general health. If an individual has a health problem, for example obesity, the diet will need to be modified to reduce the energy (kilocalories) provided. If tooth decay is present, the diet will need to be modified to reduce free sugars. If the health problem is coeliac disease, a gluten-free diet will be necessary. (See page 162 for more information on special diets.)

Nutritional analysis of recipes

A **nutritional analysis** lets you find out the nutritional value of a recipe, meal or diet. You can do this using either food tables printed in books, or using a website. Alternatively, a quicker way to find out the nutrients in a recipe or meal is by using special software, which has been designed to calculate and analyse the nutrients for you. Some will compare the nutrients with an individual's dietary reference values (DRVs). This is really helpful as it lets you see if you or your target group are having too much or too little of a particular nutrient.

Food tables

Food tables may be used to find out the nutritional value of foods or a recipe. These tables are usually listed in alphabetical order and show the amount of nutrient per 100 g of food.

The table below shows an example of how you can calculate how much iron is in a recipe for blueberry pancakes.

- Food tables have been used to look up the amount of iron in 100 g of each ingredient (this was done using a book, but this information is also available on the internet).
- The right-hand column shows how the amount of iron in each ingredient in each recipe has been calculated.
- The total amount of iron in the recipe has been calculated by adding up how much iron is in each of the ingredients.
- This recipe serves four; therefore the amount of iron in one serving has been calculated by dividing the total iron in the recipe by four.

Ingredient	Amount of iron in 100g of ingredient	Amount of ingredient in recipe	Amount of iron in ingredient used
Plain flour	1.94 mg	100 g	1.94 x 1 = 1.94 mg
Eggs	1.72 mg	100 g	1.72 x 1 = 1.72 mg
Semi-skimmed milk	0.02 mg	300 g	0.02 x 3 = 0.06 mg
Sunflower oil	0.1 mg	20 g	0.1 x 0.2 = 0.02 mg
Blueberries	0.55 mg	150 g	0.55 x 1.5 = 0.83 mg
Total iron in recipe (serves 4)			**4.57 mg**
Total iron in one serving			**1.14 mg**

Table 2.3.8 Analysing recipes using food tables: how much iron is in blueberry pancakes?

Extension activity

From Table 2.3.8 you can see that the blueberry pancakes are fairly low in iron; they contain only 1.14 mg per serving.

Teenage girls require 14.8 mg of iron a day compared with 8.7 mg a day for teenage boys. Calculate the percentage of the DRV of iron that one serving of the pancakes provides:

a) for a teenage girl
b) for a teenage boy.

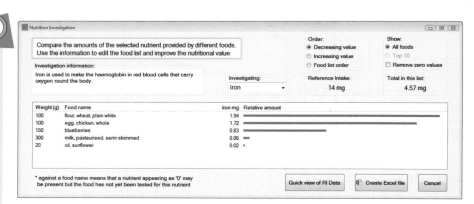

Figure 2.3.30 Nutritional analysis of blueberry pancakes

AQA GCSE Food Preparation and Nutrition

Nutritional analysis of recipes using computer programs

Nutritional analysis can help you to decide if the dish, meal or diet you have planned is suitable for your **target group**, and/or if it is healthy.

For example, if your target group are young children, aged 1–4 years, the meal should contain a suitable amount of energy for this age group for their active lifestyle and also provide the important nutrients such as calcium and vitamin D for strong bones and teeth (more information on this is on page 184–185).

> **Teacher's tip**
>
> Millilitres and grams are almost the same, so when carrying out **nutritional analysis** you can easily convert them; for example, 100 ml orange juice = 100 g orange juice.

Using food tables can be time-consuming, especially if you have several recipes or a whole day's meals to analyse, in which case you will find it quicker to use a computer program. In a computer program, you can input the ingredients and amounts, it analyses the ingredients and comes up with a table or chart to show the nutrients provided. Some programs will compare the nutrients in a recipe with the amounts an individual should be consuming (their DRV).

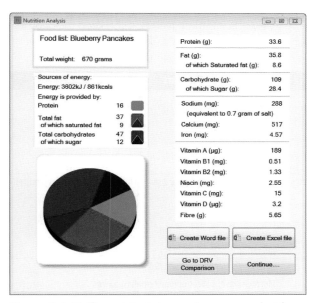

Figure 2.3.31 The nutrients in a recipe compared with the DRV for a boy aged 11–14 years

Analysing the nutritional value of meals

Sometimes you will need to plan and modify meals for a special dietary group, such as vegans. For this, you will need to input a list of the foods for the meal along with the amounts. You will also need to know the type of food, for example if bread is included, is it white, brown or wholemeal?

Good nutritional analysis software will include information on:
● the portion sizes of the foods you select
● the number of portions the meal provides
● the types of ingredients
● the gender and age of the target group you are planning the meal for.

Once you have analysed the nutrients in a meal, a graph or chart will be generated which compares the nutrients in your meal with the DRVs of an individual (your target group).

Analysing diets

If you want to find out if your diet provides you with all the nutrients you need in the correct amounts, you can find this out by keeping a **dietary diary**.

A dietary diary should include all the food, drinks and snacks eaten by you throughout the day. As you will probably eat differently at the weekends, it is more realistic if you keep the diary for a weekend day as well.

Day	Food eaten and type	Approximate amount
Breakfast	Weetabix with whole milk and banana slices	2 Weetabix
	Milky coffee made with whole milk	200 ml milk
	Apple	1 small banana
		250 ml milk
		1 large apple
Lunch	Cheddar cheese and tomato sandwich made with white bread and butter	40 g cheese, 1 small tomato, 2 slices white bread, 1 small knob butter
	Strawberry yoghurt (low fat)	1 small yoghurt
	Salt and vinegar crisps	1 small packet crisps
	Orange	Small orange
	Bottle of water	500 ml
Dinner	Chicken tikka masala with white rice	Medium portion of curry and rice
	Side salad, lettuce, onions and tomatoes	4 lettuce leave, 4 slices onion, 2 small tomatoes
	Fresh fruit salad and double cream	Small bowl fruit salad, 2 tablespoons double cream
	Orange juice carton	300ml juice
Snacks and other drinks	Bag of mixed nuts and raisins (unsalted)	Small bag
	Malt loaf and butter	2 slices
	Bottle of water x 2	500 ml x 2
	Cup of tea x 2	2 mugs

Table 2.3.9 A dietary diary listing all the food and drink consumed in one day by a teenage boy

1 Take the dietary diary in Table 2.3.9 and use a nutritional analysis program to calculate the day's nutrient intake.
2 Compare the nutrients in this day's food intake to the DRVs of a 15-year-old boy. Make suggestions for improving the diet by changing or removing some foods or adding new ones.
3 How do the percentages of energy from the nutrients compare with the recommended amounts of 15 per cent from protein, 50 per cent from carbohydrate and 35 per cent or less from fat?

Key word

Nutritional analysis means finding out the nutrients and energy in a recipe, meal or diet.

Target group is the group you are planning recipes, meals or diets for.

Dietary diary is a record of all the food and drink consumed over a set period of time.

Check your knowledge and understanding

1 Explain why it is important to use a wide variety of ingredients when planning meals.
2 Give **two** ways in which a recipe may be adapted to make it healthier.
3 Explain why wholegrain cereals are better than refined cereals.
4 Name **three** factors to consider about your target group when meal planning.
5 Describe the **two** main ways to carry out nutritional analysis.
6 Discuss the advantages of using a nutritional programme to analyse the nutrients in food.
7 Describe in detail the information that needs to be recorded in a dietary diary to ensure that it is accurate.

Diet, nutrition and health

Learning objectives

In this section you will learn about:
- how diet can affect health
- how nutritional needs change in relation to:
  - obesity
  - cardiovascular health – coronary heart disease (CHD) and strokes
  - bone health – rickets and osteoporosis
  - dental health
  - iron deficiency anaemia
  - type 2 diabetes.

The relationship between diet, nutrition and health

The food you eat affects how healthy you are. Generally, if you follow the principles of the Eatwell Guide and do not over-eat or under-eat, you will achieve a healthy balanced diet.

If you do not have a healthy diet, you can become ill. This may be caused by:
- **over-nutrition** (eating too much food, or too much of a certain nutrient); or
- **under-nutrition** (eating too little food or too little of a particular nutrient to meet dietary needs).

In the UK over-nutrition is more of a problem than under-nutrition. Under-nutrition is less of a problem in the UK, but it still occurs, particularly with the micronutrients such as calcium and iron.

Key words

Over-nutrition is an oversupply of a nutrient or nutrients.

Under-nutrition is an undersupply of nutrients.

Obesity is being very overweight.

Body mass index (BMI) is an index of your weight in relation to your height. It is used to classify people into four groups – underweight, healthy, overweight and obese.

Obesity

Obesity, or being obese, means being very overweight. One in four UK adults and one in five UK children are obese. This is higher than any other country in Western Europe.

You can use the **body mass index (BMI)** to see if your weight falls into the normal range and is suitable for adults and children. You will need to know your height and weight to calculate your body mass index (BMI).

$$Body\ mass\ index = \frac{weight\ (in\ kilograms/kg)}{height\ (in\ metres\ squared/m^2)}$$

Body mass index is used to classify people into four groups: underweight, healthy, overweight and obese.

For adults, a BMI of over 30 is considered obese.

Sometimes BMI is not accurate for someone who is very muscular but not carrying extra fat, but for most people it is a very good indication of whether you need to lose weight or not.

Another measure of obesity is by measuring your waist. Adults have a higher risk of health problems if waist measurements are above 94 cm for men and 80 cm for women.

Health problems linked to obesity are:
- **Type 2 diabetes** – see page 189.
- **Coronary heart disease** – see page 180.
- **Stroke** – see page 181.
- Some **cancers** – many more women than men get breast cancer, but being obese increases your risk, which may be due to hormonal changes in women as they get older. Bowel cancer is very common in the UK – about one in 20 people will develop this form of cancer. Being obese increases your chances of developing it.
- **Arthritis** – obesity can put a strain on the bone joints, which leads to arthritis.
- **Depression** – this is feeling sad for weeks or months. Being obese can make you feel hopeless and sad. Your doctor will have different ways of treating depression to help you recover.

Figure 2.3.32 To find out your body mass index (BMI), you will need to measure your height and weight

Treating obesity

Losing weight and reaching a healthy BMI is possible. If you have a healthy diet following the Eatwell Guide, if you reduce the energy (kilocalories) in your diet and exercise regularly you will have more of a chance.
- Children should exercise for at least 1 hour per day.
- Adults should exercise for about 4 hours per week.

Also, talking to a family member, nurse or doctor may help you to understand why being a healthy weight is important and help you to want to lose weight if you need to.

Losing weight gradually is better as you are more likely to be able to keep up this diet and stop the weight returning once you have lost it. Losing excess body fat and achieving a healthy body weight gives you more energy and means you are less likely to become seriously ill.

Figure 2.3.33 Regular exercise helps to prevent obesity

Cardiovascular disease

Cardiovascular disease covers a group of diseases, including diseases of the heart and blood vessels.

When your heart beats it pumps blood around your body to give your body cells oxygen, energy and the nutrients it needs. The blood then takes away the waste products from your body.

Two main types of cardiovascular disease are:
- coronary heart disease (CHD)
- stroke.

If the blood flow is reduced or stopped by a **blood clot** or narrowing of the **blood vessels** (caused by a build-up of fatty substances in the blood vessels), damage may be caused to the body. If this happens in the heart it can cause a **heart attack**. If this happens in the brain, the person will have a stroke.

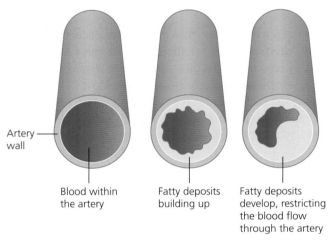

Artery wall

Blood within the artery

Fatty deposits building up

Fatty deposits develop, restricting the blood flow through the artery

Figure 2.3.34 How fatty deposits build up in the blood vessels

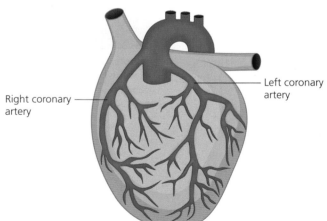

Right coronary artery

Left coronary artery

Figure 2.3.35 If the coronary arteries become blocked it can cause a heart attack

Coronary heart disease

Coronary heart disease occurs when blood vessels to the heart (the coronary arteries) become blocked with fatty deposits. This can cause **angina** if the blood flow is restricted or a heart attack if the blood supply is cut off completely. It is the main cause of death in the UK.

Stroke

A **stroke** occurs when the blood supply to the brain is cut off. The brain needs oxygen and nutrients to work properly. Without these, the brain cells begin to die. A stroke may lead to physical disability, brain injury or even death. It is the third largest cause of death in the UK after heart disease and cancer.

Risk factors for cardiovascular disease

The risk factors for cardiovascular disease are:

- **high blood pressure**
- smoking
- **high blood cholesterol**
- diabetes
- not exercising enough
- being obese or overweight
- having a blood relative with cardiovascular disease
- your ethnic background – in the UK, coronary heart disease rates are the highest in South Asian communities.

Reducing the risk of cardiovascular disease

You can reduce the risk of cardiovascular disease by:

- following the Eatwell Guide and not over-eating
- not drinking too much alcohol – men and women are advised not to regularly drink more than 14 units a week. This should be spread over three or more days if as much as 14 units of alcohol is consumed
- exercising regularly – children should exercise for at least 1 hour a day and adults about 4 hours a week
- not smoking.

Preventing cardiovascular disease

It is important that children learn good eating habits and have regular exercise so that these are seen as normal as they grow up and become adults.

The focus for a healthy lifestyle should be:

- watching the fat in your diet – not more than 35 per cent of total energy (kilocalories) should come from fat
- reducing the salt in your diet
- reducing the sugar in your diet.

Standard wine

Normal strength beer

Alcopops

Spirits

Figure 2.3.36 Alcohol consumption needs to be monitored, as too much can lead to cardiovascular disease

Reducing the salt in your diet

Table 2.3.10 shows the recommended guidelines for the maximum daily amount of salt in the diet for children and adults.

Age	Amount of salt in the diet (per day)
1–3 years	2 g
4–6 years	4 g
7–10 years	5 g
11 years to adult	6 g

Table 2.3.10 Recommended guidelines for the maximum daily amount of salt in the diet

> **Key word**
>
> **Sodium chloride** is the proper name for 'table salt'.

Salt is made from sodium and chloride (its proper name is **sodium chloride**). When looking at food labels, if sodium rather than salt is named, the amount of sodium (in grams) is multiplied by 2.5 to calculate the amount of salt.

Salt = sodium × 2.5

Activity

1 Copy and complete the table below to convert the amount of sodium in these foods into salt.

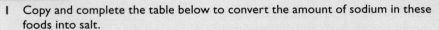

Food	Sodium in 100g food	Salt in 100g food
Grilled sausage	0.9 g	
Ready salted crisps	0.6 g	
Salted peanuts	0.5 g	
Bacon	1.7 g	
Oat cakes	0.5 g	
Rice cakes (lightly salted)	0.1 g	

1 Which food is the highest in salt?
2 Which food is lowest in salt?
3 Plan a low-salt snack using at least one the foods in the table above.

Activity

Reduce the fat and salt in a savoury recipe by swapping ingredients and choosing suitable cooking methods so it helps to prevent the risk of cardiovascular disease.

Use a nutritional analysis program to find out how much fat and salt are in both the traditional and adapted recipes.

Reducing the sugar in your diet

Eating too much sugar is a risk factor for cardiovascular disease. You should get around 50 per cent of your energy (kilocalories) from carbohydrates, but only 5 per cent of this should come from **free sugars**.

Free sugars are sometimes called 'added sugars' and include **sucrose** and honey. Sucrose is added to lots of different foods. Soft drinks including fizzy drinks are a major source of free sugars, especially for children. Where possible, you should drink water or milk and sometimes sugar-free soft drinks. From 2018, the government has decided to tax soft drink makers who put large amounts of sugar in their products. Soft drinks with more than 5g sugar per 100ml will be taxed. Drinks with more than 8g of sugar per 100ml will be taxed at a higher rate. Fruit juice and milk-based drinks will not be included in this taxing system.

Sugar is often added to breakfast cereals, either by the manufacturer or at the table when serving.

Sugars that are in fruits and vegetables (**fruit sugars**) do not count as free sugars. These sugars are part of the cell wall of plants.

Figure 2.3.37 Children need at least 1 hour of exercise a day to stay healthy and to help prevent diseases such as cardiovascular disease

Bone health

The strength of your bones depends on your diet, your exposure to sunlight and how much exercise you do. The nutrients that increase bone strength are the micronutrients calcium and vitamin D. Vitamin D may be obtained from our diet or from exposure to sunlight.

A baby's skeleton begins to grow in the womb, so the diet of a pregnant woman is very important. During this important time in the womb and childhood, the bones are being built. Up to around the late 20s, the skeleton gets stronger as it lays down calcium aided by vitamin D.

Rickets

If insufficient vitamin D or calcium is eaten in the diets of children this may lead to **rickets**. Children with rickets have weak and soft bones. This may cause the leg bones to change shape and bow outwards, as they are not strong enough to support the body weight. There has been an increase in rickets in recent years. This may be due to a lack of exposure to sunlight due to children playing indoors more and a lack of vitamin D in the diet. Children aged 6 months to 5 years should be given **vitamin drops** that contain vitamin D, as it is difficult to get enough in the diet.

Osteoporosis

In adults, a condition known as **osteoporosis** can develop, which can be caused by a lack of vitamin D and calcium from early childhood through to the late 20s. Adults with osteoporosis are much more likely to break a bone if they fall, as their bones are weaker and more brittle. Eating a healthy diet including calcium and vitamin D, as well as exercising, can help to prevent osteoporosis.

> **Key words**
>
> **Free sugars** are sugars that are added to food (they are not part of the cell wall of a plant).
>
> **Rickets** is a condition found in children, where a lack of calcium and vitamin D in the diet causes the bones to soften.
>
> **Vitamin drops** containing vitamins A, C and D are recommended for children aged 6 months to 5 years in the UK.
>
> **Osteoporosis** is a condition in adults, where a loss of calcium from bones makes them weak and more likely to break.

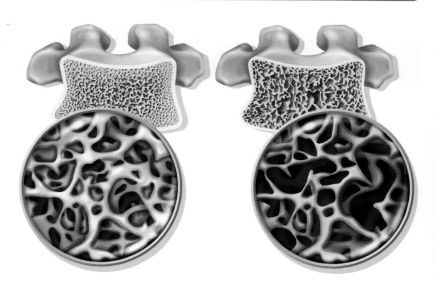

Figure 2.3.38 Osteoporosis is a condition in adults that weakens bones, making them fragile and more likely to break

Dental health

Your dental health is important to keep your teeth and gums healthy. You should have regular check-ups with your dentist. The time between visits depends on your own teeth and gums.

As soon as the first baby tooth appears, tooth brushing should begin. Babies and children aged under 7 years should have help when cleaning their teeth to make sure all surfaces are cleaned.

Teeth should be cleaned twice a day, ideally for 2 minutes each time. A **fluoride toothpaste** is recommended as it helps to prevent tooth decay.

Sugar

Eating foods with high amounts of free sugars in them, such as fizzy drinks, biscuits, cakes, sweets, chocolates and desserts, can cause **tooth decay**. If foods containing free sugars are eaten regularly throughout the day, for example for snacks and sugary drinks, this can increase the risk of tooth decay. Free sugars are sugars that have been added either by a food manufacturer, cook or consumer to a food.

- They include sugars naturally found in fruit juice, honey and syrups.
- They do not include sugars naturally found in milk and milk products nor in fruit and vegetables.

You don't need to have 'free sugar' in your diet, but if you do, it is better to eat foods and drinks that contain free sugar at mealtimes so that the teeth have less exposure to it.

Fruit juices contain large amounts of free sugar, and should be limited to a small 150 ml glass a day, which may be diluted with water to reduce the sugar and acidity of the drink overall. Regular daily drinks ideally should be water or milk between meals. If other soft drinks are consumed these should be the sugar-free versions.

The more times during the day when sugary foods and drinks are consumed, the more likely you are to develop tooth decay and need dental treatment.

Foods containing sugar should not be eaten more than three times a day nor exceed the amounts on the chart below. For children up to 3 years, do not add sugar to their food, especially during **weaning** as a sweet tooth may be formed, which will be difficult to change as the child becomes older.

Public Health England has calculated these as maximum amounts of free sugar to be eaten per day.

Ages	Maximum free sugar intake – per day
4–6 years	19 g
7–10 years	24 g
11 years to adult	30 g

Table 2.3.11 Maximum amounts of free sugar to be eaten per day (calculated by Public Health England)

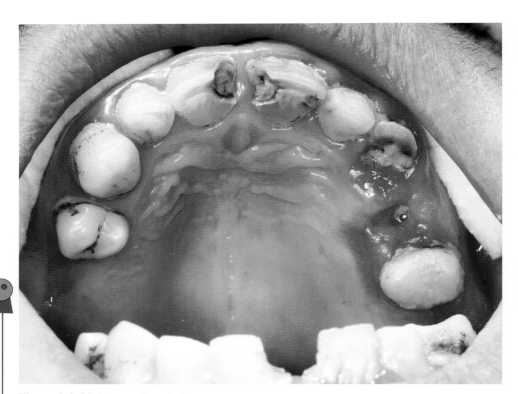

Figure 2.3.39 Advanced tooth decay

What causes tooth decay?

Tooth decay begins with **plaque** forming on your teeth and gums that contains bacteria. Over time, this bacteria can interact with the sugars in the food you eat to make acid. This acid attacks your tooth enamel and can cause tooth decay. Tooth decay may lead to fillings or the loss of teeth.

Key words

Fluoride toothpaste is a type of toothpaste that helps to strengthen the enamel on your teeth to prevent decay.

Tooth decay refers to the acids in your mouth that attack tooth enamel.

Plaque is a mixture of bacteria on teeth and the sticky substances produced by them.

Iron deficiency anaemia

Iron deficiency anaemia is a condition of the blood. It occurs when there are not enough red blood cells available. The red blood cells have an important job of transporting oxygen around the body. When there are not enough red blood cells, the body becomes short of oxygen, which can cause:

- a pale complexion
- breathlessness
- **heart palpitations**
- tiredness
- dizziness or fainting

This type of anaemia can be diagnosed by having a simple blood test at your doctor's surgery.

Figure 2.3.40 Iron deficiency anaemia can cause a pale complexion and tiredness

What causes iron deficiency anaemia?

For girls and women who have monthly periods (menstruation) it can be caused by having heavy periods, where there is more blood loss than normal. Also, pregnant women may become anaemic as they need iron for the growing baby.

Sometimes men and older women (who have passed the **menopause**) may develop iron deficiency anaemia as a result of bleeding in the **intestines** and stomach. This is not due to a lack of iron in the diet and would need separate and specialist treatment.

How to treat iron deficiency anaemia

Your doctor may give you iron tablets to take daily and will check your iron levels have returned to normal after a few months. Iron is more easily absorbed if vitamin C is eaten at the same time (see page 159).

Figure 2.3.41 These foods contain useful amounts of iron

What happens if iron deficiency anaemia is left untreated?

If anaemia is left untreated it can make you more likely to get infections and other illnesses as the body needs iron for its **immune system**.

Activity

Plan a healthy packed lunch for a teenage girl that is high in iron and vitamin C.

Use a nutritional analysis program to find out how much iron and vitamin C the lunch contains and the percentage of her daily iron and vitamin C the lunch provides.

Key words

Heart palpitations are when your heart beats suddenly become more noticeable.

Menopause is when a woman's periods (menstruation) stop, around the age of 50 years.

Intestines are part of the digestive system.

Immune system refers to the parts of your body and processes that protect against disease.

Type 2 diabetes

Diabetes is a condition when the sugar in a person's blood gets too high. Once someone has diabetes, they have it for the rest of their life. Type 2 diabetes is the most common type of diabetes in the UK. More and more people are developing type 2 diabetes, but there are things you can do to help prevent getting it yourself.

You are more likely to develop type 2 diabetes if:
- you are overweight or obese
- you are over 40 years old
- you eat fatty, salty and sugary foods often
- you have high blood pressure
- you do not exercise regularly.

Many people have diabetes, but do not realise it. This is because the symptoms can be mild to start off with. If someone thinks they may have diabetes, they should visit their doctor as soon as possible, otherwise the condition can get worse and other health problems can develop.

The main symptoms of diabetes are:
- feeling tired all the time
- feeling thirsty
- passing more urine than normal.

Diabetics should follow the Eatwell Guide and make sure they eat regular meals throughout the day. By following the Eatwell Guide, they will be eating mainly **starchy carbohydrates**, which release sugar more slowly into the bloodstream. Diabetics may have *some* free sugar in their diets (see page 110), but it should be a reduced amount.

Figure 2.3.42 Pasta dishes are a good source of starchy carbohydrates

Group activity

Reduce the sugar in one traditional pudding recipe (for example, rice pudding, microwave sponge pudding or a recipe of your choice). Only one type of pudding should be made so it is a fair test.

Use the table below to work out how much sugar your group needs to add to the recipe.

Group	How much sugar to use compared with the recipe
Group 1	All
Group 2	$\frac{3}{4}$
Group 3	$\frac{1}{2}$
Group 4	$\frac{1}{4}$

Carry out sensory analysis by **ranking** all of the samples of puddings to decide which one you like best.

Why do you think it is best to taste the pudding with the least amount of sugar first?

Key words

Diabetes is a condition when the body's sugar levels cannot be controlled properly.

Starchy carbohydrates are carbohydrates such as bread, rice, potatoes, pasta and chapatis.

Ranking means putting samples in order of preference (for example, the one you like best comes first).

Check your knowledge and understanding

1 State the maximum adult BMI before you are considered abese.
2 Name **three** conditions which are more likely if you are obese.
3 What are the **two** main types of cardiovascular disease called?
4 Name or identify the main cause of death in the UK.
5 Describe how cardiovascular disease may be prevented.
6 Name the condition that causes soft bones in children and suggest ways to prevent it.
7 Explain what osteoporosis is and how may it be prevented.
8 Describe the different types of sugars which are bad for the teeth.
9 Name the vitamin which helps the body to absorb iron.
10 Identify the type of diet people with type 2 diabetes should follow.

AQA GCSE Food Preparation and Nutrition

Section 2 Practice questions: Food, nutrition and health

Multiple choice questions

1 Which food is a source of high biological value protein? (1 mark)
   a) Wheat
   b) Peas
   c) Eggs
   d) Rice

2 Which vitamins are found in fats and oils (1 mark)
   a) Vitamin A and B
   b) Vitamin A and C
   c) Vitamin B and D
   d) Vitamin A and D

3 Which of the following foods is a source of starch? (1 mark)
   a) Honey
   b) Potatoes
   c) Red meat
   d) Butter

4 Which vitamin is an antioxidant? (1 mark)
   a) Vitamin B
   b) Vitamin K
   c) Vitamin D
   d) Vitamin E

5 Which vitamin helps the absorption of iron? (1 mark)
   a) Vitamin A
   b) Vitamin B1
   c) Vitamin C
   d) Vitamin D

6 How many glasses of water should you drink each day? (1 mark)
   a) 1–2
   b) 3–4
   c) 5–6
   d) 7–8

Other question types

7 Give **three** functions of protein in the body. (3 marks)

8 Give **three** examples of protein foods that have a high biological value (HBV). (3 marks)

9 Explain the meaning of the term 'protein complementation'. (2 marks)

10 Suggest **one** example of how protein foods can be combined to complement each other. (1 mark)

11 Explain why some people need more protein than others. (2 marks)

12 Give **two** plant sources of fat in the diet. (2 marks)

13 Name **two** vitamins that are found in fatty foods. (2 marks)

14 Explain the difference between saturated and unsaturated fats. (5 marks)

15 Give **two** plant sources of starch in the diet. (2 marks)

16 Explain the term 'free sugar'. (2 marks)

17 Give **two** functions of dietary fibre in the body. (2 marks)

18 Name **two** water-soluble vitamins. (2 marks)

19 Name the **two** vitamins which are added to margarine by law. (2 marks)

20 Explain why raw vegetables contain more vitamins than cooked vegetables. (2 marks)

21 Complete the table below. (6 marks)

Vitamin	Functions in the body	Main food sources
B2 (Riboflavin		
Folic Acid		
C (Ascorbic acid)		

22 Give **two** sources of calcium in the diet. (2 marks)

23 Give **three** functions of calcium in the body. (3 marks)

24 Name a deficiency of calcium. (1 mark)

25 Give **two** reasons why water is an important part of a healthy diet. (2 marks)

26 Name **three** different foods with a high water content. (3 marks)

27 This is an example of the daily diet of a teenage girl who is a vegetarian.

Breakfast	• Sugar-coated cereal bar	• Black coffee
Lunch	• Pizza slice • Chips	• Fizzy drink
Supper	• Vegetarian sausages • Mashed potato	• Carrots • Doughnut
Snacks	• Salted crisps	• Fizzy drink

a) Name **two** nutrients that may be low in this diet. (2 marks)

b) Explain **four** ways in which this diet could be improved to meet current dietary guidelines. (8 marks)

28 a) Suggest ways a family on a low income can save money when buying food. (6 marks)

29 Discuss the nutritional needs of the elderly. Give examples of how you could make sure the elderly receive the right nutrients. (10 marks)

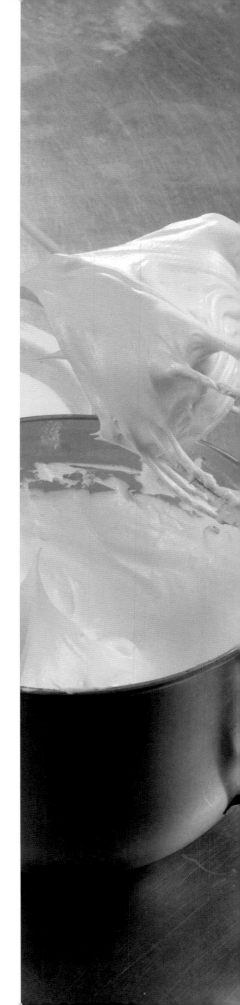

SECTION 3
Food Science

This section includes the following topics:

3.1 Cooking of food and heat transfer

3.2 Functional and chemical properties of food

Section 3 Practice questions

TOPIC 3.1 COOKING OF FOOD AND HEAT TRANSFER

Why food is cooked and how heat is transferred to food

Learning objectives

In this section you will learn about:
- the **reasons** why food is cooked
- the different ways in which **heat is transferred** through food.

Why is food cooked?

The table below shows the different reasons why we cook food and gives an explanation for each reason.

Reason why food is cooked	Explanation
To make food safe to eat	Cooking destroys harmful bacteria, e.g. in chicken.
To improve the flavours of food	Some raw foods can lack flavour. Courgettes taste better when cooked with seasoning.
To improve the appearance and smell of food	Some foods look and smell better when cooked, e.g. fish and chicken.
To improve the texture of food	Cooking improves the texture of meat. It makes it easier to chew and digest.
To improve the shelf life of food	Cooked fruits can be stored for a long time, e.g. jams.
To give variety to the diet	Different cooking methods can add flavours to food and give you more choices, e.g. barbecue.

Table 3.1.1 Reasons why food is cooked

Research activity

Eating raw meat and seafood

Investigate one cultural tradition of eating uncooked meat and seafood such as crudos, steak tartare, sushi, sashimi or raw oysters. Describe what is eaten and how it is eaten.

Figure 3.1.1 Raw oysters are a luxury food

Figure 3.1.2 Cakes rise when heated in an oven

The ways that preparation and cooking affects food

Heat can change the appearance, colour, flavour, texture and smell of food. When food is prepared and cooked you may see one or more of the changes indicated below.

Appearance	Bread dough and cakes will rise. Biscuits and pastry will set. Eggs will set.
Colour	Foods containing starch will brown. Some vegetables will brighten when cooked but they will eventually take on a dull colour, if they are cooked for too long.
Size	Meat shrinks as water is lost. Rice and pasta swell as water is absorbed.
Texture	Sauces will thicken, vegetables will soften, eggs will set and sugar will dissolve and caramelise.
Smell	Chemicals are released into the air as food is cooked. When they reach the nose, they create an attractive aroma or smell.

Table 3.1.2 The effect of heat on food

How is heat transferred?

Food is cooked by heat energy. The three ways that heat energy can be passed through food are:

- conduction
- convection
- radiation.

Conduction

Conduction is when the heat travels through solid materials such as metals and food.

Heat is conducted from molecule to molecule in a liquid or solid. For example, when a gas flame warms the base of a metal saucepan, the heat is conducted around the pan. The heat will be conducted into the food and the food will cook.

Figure 3.1.3 **Butter melting in a saucepan due to conduction**

Heat can also be conducted through the food when it is roasted.

Figure 3.1.4 **In roasting, the heat travels through the food**

- Metals conduct heat quickly so many cooking pans, utensils and baking trays are made from steel, copper or aluminium.
- Water is a good conductor too, so boiling food is a quick method of cooking.
- Plastic and wood are poor conductors, so they are used for pan handles or tools for stirring food that is cooking.

Convection

Convection is when heat travels through air or water. The movement of heat in water or in the air is called the **convention current**. Convention currents happen because hot air will rise and cool air will fall. Ovens are heated by convention currents. The hottest part of the oven is the top shelf and the coolest part is the bottom shelf (except in fan-assisted ovens, where the fan circulates the heat and keeps all shelves at the same temperature). Baking food in an oven, boiling, poaching and steaming all use convection currents to cook food.

Figure 3.1.5 In poaching, the convection currents in water cook the egg

Radiation

Radiation is when heat rays directly warm and cook food.
- Heat travels from one place to another.
- Food that is grilled or toasted is cooked by radiation.
- Radiation requires a direct heat source such as a grill or barbecue.

Figure 3.1.6 Grilling is heat transfer by radiation

Key words

Conduction is when heat travels through solid materials such as metals and food.

Convection is when heat travels through air or water.

Convection current is the movement of heat in water or in the air.

Radiation is when heat rays directly heat and cook food.

Cooking method	Method of heat transfer
Stir-frying vegetables	
Boiling an egg	
Baking a potato	
Toasting bread	
Steaming vegetables	
BBQ a chicken thigh	
Roasting beef	

Table 3.1.3 Cooking methods

Most food is cooked by a **combination of the methods** of heat transfer. For example, when baking a tray of biscuits, the heat is transferred to the biscuits by conduction from the metal baking tray. Then, the heat is transferred to the biscuits by convection using the hot air inside the oven.

Figure 3.1.7 Oatmeal cookies involve conduction and convection

Microwave ovens

Cooking food in a microwave oven is another example of radiation cooking food. The **magnetron** inside a microwave oven produces **electromagnetic rays**, which heat and cook food.

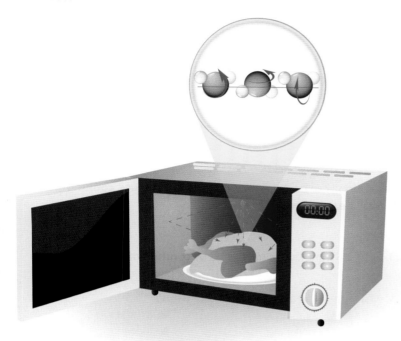

Figure 3.1.8 Electromagnetic rays inside a microwave

- Electromagnetic rays produced inside a microwave oven will heat food up by causing water molecules to vibrate.
- The electromagnetic rays are absorbed by water molecules, which makes them vibrate.
- The vibration causes the food to heat up and cook.
- The rays will pass through glass, plastic and tableware. Glass, plastic and tableware will become warm in a microwave as the food inside them warms up.
- Metals and foils will reflect the electromagnetic rays and can damage the microwave, so they should never be used in microwave cooking.

Check your knowledge and understanding

1 Explain **three** reasons why we cook food.
2 Describe how food is cooked by conduction.
3 Explain why some saucepan handles are made of wood.
4 Explain how convection currents heat food.
5 Name **one** cooking method that uses radiation.
6 Name **three** foods that can be cooked by radiation.
7 Explain how microwave ovens heat up food.
8 Discuss the advantages and disadvantages of using microwave ovens to cook food.

Selecting appropriate cooking methods

Learning objectives

In this section you will learn about:

- the methods of cooking that will **conserve** and **modify** the nutrients in food
- how the choice of cooking method will affect the **appearance**, **colour**, **flavour**, **texture**, **smell** and overall **appeal** of food.

Choice of cooking methods

The ways in which we cook food can be divided into the following groups: **cooking with water**; **cooking with 'dry' heat** and **cooking with fat**.

Cooking with water

Heat will pass through water very quickly. It is transferred by **conduction** and **convection currents**.

The cooking methods which use water are:

- blanching
- boiling
- braising
- poaching
- simmering
- steaming.

Cooking with 'dry' heat

Heat will pass through the air in **convection currents** in the oven and as **radiation** from a grill or barbecue.

Figure 3.1.9 Heat passing through water to cook food

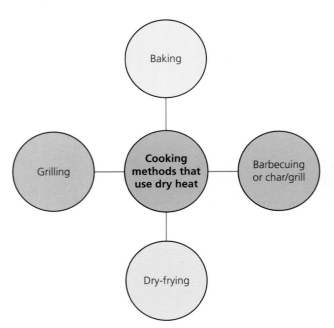

Figure 3.1.10 Cooking methods that use dry heat

Figure 3.1.11 Dry heat from a barbecue cooking food

Cooking with fat

Heat will pass through oil or fat by **conduction** or **convection currents**.

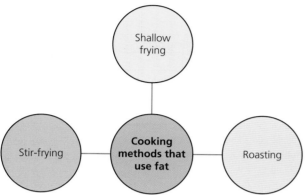
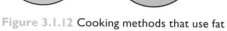

Figure 3.1.12 Cooking methods that use fat

Figure 3.1.13 Roasting beef and potatoes

Activity

Complete the following using these words. Use each word once only.

convection   boiling   grilling   braising   water
roasting   baking   dry   stir-frying

Heat will pass through .... very quickly. .... and
.... are cooking methods that use water.

In the oven and under the grill, ... heat cooks food quickly. Methods of cooking
that use dry heat include .... and ....

Heat will pass through oil or fat using .... currents. Examples of cooking
methods that use oil and fat are .... and ....

Key words

Cooking with water uses the convection currents in water to cook food.

Dry heat uses convection currents or radiation to cook food.

Cooking with fat uses the convection currents in hot oil or fat to cook food.

Activity

Copy the following table and match the correct cooking method with the correct definition.

Cooking method	Definition
Baking	Cooking food in boiling water
Barbecuing or char/grill	Using the steam from boiling water to cook food
Poaching	Cooking food in a saucepan for a long time in a hot liquid, just below boiling point
Boiling	Cooking delicate foods (eggs, fish and fruit) gently in water just below boiling
Braising	Cooking foods that are high in fat in a non-stick pan where only the melted fat inside the food is used for frying
Dry-frying	Cooking food by dry heat in an oven
Grilling	Cooking food by applying heat to the surface of food
Roasting	Cooking food using glowing hot charcoal
Shallow frying	Cooking food in a small amount of fat or oil in a shallow pan
Simmering	Cooking food in deep oil at a high temperature
Steaming	Cooking food in a wok or frying pan with a small amount of oil
Stir-frying	Hot air and a small amount of fat cooks the meat or vegetables in the oven

Activity

Copy and complete the table below. Give examples of three foods which can be cooked by each of the methods.

Cooking method	Examples of food cooked by this method
Baking	
Barbecuing or char/grill	
Boiling	
Braising	
Dry-frying	
Grilling	
Roasting	
Shallow frying	
Simmering	
Steaming	
Stir-frying	
Poaching	

The factors to consider when choosing a cooking method

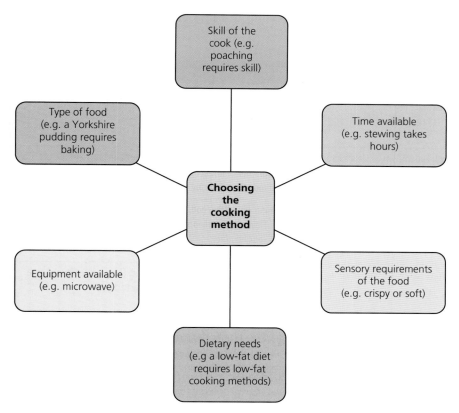

Figure 3.1.14 Factors to consider when choosing a cooking method

Activity

1 Copy the diagram above and add more example to support each point.
2 Discuss with a partner the factors that you consider when choosing a cooking method. Add new ideas to a diagram.
3 Add any special equipment to the diagram that some cooking methods require.

Cooking with water

Cooking with water involves relatively low temperatures. Water boils at 100°C. The cooking methods that use water are **blanching**, **boiling**, **braising**, **poaching**, **simmering** and **steaming**.

Cooking method	Effect on nutrients	Effect on sensory qualities (e.g. appearance, colour, flavour, texture, smell)
Blanching	Vitamin C, vitamins from the B group, iron and calcium will leach into the cooking water. Blanching is very quick so the loss of nutrients is small.	Blanching retains the crisp texture of vegetables. The colour of vegetables is retained too.
Boiling	Vitamin C, vitamins from the B group, iron and calcium will leach into the cooking water. Boiling is a relatively quick method of cooking so the loss of nutrients is not too large.	Boiling will soften food. It tenderises meat giving a soft texture. The flavours will be lost in the cooking water. Overcooking can make the food too soft and mushy. Fruit and vegetables will lose some colour.
Braising	Vitamin C, vitamins from the B group, iron and calcium will leach into the cooking water. Braising is a very slow cooking method so the loss of nutrients is large. But the cooking water is usually eaten with the meal as gravy, so the nutrients will be eaten. However, the heat will destroy water-soluble vitamins.	Braising will soften food. Tough, chewy meats become tender and soft. Flavours are enhanced. Vegetable colour can be lost due to the long cooking time.
Poaching	Vitamin C, vitamins from the B group, iron and calcium will leach into the cooking water.	Poaching will soften and tenderise food. Flavour is retained. Some colour will be lost. Poached food is easy to digest.
Simmering	Vitamin C, vitamins from the B group, iron and calcium will leach into the cooking water. Simmering takes a long time so nutrient losses are greater than when boiling food.	Simmering will soften food. It tenderises meat giving a more appetising texture. Flavour will leach into the water, and overcooking can make the food soft and mushy.
Steaming	No contact with water so vitamin C, vitamins from the B group, iron and calcium will not leach into the cooking water. There is some loss of water-soluble vitamins from the heat.	Steaming gives a light and fluffy texture to food. It tenderises meat. Fruit and vegetables may lose their colour. Steamed food is easy to digest because it does not use added fat.

Table 3.1.4 How water-based cooking methods affect food

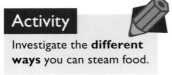

Activity

Investigate the **different ways** you can steam food.

Figure 3.1.15 Steaming is considered a very healthy method of cooking

Cooking with dry heat

There are four ways of cooking with dry heat. They are **baking**, **barbecuing** or **char/grill**, **dry-frying** and **grilling**. The oven, hob or grill can be used to produce dry heat.

Cooking method	Effect on nutrients	Effect on sensory qualities (e.g. appearance, colour, flavour, texture, smell)
Baking	Baking does not affect calcium and iron. Vitamin C and vitamin B1 are lost due to the heat.	Baking will give a crispy texture and a golden brown colour to the surface of food. Baking will tenderise meat, giving it a softer, more appetising texture.
Barbecuing or char/grill	Vitamin C and vitamin B1 are lost due to heat. No water is involved, so there is no leaching of the other water-soluble vitamins. If the fat melts and runs out of the food, vitamins A and D will be lost.	Barbecuing or char/grill are not suitable for tough or very thick cuts of meat. Food will brown. Food will become crispy and the flavour and smell are improved. Overcooking can produce a bitter flavour and a black colour.
Dry-frying	The fat-soluble vitamins A and D are retained. Vitamin C and vitamin B1 are lost due to the heat. There is no added fat, so it is healthier than other methods of frying.	Food will brown and become crispy. The flavour and smell are improved.
Grilling	Iron and calcium will be retained. But some vitamin C and vitamin B1 are lost due to the intense heat. Fat-soluble vitamins are lost when the fat melts because they will run out of the food. Fat drains off the food so this reduces its fat content, making it healthier.	Not suitable for tough cuts of meat or very thick foods. Food will brown. Food becomes crispy and the flavour and smell are improved. Overcooking can produce a bitter flavour and a black colour.

Table 3.1.4 How dry heat cooking methods affect food

Cooking with fat

There are three ways of cooking with fat:
- roasting
- shallow frying
- stir-frying.

The choice of fat for frying is important.
- Low-fat spreads are not suitable for frying because they contain water. Water will cause the fat to split and separate when heated.
- Vegetables oils, **ghee** (a type of butter that originated in India), butter and lard can all be used.

Figure 3.1.16 Dry-frying in a preheated pan

Cooking method	Effect on nutrients	Effect on sensory qualities (e.g. appearance, colour, flavour, texture, smell)
Roasting	Roasting does not affect calcium and iron. Some vitamin C and vitamin B1 are lost due to the heat. This can be large as roasting can take a long time.	The surface of meat will brown and crisp. It tenderises meat, giving it a softer, more appetising texture. Fruit and vegetables may lose their colour.
Shallow frying	Most vitamins and minerals are retained. It is a quick method of cooking. The fat content of the food will increase as fat is absorbed into the food.	Seals food quickly and produces an interesting crispy texture. It tenderises meat, giving it a softer, more appetising texture. Bright colours can be reduced.
Stir-frying	It is quick so most vitamins and minerals are usually not lost. A small amount of oil means that it is healthy too.	Crisp texture and good colour in vegetables is retained.

Table 3.1.6 How fat-based cooking methods affect food

The quality of the fat used for frying is important. The fat will absorb flavours and these can be passed on to the food. It is not advisable to reuse fat many times for deep frying as the structure of the fat will break down and it will develop an 'off' flavour. Frying involves heating fat to very high temperatures which requires careful supervision.

Methods of cooking that conserve nutrients

The methods of cooking that retain vitamins and minerals use only small amounts of fat or water and don't require a long time. They include:

- steaming
- grilling
- barbecuing
- dry frying
- poaching
- stir-frying.

Figure 3.1.18 Stir-frying is healthy

Braising is one of the most damaging cooking methods to nutrients. It involves using water and lasts a long time. Braising produces very tender and soft food. The cooking liquid should always be eaten with braised food to maximise nutrient intake.

Deep frying and roasting can damage or destroy heat-sensitive vitamins. However, the fat used in deep frying seals in the water-soluble vitamins and because it is quick the vitamin loss is reduced.

It is best to steam or microwave vitamin C-rich potatoes. Deep frying and roasting also add fat to the food.

Research activity

Many people wish to reduce the amount of fat they eat. However, fried food is popular with all age groups and in almost all cultures. Investigate the different fried foods eaten by different cultures and the possible harmful effects of eating too much fried food.

Figure 3.1.19 Pancakes are part of British cultural food

Research activity

Find an image and write a description about each of the following methods of cooking. Include references to the cultural origin of the cooking method, if appropriate.

- sauté
- fondue
- slow cooking
- tandoori oven
- pressure cooking.

AQA GCSE Food Preparation and Nutrition

The effect of microwaving on food

Microwaves are versatile and can be used to cook and heat a wide range of foods.

- Food is cooked very quickly in a microwave. This means that there is less chance of the vitamins in the food being destroyed.
- Water, not fat, is used to transfer the heat to food so no additional fat is added to food either.
- The bright colours of fruit and vegetables are retained because the cooking time is short.

Microwaves can be used to cook and heat a wide range of foods.

It is important to follow the manufacturer's instructions for cooking foods in a microwave. Different power settings can make it easy to overcook or undercook food.

Some foods do not cook well in a microwave. Microwaves are not very good at browning food or giving a crisp crust. This means that food that requires a crispy crust, such as pastries, breads and cakes, are not usually suitable for microwaving. Some types of microwave oven do have a browning facility. These are called **combination microwaves**. Combination microwave ovens have grills, which will give some browning and crispiness to food.

Practical activity

Plan and cook a dessert using only a microwave oven. The ingredients need to be cooked in the microwave and not simply reheated.

Check your knowledge and understanding

1 Describe **six** factors that might determine choice of cooking method.

2 Name **two** water-soluble vitamins which are lost when food is cooked in water.

3 Explain how the cooking water could be used to reduce vitamin and mineral loss.

4 Explain why dry-frying is healthier than other types of frying.

5 Discuss why steaming is a good cooking method for families.

6 Name **two** cooking method that retain the colour in vegetables.

7 Name **two** cooking methods that add a crispy texture to food.

8 Name **two** cooking methods that produce a soft and mushy texture to food if used incorrectly.

9 Name **one** cooking method that produces black and bitter-tasting food if used incorrectly.

10 Name **three** foods that do not usually cook well in a microwave oven.

Proteins

Learning objectives

In this section you will learn about:
- protein denaturation
- protein coagulation
- gluten formation
- foam formation.

What is protein denaturation?

Denaturation is a change in the structure of a protein. The long chains of amino acids that make up the proteins unfold from their coiled state.

Protein is denatured by: heat, acids and mechanical action. Heating and acids change the shape and structure of proteins permanently. This change is irreversible. You can visibly see the changes in the protein. However, mechanical action such as whisking egg white can be reversible if the egg foam is left to stand, the foam can return to its liquid state.

Proteins can be denatured by:
- acid
- mechanical action
- heat.

Figure 3.2.1 Marinating meat before cooking

Using an acid

Marinating

Marinating is the process of soaking meat or vegetables in liquid before cooking.
- A **marinade** is a highly seasoned liquid, which is used to give flavour, keep food moist and assist in tenderising foods.
- The marinating liquid can be an acidic or a salty solution.
- The acids often used for marinating are lemon juice or vinegar.

Marinating will tenderise the tougher cuts of meat. The acid causes the meat fibres to break down and this allows more moisture to be absorbed into the meat, making the meat juicy and tender.

Curdling

Acids can also be used to denture the protein in milk. This is known as **curdling**.

Curdling is when milk develops a slightly lumpy appearance because all the protein in the milk has clumped together. Curdling will occur naturally when milk starts to 'go off', but it can also be caused by adding an acid, heat or enzymes to milk.

Curdling is used in the cheese-making process to separate the protein 'curds' away from the liquid 'whey' part of the milk. The curds are then pressed into cheese.

You will learn more about the cheese-making process in Topic 6.2 Food processing and production. See page 404.

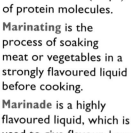

Key words

Denaturation is a change in the structure (shape) of protein molecules.

Marinating is the process of soaking meat or vegetables in a strongly flavoured liquid before cooking.

Marinade is a highly flavoured liquid, which is used to give flavour, keep food moist and assist in tenderising foods. The liquid can be acidic or a salty solution.

Curdling is when milk denatures. It develops a slightly lumpy appearance because all the protein in the milk has clumped together.

Practical activity

(Teacher demonstration or small group activity)

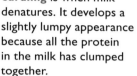

To show how an acid can curdle milk

Makes 250 ml curdled milk

Resources required

Ingredients

250 ml milk

5–20 ml (1–4 tsp) lemon juice

Equipment

Saucepan

Whisk

J cloth or similar

Method

1. Gently warm the milk in a saucepan. Heat speeds up the process.
2. When the milk releases steam, stir in the lemon juice teaspoon by teaspoon.
3. Whisk the milk to incorporate the lemon juice thoroughly.
4. The more lemon juice you add, the larger your curds will be and the faster they will form. For smaller 'clumps' of curds, use a smaller amount of lemon juice.
5. Remove the saucepan from the heat and let the acidic milk stand, uncovered, for 5–10 minutes at room temperature. Do not stir the milk during this time.
6. Strain by pouring the contents of the saucepan through the J cloth.
7. The curds will be trapped in the J cloth and the whey is the watery liquid that passes through.

Evaluation

1. Explain why the curds develop.
2. What will speed up the process?
3. Explain how you can achieve larger curds.

Using mechanical action

The physical act of whisking will cause a protein to denature. Eggs are a good source of protein and will stretch when whisked. The protein stretches into strands and forms a structure that allows air to be captured. Tiny air bubbles are held together by a mesh of protein. With continued whisking, a foam is produced.

Figure 3.2.2 Mechanical action produces a foam

The physical act of kneading in the bread-making process can also cause proteins to denature. The protein in the flour becomes very stretchy when the bread dough is kneaded. This is a permanent change in the structure of the dough. In addition, the mechanical pounding, cutting up and mincing of meat helps to break up long muscle fibres. This is a permanent change to the physical structure of the meat and makes it easier to eat.

Using heat

Proteins will also denature (change shape) if heat is applied to them. With continued heating they will then set or coagulate. This process is known as the **coagulation** of protein.

Protein coagulation

Coagulation is when the protein in food sets. This occurs when the protein is heated. If protein is heated too much, it will become hard, tough and difficult to digest.

Heated protein foods will coagulate in different ways.

Table 3.2.1 shows the effect of heat on different protein foods.

Protein food	Effect of heat
Meat and poultry	Meat proteins shrink as they coagulate. Overheating can make meat chewy. Heating meat proteins in a liquid will change the structure of the muscle fibres. The protein collagen will change to gelatine.
Fish	Fish proteins shrink as they coagulate. Overcooking will make the fish tough.
Eggs	Egg white becomes solid and turns white as it coagulates at 60°C. Egg yolk becomes solid and will eventually become dry as it coagulates at 70°C.
Wheat	The protein in wheat is called gluten. Gluten will set and give cakes, breads and biscuits their firm structure.
Milk	The milk proteins will coagulate and form skin on heated milk, just below boiling point.
Cheese	The fat in cheese melts. The proteins in the cheese denature and then coagulate, if overheated it will become rubbery. The cheese will brown too.

Table 3.2.1 **The effects of heat on different protein foods**

Figure 3.2.3 Egg whites become solid after coagulation

Figure 3.2.4 **The process of milk curdling**

Syneresis results from the over-coagulation of egg protein. Water is pushed out of the egg. This can be seen in overcooked scrambled eggs.

> ### Teacher's tip
> This activity might be useful for an NEA Task 1. The activity could be presented as an investigation and follow the structure of the NEA.

> ### Key words
> **Coagulation** is the setting of protein brought about by heat and acids. This change is irreversible.
>
> **Syneresis** usually refers to eggs; if overcooked, the proteins shrink as they coagulate and separate from the watery liquid.

Practical activity

(Teacher demonstration or small group activity)

Tests to show the effect of heat on protein foods

Cheese test

Resources required

Ingredients

10 g cheese

Quarter of a slice of bread

Equipment

A small piece of foil

Process

1   Slice the cheese thinly.
2   Put half the cheese on the bread and half on the foil.
3   Heat both under a grill until golden brown.
4   Observe carefully what happens.

Evaluation

1   Describe what happened to the cheese.
2   Explain what happened to the fat in both pieces of cheese.

Milk test

Resources required

Ingredients

50 ml milk

Equipment

Saucepan

Sieve lined with a J cloth

Process

1   Heat the milk in a small saucepan. Be careful not to allow the milk to boil over.
2   When the milk boils, strain it through the sieve.
3   Observe carefully what happens.

Evaluation

1   What is the substance in the sieve?
2   Describe the difference between water and milk when boiled.
3   Explain why all the milk does not set.

Gluten formation

Gluten is a general name for all the proteins found in flour. Two proteins called **gliadin** and **glutenin** are important when using flour to make baked products.

Bread-making flour, sometimes called **strong flour**, contains a large amount of both these proteins. These proteins give bread dough special qualities:

- **Glutenin** gives the dough strength and elasticity.
- **Gliadin** binds the dough together into a sticky mass.

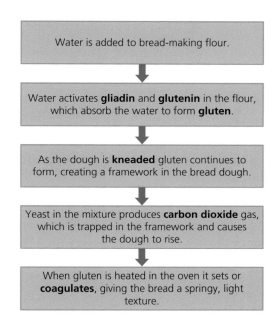

Water is added to bread-making flour.

Water activates **gliadin** and **glutenin** in the flour, which absorb the water to form **gluten**.

As the dough is **kneaded** gluten continues to form, creating a framework in the bread dough.

Yeast in the mixture produces **carbon dioxide** gas, which is trapped in the framework and causes the dough to rise.

When gluten is heated in the oven it sets or **coagulates**, giving the bread a springy, light texture.

Figure 3.2.5 Gluten formation in bread-making

Figure 3.2.6 Kneading dough to create gluten

Practical activity

Test to find out which flour contains the most the gluten

Resources required

Ingredients

50 g strong plain white flour

50 g plain flour

50 g self-raising flour

Equipment

3 squares of J cloth about 10cms square

3 tie closures

Method

1 Mix the strong white flour with enough water to make a soft dough.
2 Knead each dough ball for 5 minutes.
3 Put the dough ball into the centre of a piece of cloth, and fasten the mixture into the cloth with a tie closure.
4 Run cold water over the dough and squeeze it gently to wash out the starch.
5 Continue the washing for about 5 minutes to ensure all the starch is washed out. A ball of gluten will remain. Put the ball of gluten to one side.
6 Repeat the process with each of the other flours, saving the gluten balls.
7 Weigh each of the gluten balls and record your results.

Evaluation

1 Which mixture contains the most gluten?
2 Which mixture contains the least gluten?
3 Which flour would give the best result for a well-risen bread? Give reasons for your choice.

Key word

Foam is when a gas is spread throughout a liquid and whisking eggs to produce a gas-in-liquid foam.

Foam formation

Eggs are excellent at **foam** formation. You can whisk egg whites, egg yolks or whole eggs into a foam. A foam is when a gas is spread throughout a liquid and whisking eggs to produce a gas-in-liquid foam.

Whisking makes the protein in the egg white unravel and **denature**. This allows tiny bubbles of air to be incorporated into the egg white making an egg white foam. This denaturation is reversible as if the foam is left to stand it will collapse back into liquid egg white.

Eventually the egg white will stand in soft peaks. When you heat the foam, the tiny air bubbles expand and the egg protein **coagulates** (sets) around them. This gives firmness to the foam. Examples of foods that rely on this property are meringues and soufflés.

Critical points to remember when whisking egg whites to make a foam:
● Use fresh eggs because they are slightly acidic and will produce a more stable foam.
● Tiny amounts of fat and egg yolk will stop the foaming of egg whites. Always ensure that the whisk and bowl are scrupulously clean.
● Use only metal or glass bowls because fat clings to plastic and they will reduce foam formation.

- The whisk used should be fine wire or have thin blades to ensure that the maximum amount of air is incorporated into the egg white quickly.
- Avoid over whisking because the air bubbles in the foam will join together and the foam will leak water. When water leaks out of the foam it is called **syneresis**.
- Adding vinegar (or any other acid) makes the mixture slightly acidic. This makes the foam less likely to suffer the effects of over whisking, for example lumpiness, loss of water, and collapse.

Practical activity

Investigating egg whites

Ingredients

2 eggs

Pinch of cream of tartar

Equipment

Whisk

Bowl

Method

1 Take two identical samples of egg white.
2 Whisk one egg white sample with a good pinch of cream of tartar until stiff foam is produced.
3 Whisk one egg white sample without cream of tartar until stiff foam is produced.
4 Allow the foams to stand for about 30 minutes.

Evaluation

1 Did it take longer to whisk to stiff peaks the egg white with cream of tartar or the egg white without cream of tartar? Explain your results.
2 Which egg white lost less water after 30 minutes?
3 Describe how cream of tartar affects egg whites when whisked.
4 Explain why would you want egg whites to be stable after whisking.

Check your knowledge and understanding

1 State three ways protein can be denatured.
2 Explain how a marinade works.
3 Explain how to make milk curdle.
4 What is the definition of is coagulation?
5 Describe what happens to egg proteins when they are heated.

6 Explain the functions of the two proteins which form gluten.
7 Explain the important points to remember to ensure egg whites make a foam.
8 Name the **two** proteins that form gluten.

Carbohydrates

Gelatinisation

Some carbohydrates are starches.

Starch grains do not dissolve in water or other liquids. They absorb water, swell and break open when heated. This causes mixtures to thicken, and is the start of a process called gelatinisation. With further heating and constant stirring gelatinisation will occur. **Gelatinisation** occurs between 75°C and 87°C. When the thick liquid cools it forms a gel that will set.

Flour is an excellent source of starch. Starch is found in tiny grains in the flour and when flour is mixed with a liquid and heated (for example, in sauce-making) it will start to thicken.

Some other foods also contain starch and when added to mixtures will thicken them. Examples are shown in the table below.

Starchy rich food	How they thicken
Cornflour	Used to thicken gravies, custards and soups
Arrowroot	Used to thicken soups, stews, gravies and sauces
Potatoes	Used to thicken soups and casseroles as they release starch
Tiny pasta shapes	Added to soups to thicken them, e.g. minestrone
Rice	Used to thicken milk puddings, e.g. rice pudding
Barley	Added to a vegetable soup or casserole to thicken it

Table 3.2.2 **Foods containing starch that thicken mixtures**

It is the presence of two molecules called amylose and amylopectin in starch that gives it the ability to thicken sauces. Amylose and amylopectin bond with each other to form a gel when heated.
- **Amylose** causes sauces to thicken, turn cloudy when cooked and get even thicker as they cool.
- **Amylopectin** produces a clear gel when it thickens and has the same thickness hot or cold.

Different starches contain different amounts of these molecules. Cornflour, for example, is made from the cereal maize. It is almost pure starch and is high in amylose; this means that cornflour will form a strong gel. It blends to a smooth cream when mixed with a cold liquid.

Key words

Starch grains are tiny particles of starch found in some carbohydrates.

Gelatinisation is the process in which moist heat is applied to starch grains, which swell, increase in size and then break open, releasing amylose, which thickens the mixture around boiling point. Stirring will prevent lumps forming.

Amylose causes sauces to thicken, turn cloudy when cooked and get even thicker as they cool.

Amylopectin produces a clear gel when it thickens and has the same thickness hot or cold.

Teacher tip

This activity might be useful for an NEA Task 1.
The activity could be presented as an investigation
and follow the structure of the NEA.

Figure 3.2.7 Custard sauce
produced by gelatinisation

Practical activity

Test to show the effect of moist heat on starch

Resources required

Ingredients

5 g (1 tsp) plain flour

Equipment

Small bowl

Saucepan

Wooden spoon

Method

1 Mix the flour with 2 teaspoons of water in a small bowl. Observe and record
   how easily it dissolves.
2 Pour the mixture into a saucepan and heat gently, stirring all the time.
   Observe and record what happens to the texture and the colour of the
   mixture.
3 Wash and dry the pan.
4 Repeat the process but do not mix the flour and water together before
   heating. Observe and record what happens to the texture and the colour
   of the mixture.

Evaluation

1 What is the process called when starch grains break open and absorb water?
2 Explain why it is important to stir the mixture throughout the heating
3 Describe the ideal method to use to produce a smooth sauce.

What can affect gelatinisation?

How well a sauce will thicken depends on a number of factors:

- **Amount of liquid:** a small amount of starch in proportion to the liquid will produce a runny sauce and a large amount of starch in proportion to the liquid will produce a thicker sauce.
- **Types of starch used:** cornflour is better than white flour for thickening because it is pure starch.
- **Temperature:** gelatinisation requires hot, moist conditions. Starch will not dissolve in cold water and cannot thicken cool liquids. In order for the starch to absorb liquid, the outside of the starch grain needs to be softened by heating. At a temperature of between **75°C** and **87°C** the sauce will start to thicken, at boiling point it stops thickening. Sauces should be gently boiled while stirring for a full 2 minutes to ensure that all the starch grains have gelatinised.
- **Stirring** is essential for the creation of a smooth, gelatinised sauce. If stirring is not used the starch grains will settle on the bottom of the saucepan. At the bottom of the saucepan, the starch grains will absorb some of the liquid around them but they will also stop liquid from reaching other grains, resulting in a lumpy texture.
- **Sugar** competes with starch for water. This means the starch does not absorb as much water. Sugar makes the sauce runnier and less likely to remain stable. Always add sugar after gelatinisation in sauce-making.
- **Acids** such as lemon juice should always be added to the sauce after it has thickened and boiled because they can break down the gel. Recipes for lemon meringue pie follow this rule.

Figure 3.2.8 Stirring the sauce continuously prevents lumps

Practical activity

(Teacher demonstration or student paired activity)

Test to show the effect of temperature, acid and sugar on gelatinisation

You are going to make four sauces.

Resources required

Ingredients

1 litre water

100 g cornflour

30 ml lemon juice

50 g sugar

Equipment

Wooden spoon

Saucepan

4 small bowls

Sticky labels

Thermometer

Method

1   Make a sauce using 250 ml of water and 25 g cornflour. First, moisten the cornflour with a small amount of water, then stir with a wooden spoon until the lumps disappear. Finally, add the remaining water and stir.
2   Place the mixture in a saucepan. Heat and stir constantly.
3   Bring the mixture to the boil for 2 minutes. Stir constantly.
4   Remove from heat and pour into a small bowl. Label **'The control'**.
5   Repeat the sauce-making process in the same way. Boil for 2 minutes and add the lemon juice, then boil for a further minute. Pour into a small bowl. Label **'Gel with acid'**.
6   Repeat the sauce-making process. Boil for 2 minutes and add the sugar, then boil for a further minute. Pour into a small bowl. Label **'Gel with sugar'**.
7   Repeat the sauce-making process except do not boil the sauce, heat to 70°C only. Remove from the heat. Pour into a small bowl. Label **'Gel at 70°C'**.

Evaluation

1   Describe the effect of adding lemon juice to a sauce.
2   Describe the effect of adding sugar to a sauce.
3   Explain how temperature affects the thickness of a sauce.
4   What are some factors to consider when making a sweet, lemon sauce to ensure a good quality outcome?

Extension activity

Investigate what a **modified starch** is and how is it used.

Practical activity

Investigate gelatinisation

Design and make a savoury dish that includes a sauce that is thickened by gelatinisation. Ideas could include macaroni cheese, lasagne, moussaka, cauliflower cheese.

Key words

Dextrinisation is when dry heat turns a starch brown.

Dextrin is formed during the baking and toasting of starchy foods.

Dextrinisation

Dextrinisation occurs when starch is broken down into **dextrin** by **dry heat** (for example, baking, grilling or toasting). Dextrin adds a sweet taste to baked products.

Figure 3.2.9 Browning on the surface of bread is dextrinisation

Dextrinisation contributes to the colour and flavour of many foods such as toast, bread and croissants.

Practical activity

Test to show the effect of dry heat on starch

Resources required

Ingredients

3 g ($\frac{1}{2}$ tsp) plain flour

12 ml (2 tsp) water

Equipment

Saucepan

Wooden spoon

Process

1 Gently heat $\frac{1}{2}$ teaspoon of flour in a saucepan. Observe and record what happens, including how it smells.
2 When it turns a slightly off-white colour, add the water and stir well with a wooden spoon until the mixture thickens. Observe and record what happens.

Evaluation

1 Explain why this is an important property of starch.
2 Explain how dextrinisation affects the smell of the starch.

Caramelisation

Caramelisation causes changes to a food's colour and also to its flavour.

It leads to a desirable golden brown colour and an attractive flavour in baked goods and drinks. Caramelisation can give a buttery, toasty or even a nutty flavour to food.

How does caramelisation occur?

Caramelisation occurs when food products containing sugar come in contact with heat. It is the process of sugar turning brown through heat being applied.

The process of caramelisation begins when sugar breaks down. As sugar is heated to high temperatures (about 180°C), it darkens and turns from clear to dark amber.

Caramelisation happens because water is released from the sugar as it is heated. The water is released as steam.

- Caramelised sugar is used to make fudge, toffee, jam and honeycomb.
- The surface of biscuits, breads and pastries are browned by caramelisation.
- Caramelisation also occurs in some vegetables such as onions, for example when they are fried for an extended period of time as in French onion soup.

If the sugar is overheated it will burn and produce a bitter taste. The sugar begins to breaks down to pure carbon at about 200°C.

Figure 3.2.10 Crème brûlée is a dessert with a hard sugar topping, achieved by using a blow touch or a very hot grill to caramelise the sugar. Brandy snaps and spun sugar are also good examples of caramelisation

Caramelisation also occurs during the dry heating, shallow frying and roasting of meat and vegetables.

Test to show the effect of moist heat on sugar

Care must be taken when completing this experiment as the hot sugar will burn you if it comes into contact with your skin.

Resources required

Ingredients

18 g (1 tbsp) white sugar

18 ml (1 tbsp) water

Jug of cold water

Equipment

Saucepan

Teaspoon

Method

1 Put the sugar and water into a saucepan and heat gently.
2 Once the mixture starts to change colour remove a very small quantity using a teaspoon and place it in the jug of cold water. Observe the mixture in cold water. Does it hold its shape?
3 As you continue to heat the mixture and add further drops into the cold water. Does the mixture become harder when dropped in the water?

Evaluation

1 What is the name of the process in which sugar turn browns when it is heated?
2 Describe how the sugar changes when it is heated.
3 What recipes make use of boiling sugar?

Fats and oils

Learning objectives

In this section you will learn about:
- shortening
- aeration
- plasticity
- emulsification.

Shortening

Fat gives foods such as biscuits, shortbread and pastries a crumbly texture. The ability of fat to do this is called **shortening**.

Shortening is when fat coats the flour particles preventing the absorption of water, which results in a crumbly mixture. The fat:
- gives the flour particles a waterproof coating
- prevents the flour from absorbing water
- reduces the development of gluten.

Gluten would make the dough stretchy and elastic, but because gluten does not develop biscuits, shortbread and pastries have a crumbly texture.

Key word

Shortening is the process in which fat coats the flour particles, preventing absorption of water, resulting in a crumbly mixture.

Figure 3.2.11 Rubbing in ensures the fat coats the flour

Aeration

Key word

Aeration is when air is
trapped in a mixture.

Aeration is when air is trapped in a mixture.

Air needs to be added to a cake mixture in order to give a springy and well-risen texture to the baked cake. When making a cake, fat and sugar are creamed together using an electric whisk or a wooden spoon. When the fat and sugar are creamed, they enclose tiny bubbles of air. The tiny bubbles of air make a stable foam, which can be baked to give the springy texture.

Figure 3.2.12 **Creaming the butter and sugar together**

Caster sugar is used for cake-making because it has a finer texture than granulated sugar. The finer texture holds more air when creamed with the fat. It helps aeration.

Plasticity

Fats do not melt at fixed temperatures but over a range of temperatures. The **plasticity** of fat is linked to their different **melting points**. Plasticity gives fats their unique character.

Plasticity describes the ability of a solid fat to soften over a range of temperatures.

Plasticity is very important when choosing which fat to use in food preparation. There are many different types of fat. Solid fats do not melt immediately but soften over a range of temperatures.

Plasticity affects the **spreading**, **creaming** and **shortening** ability of the fat.

The fat chosen for shortening must have **good plasticity**. This is because it needs to spread over a large area of flour and coat it with a film of oil. If the fat is too hard, it will have poor spreading power. If the fat chosen is a liquid, an oil, it will clump rather than make a coating over the flour.

Fats can be processed to change their chemical structure and alter their melting point.

Some fats have been developed so that their melting points are low and you can spread them straight from the fridge, for example spreadable fats, spreadable cheeses. Chocolates that 'melt in the mouth' are also made with fats with low melting points.

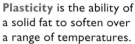

Key word

Plasticity is the ability of a solid fat to soften over a range of temperatures.

Figure 3.2.13 When butter is heated it melts and the plasticity increases

Emulsification

Fats and oils do not mix with water. This means they are '**immiscible**' and they cannot be mixed.

Figure 3.2.14 Oil and water are immiscible or unmixable

When two unmixable liquids are forced together, tiny droplets of one will be spread throughout the second liquid. This forms an **emulsion**.

An emulsion is a special type of liquid where tiny droplets of one liquid, such as oil, are spread throughout another liquid such as water.

There are two types of emulsions:

1   **An oil-in-water emulsion.** This forms when the amount of water is more than the amount of oil. Tiny droplets of oil are spread throughout the water. Milk is a good example of this type of emulsion: it contains about 4 per cent fat and 96 per cent water. The small droplets of fat are spread throughout the milk.

2   **A water-in-oil emulsion.** This forms when the amount of oil or fat is more than the amount of water. Tiny droplets of water are spread through the fat or oil. Butter and fat spreads are water-in-oil emulsions.

Emulsifiers

In all foods, we want emulsions that will last and not separate out. Sometimes, if liquids are allowed to stand for a long time, the oil or water will separate out from the mixture.

Figure 3.2.15 A salad dressing where the olive oil can be seen floating on the surface

The formation of an emulsion will depend on the presence of an **emulsifier**. An emulsifier is a substance that will allow two immiscible liquids (substances that do not mix) to be held together.

How do emulsifiers work?

An emulsifier consists of two parts:
- a water-loving part, which we describe as **'hydrophilic'**
- a water-hating part, which we describe as **'hydrophobic'**.

One part of the emulsifier attracts the water and one part attracts the oil. This combination holds the oil and water together. The emulsifier lowers the surface tension between the two liquids so that they can combine to form **a stable emulsion**.

Emulsions are very important in food production. Products such as ice cream, mayonnaise and salad dressing all require an emulsifier. **Lecithin** found in egg yolk is an emulsifier. Lecithin is used to produce mayonnaise. It helps to stop the oil and vinegar from separating out in the mayonnaise.

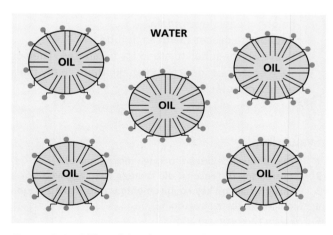

Figure 3.2.16 The oil droplets are held into the water by an emulsifier, which has a hydrophilic head in red and hydrophobic tail in black

Key words

Emulsifier is a substance that will allow two immiscible liquids (substances that do not mix) to be held together.

Lecithin is a natural emulsifier found in egg yolk.

A test to find out what makes an emulsion more stable

Resources required

Ingredients

4 tsp vinegar

1 tsp egg yolk

4 tsp oil

1 tsp egg white

Pinch of mustard powder

Equipment

Ruler

4 test tubes (labelled 1, 2, 3 and 4)

Test tube rack

Method

1 Put 1 teaspoon of oil and 1 teaspoon of vinegar in each test tube. Label the test tubes 1, 2, 3 and 4.
2 Add nothing to test tube 1; this is your control, Tube 1.
3 Add the following to the other tubes:
    Tube 2   1 teaspoon of egg yolk
    Tube 3   1 teaspoon of egg white
    Tube 4   Pinch of mustard powder
4 Measure and record the height of the vinegar (bottom layer) and the total height of the liquid in each tube.
5 Put your thumb over the top of tube 1 (the control) and turn the tube upside down five times.
6 Observe the tube straight after this mixing process. Describe the size of the oil droplets. Measure the height of each layer again.
7 Repeat the process with each tube.
8 Leave all the tubes to stand for 5 minutes. Then observe the results again.
9 Take each tube in turn and shake them really thoroughly. Observe what happens after shaking and again after 5 minutes.

Evaluation

1 What difference does thorough mixing make?
2 Considering the results, did the egg yolk, egg white or mustard powder produce the best emulsion?
3 Explain what the key requirements are to make a good emulsion.
4 Explain the term shortening.
5 Explain the term aeration.
6 Explain the term plasticity of fat.
7 Explain the term emulsification.

Raising agents

Learning objectives

In this section you will learn about the three types of raising agent:
- chemical
- mechanical
- biological.

What are raising agents?

Raising agents are used to make mixtures rise. Raising agents work by introducing gas into a mixture. When you heat a mixture, which contains a raising agent, the gas expands and makes the mixture rise. Some gas escapes and some is trapped in the mixture as it cools and sets. This makes the baked item have a light, open texture. Many baked items, such as cakes, pastries, breads and biscuits, depend on raising agents for their soft, springy texture.

The gases that are used as raising agents are **air**, **steam** and **carbon dioxide**.

Key word

Raising agent is an ingredient or process that incorporates a gas into a mixture to lighten it.

Figure 3.2.17 Scones depend on a chemical raising agent for their light texture

The three types of raising agents are chemical, mechanical and biological.

Chemical raising agents

Chemical raising agents produce carbon dioxide when they are heated with a liquid. The two most common chemical raising agents are baking powder and bicarbonate of soda.

Baking powder

Baking powder is a mixture of two chemicals, which react with moisture and heat to produce the gas carbon dioxide. **Self-raising flour** has baking powder added to it during production so that items made with it can have a light texture.

Figure 3.2.18 Small cakes rely on self-raising flour for their soft texture

Bicarbonate of soda

Bicarbonate of soda is a chemical that is used to raise soda breads and strong-flavoured cakes, such as gingerbread, fruit cake, chocolate cake and carrot cake.

● Bicarbonate of soda can add a soapy taste to baked items, so it is used in recipes where this can be disguised by other flavours.

● It needs moisture and an acid to work so it so is often combined with yoghurt, buttermilk or milk in recipes.

Bicarbonate of soda works by producing carbon dioxide when heated. The carbon dioxide forms small bubbles in the mixture. Once the mixture is cooked and set, the carbon dioxide is replaced by air, leaving a light cake or bread.

Figure 3.2.19 Soda bread relies on bicarbonate of soda for its soft texture

---

Practical activity

1   Plan and make a recipe using a chemical raising agent. Your choice of dish will also provide an opportunity to develop your skills in using electrical equipment, for example mixers, food processor, sieve. Possible practical ideas could include cheese scones, savoury muffins, cupcakes.

2   Describe how the raising agent has worked to develop the texture of your dish.

Mechanical raising agents

Mechanical raising agents use **air** and **steam**.

Air

Air can be introduced into a mixture mechanically. The main ways to do this are shown in Table 3.2.3.

Method	Process of adding air	Examples
Whisking	Eggs or egg whites are whisked with sugar at high speed. This traps air bubbles in the egg white.	Roulades and meringues, whisked sponges
Beating	Liquids are beaten and air bubbles are trapped in the liquid.	Batter
Folding	Layers of air are trapped between the layers of pastry when the pastry is folded. During baking, the air expands between the layers and lifts the pastry.	Flaky pastry
Sieving	Sieving flour traps air between the flour particles.	Cakes, pastries and scones
Creaming	Beating fat and sugar together traps tiny air bubbles into the mixture. When heated, the mixture sets and stops the bubbles from escaping.	Cakes
Rubbing in	Rubbing the fat into flour. This traps air in the mixture.	Pastry and scones

Table 3.2.4 Methods of adding air into a mixture

Key words

Mechanical raising agents are air and steam.

Whisking at high speed adds air.

Beating a liquid or mixture adds air.

Folding layers into a dough adds air between the layers.

Sieving dry ingredients through a sieve adds air.

Creaming fat and sugar together adds air.

Rubbing in fat into flour adds air.

Figure 3.2.20 Whisking egg whites adds air bubbles and turns the mixture into a thick foam

Figure 3.2.21 Folding puff pastry to add air between the layers

Figure 3.2.22 Roulade sponge relies on air whisked in the mixture for its light texture

Some dishes depend on air entirely as the raising agent. They include:

- whisked sponges
- soufflés
- roulades.

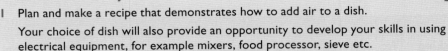

Practical activity

1 Plan and make a recipe that demonstrates how to add air to a dish.

Your choice of dish will also provide an opportunity to develop your skills in using electrical equipment, for example mixers, food processor, sieve etc.

2 Describe how the raising agent has worked to develop the texture of your dish.

Figure 3.2.23 Yorkshire puddings rely on steam for their light texture

Steam

Steam is produced during cooking from water or other liquids in the mixture. Steam is produced as the mixture is heated to boiling point in the oven. The oven temperature must be hot to ensure this happens.

Steam is used in making Yorkshire puddings, choux, puff and flaky pastry. Choux pastry has a high water content. When cooked, the water is converted into steam. This makes a pastry shell that, when cool, can be pierced and filled.

Flaky pastry also has a high water content. The dough is folded to incorporate air and baked in a hot oven, which allows steam to push the folds into crispy layers.

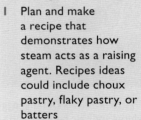

Practical activity

1 Plan and make a recipe that demonstrates how steam acts as a raising agent. Recipes ideas could include choux pastry, flaky pastry, or batters

Your choice of dish will also provide an opportunity to develop your skills in using electrical equipment, for example mixers, food processor, sieve

2 Describe how the raising agent has worked to develop the texture of your dish.

Figure 3.2.24 Vol au vents rely on the folding of the pastry and the steam produced from the water, in the recipe, for their light crispy texture

Biological raising agents

Yeast is a biological raising agent. Yeast is a living plant (a type of fungus). It produces the gas carbon dioxide by **fermentation**. It needs **warmth**, **food** and **liquid** to ferment.

Fermentation requires:

- a warm temperature of 25–29°C
- sugar as a food supply
- a liquid, usually water or milk to help the gluten form.

The carbon dioxide collects in small bubbles throughout the dough and will make the dough rise. Yeast is used as a raising agent in bread doughs, doughnuts and buns.

It is available to buy in two main forms: fresh and dried.

- **Fast-acting 'easy blend' dried yeast** will keep for many months. It is usually mixed with the flour during the dough-making process.
- **Fresh yeast** is a firm, moist cream-coloured block that must be stored in a refrigerator. It is blended with warm water when required for dough-making.
- **Dried yeast** (or active dried yeast) comes in small granules that are first re-formed with warm water and sugar before use.

Figure 3.2.25 Bread rolls rely on yeast to produce carbon dioxide, which makes a light, fluffy texture

Test to find out what yeast needs to ferment

Resources required

Ingredients
50 g dried yeast
40 g sugar
Kettle containing very hot water
Some ice cubes
Equipment
5 plastic bottles of the same size
5 balloons

Method

1 Label the plastic bottles A, B, C, D and E.
2 Prepare the bottles as follows:

Bottle A	10 g yeast	10 g sugar	5 cm warm water
Bottle B	10 g yeast	No sugar	5 cm warm water
Bottle C	10 g yeast	10 g sugar	No water
Bottle D	10 g yeast	10 g sugar	5 cm cold water
Bottle E	10 g yeast	10 g sugar	5 cm boiling water

3 Attach an un-blown balloon over the open end of each plastic bottle, and leave to stand for about 20 minutes.
4 Observe the results every 5 minutes.
5 After 20 minutes, place bottle D into a bowl of warm water and observe the results.
6 The yeast should start to produce carbon dioxide gas. Explain why.
7 Copy the results into chart like the one below and fill out your results.

Yeast experiments					
Method	A	B	C	D	E
Did the yeast produce carbon dioxide?					

8 Describe each method used. What are your conclusions?

Evaluation

1 What slows the growth of yeast?
2 What kills yeast?
3 Describe the conditions in which yeast grows best.

Practical activity

Bread-making

An excellent way to understand how yeast works is to make some bread rolls. The basic ingredients for 4 bread rolls:

250 g strong flour

2 tbsp oil

1 level tsp salt

$\frac{1}{2}$ tsp fast-action dried yeast

125–145 ml warm water

1 level tsp sugar

Before you start the process, copy the table and add the **correct explanation** for each step of the process. The steps are in the boxes below.

To make the bread follow these steps:

Steps in bread-making	Explanation of the process
Select and weigh out the flour, yeast, sugar, salt and warm water carefully.	
Mix the flour, salt, sugar and yeast together in a large bowl and make a 'well' in the middle.	
Mix the water and oil together and pour the liquid into the flour mixture. Mix to make a soft but not sticky dough.	
Knead for 10 minutes by hand on the work surface.	
Bring the dough together, cover and leave in a warm place to rise, if time allows.	
The risen dough is kneaded again.	
Shape the dough into four bread rolls. Cover the bread rolls and allow the dough to rise again for about 20 minutes in a warm place.	
Bake the bread rolls in a hot oven.	

The yeast ferments producing carbon dioxide. Enzymes break the starch and sugar into **glucose**, which is food for the yeast. Large bubbles of **carbon dioxide** are produced. The gluten stretches to hold the carbon dioxide and can look like a honeycomb.

This develops the gluten framework.

Strong flour is required for gluten formation. Yeast is the raising agent. Sugar feeds the yeast. The amount of warm water used can vary but the temperature must be **warm.**

During baking, the dough rises rapidly at first. The yeast is then killed by the heat and no more carbon dioxide gas is produced.

The large bubbles of carbon dioxide are broken into small, evenly sized bubbles by kneading.

The dough continues to expand, but does it more evenly than during the rising.

The yeast begins to become active due to the warm water and presence of the sugar in the mixing. The protein in the flour absorbs the water to form gluten.

The ingredients are ready to receive the warm water and the water will spread evenly throughout the mixture.

Check your knowledge and understanding

1 Explain why it is important to add a raising agent to some food products.
2 Name **one** chemical raising agent.
3 Describe **three** ways that air can be added to a mixture.
4 Give examples of **two** dishes that depend on air as the main raising agent.
5 Describe how water acts as a raising agent.
6 Give examples of **two** dishes that depend on steam as the main raising agent.
7 Explain the conditions required for yeast fermentation.
8 Name the gas produced during fermentation of yeast.

Section 3 Practice questions: Food science

Multiple choice questions

1. When heat travels through a solid material it is called: (1 mark)
   a) Radiation
   b) Convection
   c) Conduction
   d) Condensation

2. Which vitamin is not lost during boiling? (1 mark)
   a) Vitamin B1
   b) Vitamin B2
   c) Vitamin C
   d) Vitamin A

3. Denaturation is a change in: (1 mark)
   a) Protein
   b) Sugar
   c) Starch
   d) Fat

4. A food source which contains significant amounts of pure starch is: (1 mark)
   a) Wheat flour
   b) Rice
   c) Potatoes
   d) Cornflour

5. Which statement best describes shortening? (1 mark)
   a) Fat absorbs water and binds the mixture.
   b) Fat works with gluten to make the dough stretchy.
   c) Fat and sugar trap air in the mixture.
   d) Fat coats the flour preventing the absorption of water.

6. The ideal temperature for yeast to grow is: (1 mark)
   a) 100°C
   b) 45°C
   c) 25°C
   d) 10°C

Other question types

7 Give **four** reasons why some foods are cooked. (4 marks)

8 Describe how heat is transferred during the baking of potatoes in an oven. (2 marks)

9 Complete the table below matching the method of heat transference to the description given. In each case give **one** example of a cooking method. (9 marks)

Radiation   Conduction   Convection

Description	Method of heat transference	Explain how the heat is transferred	Example of cooking method
Heat travels through liquids and gases			
Heat travels through solids			
Heat travels directly onto food by radiation			

10 Discuss the advantages and disadvantages of grilling, frying and roasting as methods of cooking meat. (12 marks)

11 Complete the table below to show **one** advantage and **one** disadvantage of boiling, steaming and roasting and barbecuing as methods of cooking potatoes. Do not repeat any of your answers. (6 marks)

Method of cooking potatoes	Advantage	Disadvantage
Boiling		
Steaming		
Roasting		

12 Explain the changes that take place when eggs are cooked. (6 marks)

13 Give the meaning of the following terms, including an example
   a) Denaturation (2 marks)
   b) Coagulation (2 marks)

14 Explain how the process of gelatinisation causes a white sauce to thicken. (5 marks)

15 Give the definition of the following cooking terms:
   a) Caramelisation (2 marks)
   b) Dextrinisation (2 marks)

16 Describe how an emulsifier works in an oil in water mixture. (2 marks)

17 Give the meaning of the following terms:
   a) Aeration (2 marks)
   b) Plasticity (2 marks)

18 Explain the term chemical raising agent. (1 mark)

19 Describe three ways that air can be added to mixtures. (6 marks)

20 Explain with examples, why gluten is important in bread-making. (6 marks)

AQA GCSE Food Preparation and Nutrition

SECTION 4
Food Safety

This section includes the following topics:

4.1 Food spoilage and contamination

4.2 Principles of food safety

Section 4 Practice questions

TOPIC 4.1 FOOD SPOILAGE AND CONTAMINATION

Micro-organisms and enzymes

Learning objectives

In this section you will learn about:
- the micro-organisms: yeasts, moulds, bacteria and their growth conditions
- enzymes, their activity and role in food spoilage
- the control of food spoilage.

Key words

Food spoilage is when food loses quality and becomes inedible.

Contaminated is when an unwanted substance is transferred onto another, for example if someone sneezes onto food.

Yeasts are tiny, single-celled fungi; a type of micro-organism.

Moulds are tiny fungi, which produce thread-like filaments; a type of micro-organism.

Bacteria are single-celled micro-organisms; some types of bacteria can cause food poisoning.

Enzymes are biological catalysts that speed up reactions.

Micro-organisms are microscopic, tiny organisms; these include yeasts, moulds and bacteria.

How does food spoilage happen?

Food spoilage happens when food is **contaminated** by **yeasts**, **moulds** or **bacteria**, which make the food unsafe or undesirable to eat. Food spoilage may also be caused by **enzyme** activity, causing colour and flavour changes as well as over-ripening of some fruits and vegetables.

Food spoilage occurs in many different ways and may happen at any stage: from when the food is harvested/caught or slaughtered, right through to the preparation and serving of food. For example, if strawberries are picked when they are very ripe and packaged while damp, this will encourage mould and/or yeast growth. Another example is food being served uncovered for a buffet meal, and flies land on it, causing contamination from the bacteria carried by the flies.

Micro-organisms

The yeasts, moulds and bacteria that contaminate food and cause food spoilage are called **micro-organisms**. Micro-organisms are tiny living things that can only be seen with a microscope.

What do yeasts, moulds and bacteria need to grow?

Yeasts, moulds and bacteria need the following four conditions to be able to grow:
- food
- moisture
- warmth
- time.

Yeasts

What are yeasts?

Yeasts are tiny, single-celled **fungi**, which reproduce by budding.

Ideal growth conditions for yeasts

Most yeasts grow best in the presence of oxygen (these are called **aerobic** yeasts), but they can grow without oxygen (called **anaerobic** yeasts) as well.

Yeasts prefer acid foods that are fairly moist. They can also grow in high concentrations of sugar and salt.

Yeasts grow best in warm conditions (around 25–29°C). However, some yeasts can grow at 0°C and below, so, although chilling food in the fridge slows down the growth, it won't stop it completely.

Yeasts are destroyed at temperatures above 100°C, and cannot grow when there is insufficient water available.

Figure 4.1.1 Yeasts reproduce by budding

Which foods do yeasts often spoil?

Yeasts can spoil food such as jam, honey, fruit, yoghurts and fruit juices. They **ferment** the sugars in these foods, which produces carbon dioxide gas and alcohol. This causes food spoilage. The food will develop 'off' flavours and may appear 'fizzy'.

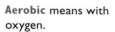

Practical activity

As well as spoiling food, yeast is widely used as a **raising agent** in bread-making. The gas it produces when it multiplies gives a soft, spongy and light texture to food.

Carry out this practical activity to show how yeast ferments and can be used to **leaven** (rise) bread rolls.

1 Find a recipe for some bread rolls using active dried yeast or fresh yeast (not fast-action yeast).
2 Mix the yeast with warm water and a little sugar to begin the fermentation process.
3 If possible, take some photographs of the yeast fermenting and note the smell and texture of the yeast mixture as fermentation progresses.

To flavour your rolls, you may want to add some extra ingredients to the flour to make them more interesting, such as seeds, dried fruit or herbs.

Key words

Aerobic means with oxygen.

Anaerobic means without oxygen.

Ferment is when yeasts reproduce by feeding on sugar, producing carbon dioxide gas and alcohol.

Raising agent is a chemical or biological substance that lightens food products.

Preservatives are chemicals added to food to increase the shelf life.

You will have learnt about using yeast as a raising agent in bread-making in the section on raising agents in Topic 3.2 Functional and chemical properties of food. See page 239.

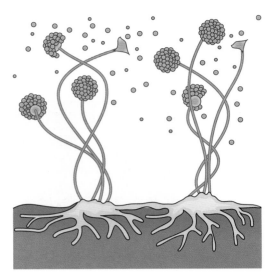

Figure 4.1.2 Mould growing

Moulds

What are moulds?

Moulds are tiny fungi that produce thread-like filaments. These filaments help the mould to spread around the food, extracting nutrients from it.

Ideal growth conditions for moulds

Moulds may be different colours and grow on many foods, including acid and alkaline foods as well as those with high sugar and salt concentrations. They grow best between 20°C and 30°C, although they can also grow at low temperatures, including in the fridge. High humidity and fluctuating temperatures can speed up mould growth. Although moulds do require some moisture to grow, they can grow on fairly dry foods such as hard cheeses.

Mould growth can be slowed down or prevented by:
- storing food in a cool, dry place (for example, kitchen cupboard)
- storing food in the fridge
- heating/cooking food
- storing in acid conditions (for example, pickled onions).

Which foods do moulds often spoil?

Moulds often grow on and spoil bread and bakery products. Some breads have **preservatives** added to prevent mould growth.

> ## Key words
>
> **Preservatives** are chemicals added to food to increase the shelf life.
>
> **Vacuum packs** are sealed packs from which the air has been removed. (Used for foods such as bacon to increase shelf life).

Ingredients

Wholemeal **Wheat** Flour, Water, **Wheat** Protein, Yeast, *Vegetable* Oil (Rapeseed, Palm), Salt, Spirit Vinegar, **Soya** Flour, Caramelised Sugar, Emulsifier (Mono- and diacetyl tartaric acid esters of mono- and diglycerides of fatty acids - Vegetable), Preservative (Calcium propionate), Flour Treatment Agent (Ascorbic acid).

Allergy Advice

For allergens, including cereals containing gluten, see ingredients in **bold**. Also, may contain other gluten containing ingredients (barley, oats, rye).

Figure 4.1.3 Bread ingredients – these bagels have a preservative (calcium propionate) added to prevent mould growth

Moulds may also spoil cheeses in **vacuum packs** if the seal is broken. Foods spoiled with mould should not be consumed, even if the visible mould is scraped off. The mould may have spread harmful substances that are not visible deep into the food.

Bacteria

What are bacteria?
Bacteria are single-celled micro-organisms. They can be divided into three groups:
- harmless bacteria
- pathogenic bacteria
- food spoilage bacteria.

Bacteria are found everywhere around us. For example, they are found on our skin, in raw food, in soil, in water and in the air. Most bacteria are harmless, but others are harmful and can cause food poisoning.
- Bacteria that cause food poisoning are called **pathogens** or **pathogenic bacteria**.
- Other types of bacteria enable food to decay; these are called food spoilage bacteria and cause food to smell and to lose texture and flavour.

Bacteria can only be seen under a very powerful microscope as they are so small.

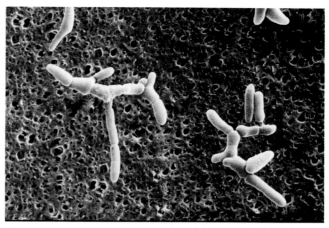
Figure 4.1.4 Pathogenic bacteria (Listeria) under a powerful microscope

Ideal growth conditions for bacteria
Bacteria need food, warmth, moisture and time to grow. Bacteria do not like acidic conditions; they grow best in **neutral conditions**. This means neither acid nor alkaline conditions.

Bacterial growth can be slowed down or prevented by:
- storing perishable food in the fridge at between 0°C and below 5°C
- cooling cooked perishable food to room temperature within 90 minutes before putting in the fridge
- reheating leftover food only once (any remaining food should be thrown away)
- using high concentrations of salt (e.g. for bacon), sugar (e.g. for jam) and acid (e.g. for pickled eggs) to destroy most bacteria.

Which foods do bacteria often spoil?
Bacteria prefer foods with a high protein content that are moist. These foods provide excellent conditions for bacterial growth, especially if kept in warm conditions. Foods that provide these conditions and are ready to eat without further heating or cooking are known as **high-risk foods**.

Most cases of food poisoning are caused by consuming high-risk foods contaminated with pathogenic bacteria. Examples of high-risk foods are:
- cooked meat and poultry
- cooked meat products such as gravy, soup and stock
- milk and eggs and dishes made from them, for example unpasteurised soft cheese
- eggs and dishes made from them, for example homemade mayonnaise
- shellfish such as mussels, crabs and lobsters
- cooked rice.

Key words
Pathogens are harmful bacteria, which can cause food poisoning.

Neutral conditions refer to pH 7 (neither acid nor alkaline).

High-risk foods are ready to eat moist foods, usually high in protein that easily support the growth of pathogenic bacteria and do not require any further heat treatment or cooking.

Practical activity
Find a recipe for curry and rice which you will make in a practical session. Make a time plan highlighting points in the process where hazards could occur, from how the ingredients will be stored (before the lesson starts) to when you reheat and serve the curry and rice at home. Make the curry and rice, following the food safety points you have identified.

Extension activity
You have been asked to make a rice salad as part of a wedding buffet.
1 Find a recipe for rice salad.
2 Describe how you would safely prepare and cook the rice salad in the morning, ready to serve in the early evening.

Enzymes

Enzymes are **biological catalysts** usually made from proteins. The job of enzymes is to speed up chemical reactions. The action of enzymes can cause browning in foods that are bruised or cut open, for example apples that are cut open. This type of browning is known as **enzymic browning**. Enzymes can be destroyed by heat or acids.

Blanching to destroy enzymes

When some fruits and vegetables, such as cooking apples and corn on the cob, are prepared for freezing they need to be blanched to destroy the enzymes. This will prevent enzymic action while the food is stored in the freezer. **Blanching** is heating fruit or vegetables in boiling water for a short time to destroy the enzymes before plunging into iced water to stop the cooking process.

Although freezer temperatures of −18°C or below are low enough to prevent the growth of yeasts, moulds and bacteria, they are not low enough to prevent enzyme activity. If food is not blanched before freezing, apple slices may go brown and corn on the cobs may undergo colour and flavour changes while stored in the freezer.

Figure 4.1.5 Corn on the cob being blanched to destroy enzymes

Figure 4.1.6 Corn on the cob being chilled before freezing

Use of acids to prevent enzymic browning

Some fruits and vegetables turn brown when you are preparing them, which spoils their appearance and can lead to food waste. To prevent this, an acid may be used to **denature** the enzymes.

Practical activity

Preserving apples experiment

Aim of experiment: To find out the best way to prepare apples before freezing

Ask your teacher to check all your equipment is ready before you slice the apple to make it a fair test.

***Method 1** – Frozen apple (unblanched)*

You will need:

- 1 cooking apple

1 Peel, core and slice the apple.
2 Put the apple slices in a freezer bag or small plastic tub with a lid.
3 Label and freeze the apple.

***Method 2** – Frozen apple (unblanched with lemon juice)*

You will need:

- 1 cooking apple
- 4 tbsp lemon juice

1 Peel, core and slice the apple. Cover in lemon juice.
2 Put the apple slices in the freezer bag or small plastic tub with a lid.
3 Label and freeze the apple.

***Method 3** – Frozen apple (blanched)*

You will need:

- 1 cooking apple
- Bowl filled with cold water and ice cubes
- 1 saucepan
- Sieve
- Kettle

1 Boil about a litre of water in a kettle. Take care with boiling water and hot steam!
2 Collect all equipment and then pour the boiling water into a large saucepan; bring the water back to the boil.
3 Peel, core and slice the apple. Put the slices into the sieve and put the sieve into the boiling water for 1 minute (this will blanch the apple slices by destroying the enzymes).
4 Shake the sieve well and then plunge the apple slices into the iced water for 2 minutes.
5 Drain the apple slices before putting them into a freezer bag or small plastic tub with a lid.
6 Label and freeze the apple.

After about 4 weeks, take your apple samples out of the freezer and compare them.

Copy the chart below and fill in your results.

Blanching apples investigation – results after 4 weeks storage in the freezer				
Method	Colour	Flavour	Texture	Which method do you think is best? (Rank order: 1st, 2nd and 3rd)
1 Unblanched				
2 Unblanched with lemon juice				
3 Blanched in boiling water				
Conclusions – discuss what you have learnt from this experiment and detail here:				

Oxidation

Enzymes can cause foods to spoil by the process of **oxidation**. Oxidation can be used to describe the loss of the water-soluble vitamins (B group and vitamin C) from some fruits and vegetables during food preparation and cooking processes.

These methods will help to reduce oxidation in fruits and vegetables:

- Minimise the amount of time prepared fruits and vegetables are in contact with the air.
- Always start with boiling water to reduce cooking times.
- Always put a lid on saucepans to speed up the cooking time.
- Allow shorter cooking times (don't overcook fruits and vegetables).
- Reduce the amount of liquid in contact with the fruit/vegetables – vitamin B group and vitamin C are water soluble.
- Use the cooking water for sauces or gravy as some nutrients will be dissolved in the cooking water.
- Serve fruit and vegetables straight away as the water-soluble vitamins are lost during storage.

Activity

For this activity, state whether statement a) or statement b) is true for each question.

To retain the water soluble vitamins when cooking green vegetables (e.g. cabbage or broccoli), you should:

1. **a)** use a large amount of water
   b) use a minimum amount of water or steaming
2. **a)** use boiling water
   b) use cold water and heat it gradually with the vegetables in the pan
3. **a)** prepare vegetables several hours ahead of cooking time
   b) prepare just before the vegetables are cooked
4. **a)** put a lid on the pan during cooking
   b) use no lid
5. **a)** cook for a long time (over 10 minutes)
   b) cook for a minimum time (3–4 minutes), until just tender
6. **a)** use the cooking water for gravy/sauces
   b) pour the cooking water away down the sink
7. **a)** drain and serve the vegetables straight away
   b) keep the vegetables warm until needed

Practical activity

Using your responses from the activity above, choose the better method each time for preparing and cooking cabbage, broccoli or a green vegetable of your choice.

Once your plan has been checked by your teacher, carry out the methods you have chosen to cook your vegetables.

Check your knowledge and understanding

1 Identify the main types of food spoilage micro-organisms.
2 Name **two** ways in which enzymes may spoil food.
3 Explain the **four** main growth conditions needed for micro-organisms to multiply.
4 Name **two** foods that yeasts may spoil.
5 Discuss what happens when yeast multiplies, and the changes which occur in foods.
6 Suggest ways of preventing mould growth in bread.
7 Explain the differences between harmless, pathogenic and food spoilage bacteria.
8 Describe what high-risk foods have in common and give **three** examples of high-risk foods.
9 Describe how to blanch food and discuss the benefits of blanching some fruit and vegetables.

The signs of food spoilage

Learning objectives

In this section you will learn about the signs of food spoilage by:
- enzymic action
- yeast action
- mould growth.

Key word

Enzymic browning is when enzymes in food react with oxygen in the air to cause the food to turn brown.

Enzymic action

On page 248, you read how enzymes may be destroyed by heat and acid such as lemon juice. Enzymes are naturally found in foods, but it is only when the foods are bruised or cut open that they react with the oxygen in the air and **enzymic browning** takes place. This browning takes place in some fruits such as apples and pears.

Enzymes can also cause over-ripening of fruits such as bananas, eventually making them inedible.

Figure 4.1.7 Enzymes convert starch to sugar in bananas which helps to ripen them, but eventually spoils them

Figure 4.1.8 Enzymic browning of apples

Figure 4.1.9 Enzymic browning of avocados

Practical activity

Aim of Practical: To prevent enzymic browning during the preparation of fruits and vegetables

Look at the recipe for guacamole below, or find a recipe containing fresh mixed fruits, for example fresh fruit tart containing apples/pears/bananas.

Guacamole

1 red chilli pepper

1 crushed garlic clove

Juice of 1 lime

2 spring onions, sliced

3 tbsp chopped fresh coriander

2 ripe avocados

2 tomatoes

Figure 4.1.10 Guacamole often has an acid ingredient to prevent enzymic browning

Top tip 1: Wear rubber gloves when you prepare fresh chilli peppers. This will prevent you accidentally getting chilli in your eyes, which can really sting!

Top tip 2: To help prevent the enzymic browning of the avocados, lime juice is added to the recipe. You can also put the avocado stones in the mixture until it is served.

Method

1 Put on rubber gloves to slice the chilli pepper down the middle and then scrape out the seeds with a teaspoon and discard. Using a paring knife, roughly chop the chilli into small pieces.
2 In a food processor, put the chopped chilli, crushed garlic, lime juice, sliced spring onions and coriander and process until it is a pulp.
3 Cut the avocados in half with the paring knife and remove the stones; don't throw the stones away.
4 In a medium bowl, mash the avocado flesh with a fork until it is a purée.
5 Stir the chilli mixture into the avocado purée.
6 Quarter and then deseed the tomatoes with the paring knife. Cut the tomatoes into small pieces and stir into the avocado mixture.

1 Identify which ingredients and/or preparation methods are used to prevent enzymic browning.
2 Prepare either the guacamole or a fresh fruit dessert.

If you are preparing a fresh fruit dessert:

● Include fruits which go brown when cut such as apples, pears and or bananas.
● For variety, include berries, such as raspberries, strawberries or blackberries if they are **in season**.
● To prepare them, wash in cold water in a **colander** under gentle running water, drain, then pat with kitchen towel gently before chilling to prevent yeast/mould growth.
3 Photograph key points in the preparation of these recipes that prevent enzymic browning and include these in your notes.

Figure 4.1.11 Raspberries washed in a sieve; all fresh fruit should be washed before eating

Key word

Ferment is when yeasts reproduce by feeding on sugar, producing carbon dioxide gas and alcohol.

Yeast action

On page 244, you have read how yeasts can grow with oxygen (aerobically) or without oxygen (anaerobically), and how they prefer to grow on acid foods. As they prefer acidic and sweet foods, they can spoil fruit juices, jam, honey and fruit yoghurts. As yeasts **ferment** the sugars in these foods, they produce alcohol and the gas carbon dioxide.

Figure 4.1.12 This honey is fermenting due to yeast action; most honey is *pasteurised* to stop this happening

Figure 4.1.13 Yeasts may ferment orange juice if it is not stored correctly or if it is kept after its 'best before' date

Figure 4.1.14 Yeasts can grow on grapes, spoiling them

Mould growth

On page 246, you have read how moulds like to grow on food in moist and warm conditions, but also how they can grow at low temperatures as well, given enough time. They grow easily on bread, cheese, jam and soft fruits.

In jam-making, the high temperature that is achieved by the boiling process destroys all moulds, but if the jam is potted into jars that are not **sterilised**, any **mould spores** in the jars can grow and spoil the jam. Also, if condensation forms on the lids of the jam jars it may dilute the sugar concentration on the surface of the jam, allowing mould growth. This is why the lids on freshly made jam should be put on either as soon as the jam is made or once the jam has completely cooled.

When moulds grow on food, they grow throughout the food to extract nutrients from it. This is why you should throw away any food with mould on it rather than just scraping the mould off the surface of the food.

Figure 4.1.15 Moulds can grow on the surface of jam

Figure 4.1.16 Mould grows easily on bread

Figure 4.1.17 Yeasts and moulds can grow on tomatoes. Once they are very ripe – store them in the fridge

Teacher demonstration

Your teacher will demonstrate tomato soup that involves **de-skinning** and **de-seeding** the tomatoes as part of the preparation. If the tomatoes are very ripe, they should be stored in the fridge before use so that yeast and mould growth is not encouraged.

Check your knowledge and understanding

1 Explain how to prevent enzymic browning when making either fresh fruit dessert or guacamole.
2 Describe ways to hygienically prepare berries before using them in a recipe.
3 Explain how yeasts can spoil food.
4 Describe the types of food yeasts prefer to grow on.
5 Explain why most honey we buy is pasteurised.
6 Explain why it is important to sterilise jam jars before use.
7 Identify at which stage the lid should be put on homemade jam.

Learning objective

In this section you will learn about:

● the use of micro-organisms in food production.

The use of yeasts in food production

Yeast is widely used in food production as a **raising agent** for bread and other yeasted doughs such as crumpets, doughnuts and currant buns. As well as bakery products, yeast is used in the brewery industry to ferment grapes into wine and hops into beer.

You will have learnt about using yeast as a raising agent in the raising agents section in Topic 3.2 Functional and chemical properties of food. See page 236.

Figure 4.1.18 Yeast is used to produce bread, beer and wine

The use of moulds in food production

Some cheeses are made with **moulds** to improve their colour and flavour. For example, Brie, Camembert and Stilton cheeses all have specific moulds grown on them. This is not an example of food spoilage, but a use of moulds to improve the flavour and variety of food in your diet.

Figure 4.1.19 Brie, Camembert and Stilton cheese all use moulds to provide distinctive colours and flavours

Figure 4.1.20 Some sausages are ripened with moulds

Figure 4.1.21 Soy sauce is made using moulds and yeasts to help develop its flavour

Moulds are also used to ripen the surface of some sausages. The mould improves the aroma (smell) and texture of the sausages and also extends their shelf life.

Soy sauce is made by mixing soya beans and other grains with a mould and yeast. Traditionally, this would have been left in the sun to ferment, but nowadays it is mainly made in factories under controlled conditions. The process forms a flavour enhancer, **monosodium glutamate**, which is popular in Chinese foods.

The use of bacteria in food production

Harmless bacteria are used to make cheese and yoghurt.

Cheese-making

The raw ingredients for making cheese are: milk, a starter culture of bacteria, **rennet** and salt.

- The milk used for cheese-making is usually pasteurised, this means the milk has been held at a minimum temperature of 72°C for 15 seconds to kill harmful bacteria.
- The pasteurised milk is warmed to between 25°C to 35°C (depending on the type of cheese being made).
- The starter culture (selected harmless/friendly bacteria) is added to the warmed milk and this sours the milk. This starter converts the milk sugar, **lactose** into **lactic acid** and this begins the cheese-making process.
- To increase the rate of curdling, rennet is also added. This contains an enzyme called rennin. Rennin was traditionally extracted from the stomach of calves, but nowadays it can be made from a vegetable or synthetic source. The rennet causes the milk to separate into **curds and whey**.
- The curds and whey are then cut to release the whey which is drained off. The curd is heated and stirred and becomes very firm. The blocks of curd are **milled** to form smaller pieces of curd. Salt is added to the curd at this stage to add flavour and to help preserve the cheese.
- These curds are then pressed into moulds and pressed again to make blocks of cheese which are firm and solid. After this, the blocks of cheese are either wrapped in large plastic bags and put into boxes or wrapped in muslin cloth (cheesecloth). The cheese goes into cool storage for weeks, months or even years depending on the type of cheese being made. Cheddar cheese uses this process of traditional cheese-making.

Yoghurt-making

In yoghurt-making, selected harmless bacteria are added to warmed, previously boiled, milk and allowed to multiply for several hours in warm (about 37°C) conditions. During this time, the milk turns from being runny into thick yoghurt. The yoghurt becomes slightly tangy as the lactose (the milk sugar) turns into lactic acid. It is the lactic acid that **denatures** and **coagulates** the protein in the milk to thicken it into yoghurt. Before yoghurt-making begins, it is important that all the equipment is sterilised so that the yoghurt does not become contaminated with pathogenic or spoilage bacteria.

Figure 4.1.22 Bacteria cultures are used to produce some cheeses and yoghurt

Key words

Rennet is an enzyme produced in the stomach of animals such as cows often used in cheese-making.

Lactose is the sugar naturally found in milk.

Lactic acid is formed during the cheese-making process, when lactose is converted into lactic acid.

Curds and whey are the products made after adding bacteria and rennet to warm milk during cheese-making. The curds are the solid and the whey the liquid.

Milling is the process of breaking the solid blocks of curd into much smaller pieces (usually carried out by machine).

Denature is when protein changes shape, either when heated, agitated or in acidic conditions.

Coagulate is when protein sets, either when heated or in acidic conditions.

Extension activity

1 Find out how to make yoghurt at home. Draw a flow chart to show the step-by-step stages of yoghurt-making.
2 If you are able to, make some yoghurt at home and video the key stages of the process to share with your group.

Practical activity

First make a bread dough, then use this to make calzone. A calzone is a folded pizza originating from Naples, Italy. Calzones are often stuffed with meat such as salami and ham, as well as Italian cheeses such as ricotta, mozzarella, pecorino and Parmesan. Vegetables such as mushrooms and spinach can be added for extra flavours and textures.

The recipe filling below is just a suggestion; you may adapt these ingredients to suit your own taste.

Making Italian calzone

Ingredients

For the dough:

250 g strong plain flour

2.5 g ($\frac{1}{2}$ tsp) salt

15 g butter or low fat spread

10 g (2 tsp) fast-action yeast

150 ml warm water

For the filling:

10 g (2 tsp) vegetable oil

50 g finely sliced mushrooms

100 g washed baby spinach leaves

120 ml passata

150 g grated mozzarella cheese

20 g fresh basil leaves

Figure 4.1.23 A calzone is a folded pizza originating from Italy

Top tip: It is better for the texture of the calzone dough to add all the water to the flour at once. If the dough is too sticky, you can add a little more flour afterwards.

Method

1. Preheat the oven to 200°C and line a baking sheet with parchment.
2. Put the flour into a large bowl and stir in the salt.
3. Rub the butter or margarine into the flour.
4. Stir in the yeast.
5. Add the warm water and mix it to a pliable dough with a table knife.
6. Put the dough onto a lightly floured surface and knead for 5–10 minutes until you have a smooth dough with no cracks.
7. Shape the dough into two large circles using a rolling pin. Cover with cling film and leave in a warm place to rise, while you prepare the fillings.
8. Heat the oil in a large frying pan and fry the mushrooms for about 2 minutes. Add the spinach and stir-fry until just wilted.
9. Spread the passata evenly over one half of each of the dough.
10. Divide the spinach mixture evenly and spread on top of the passata. Sprinkle the mozzarella cheese and torn basil leaves onto each dough. To seal each calzone, carefully lift the far edge of the dough and pull it over the top towards you. This is like folding the dough in half.
11. Crimp the edges of the calzones to seal so the mixture won't escape when cooking.
12. Put the calzones on the baking sheet and bake for about 15 minutes until the dough is golden brown all over.
13. Cool on a wire rack and serve hot with some salad.

Check your knowledge and understanding

1   Describe **two** uses of yeast in food production.
2   Name **two** cheeses that rely on mould for their colour and flavour.
3   Describe the effect of adding bacteria to milk at the beginning of the stages to make cheese.
4   Explain why it is important that all the equipment for yoghurt-making is free from micro-organisms.
5   Describe the effect of adding lactic acid to milk protein during yoghurt-making.
6   Name the ingredients in the calzone pizza which are micro-organisms or rely on micro-organisms for their food production?

Extension activity

Watch a video on how to make cheese in a large processing plant compared to small farm production. Produce flow charts to show the different stages of production and highlight at which stages micro-organisms are important for the manufacture and maturing of the cheeses.

You may want to use this link: https://www.youtube.com/watch?v=hXhXTs5uwyg

Bacterial contamination

Learning objectives

In this section you will learn about:

- the different **sources** of bacterial contamination
- the main **types** of bacteria that cause **food poisoning**
- the main **sources** and **methods of control** of different types of food poisoning bacteria
- the general **symptoms** of food poisoning.

The different sources of bacterial contamination

Foods may become contaminated with bacteria from many different places.

Raw food contamination

Many raw foods carry a lot of bacteria.

> **Key word**
>
> **Slaughter** means to kill animals for food.

- Many types of bacteria live in the intestines of animals. When the animal is **slaughtered** the bacteria can get onto the meat and poultry. These bacteria could multiply to cause food poisoning if the meat and its juices are allowed to come into contact with other foods and equipment. It is safest to assume that all raw meat and their juices carry food poisoning bacteria, and to take extra care to make sure that, when storing, handling and cooking raw meat and poultry, these cannot contaminate other food or equipment.
- Other types of raw food that carry bacteria are raw eggs, which may have bacteria on the inside and outside of their shell, as well as shellfish, for example mussels and oysters.
- As well as these animal foods, plant foods such as rice and vegetables can be contaminated with bacteria from the soil.

> **Teacher's tip**
>
> When handling raw foods, such as raw meat and poultry, raw eggs, shellfish, rice and vegetables, it is important to follow the rules for preparing and cooking food on pages 276–282.

AQA GCSE Food Preparation and Nutrition

Work surface and equipment contamination

Work surfaces and equipment can become contaminated with bacteria from raw foods, and unwashed hands.

- Bacteria are so small you cannot see them without a powerful microscope, so always clean work surfaces before you begin any food preparation.
- Any work surfaces and equipment that have been in contact with raw meat and poultry should be thoroughly cleaned with hot soapy water before they are re-used for other food preparation. Ideally, separate chopping boards, utensils and equipment should be used for raw and cooked food, and these should be washed in very hot water or in the dishwasher.
- All equipment and work surfaces should be cleaned regularly both before and after use so that they are clean for the next stage of preparation to avoid contamination.
- Colour-coding of equipment can help to reduce contamination from bacteria.
- Dishcloths used to wipe work surfaces pick up bacteria each time they are used. If there are juices from raw meat or poultry to be wiped up, it is better if this is carried out with a disposable cloth, such as paper kitchen towel, before using an **anti-bacterial spray** or hot soapy water to clean the work surface.
- Use clean dishcloths and tea towels every day, and make sure they are washed in very hot water.

Key word

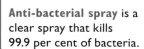

Anti-bacterial spray is a clear spray that kills 99.9 per cent of bacteria.

Figure 4.1.24 Colour-coded chopping boards are useful to prevent the transfer of bacteria between different foods

Food handler contamination

When you are preparing and cooking food, you can contaminate the food with bacteria that are naturally present on you. To avoid this, you should:

- Use tongs or other utensils to pick up food.
- When you taste food during food preparation to check the flavour, use a clean teaspoon and don't double-dip!
- Don't lick your fingers, for example, to open a plastic bag, as this will spread bacteria from your mouth onto your hands.
- Avoid touching parts of utensils that come into contact with food; for example, when picking up cutlery, use the handles. When picking up cups and mugs, use the handles, don't put your hands inside to lift them as this will spread bacteria.

Pest contamination

Pests, such as flies, insects, birds, mice and even rats, can contaminate food. They carry bacteria on their bodies and in their urine and droppings. They can contaminate the actual food or areas where food may be stored or prepared.

Figure 4.1.25 Pests, including rats and flies, carry bacteria that may lead to food poisoning

You should try to keep pests out of the kitchen by keeping windows and doors shut if possible and using extractor fans to cool the kitchen. Also keep all rubbish bins covered.

It is impossible to keep all pests out of kitchens, but there are other things you can do to prevent them from contaminating food:

- Keep all work surfaces clean so that pests have no food source.
- Wash up straight away, don't leave dishes lying around in the kitchen as this will be a food source for pests.
- Make sure your kitchen is very clean after each cooking session.
- Don't leave food out overnight as some pests are **nocturnal**.
- Empty bins regularly and clean the bins at least once a week.
- Domestic pets, including cats, dogs and birds carry food poisoning bacteria and should not be allowed in food preparation areas.

Waste food and rubbish contamination

Bacteria can multiply in waste food and rubbish bins. To avoid possible contamination onto food the following precautions should be taken:

- Only use bins with lids.
- Use thick bin bags.
- Empty bins as soon as they become full and always at the end of each day.
- A bin with a lid that is foot-operated is better as it means you avoid touching the bin with your hands, which could become contaminated with bacteria from the lid.
- Bins should be washed regularly, inside and out, and then disinfected. The floor area underneath the bin should be washed every day.

At-risk groups

Food poisoning is very unpleasant for anyone but for some groups of the population, the outcomes can be more serious. These groups are:

- babies and very young children
- pregnant women
- elderly people
- those with reduced immunity (due to illness or medical treatment).

The outcomes of food poisoning can be serious, and death is more frequent in these at-risk groups.

Food poisoning may be caused by:

- eating or drinking contaminated water
- eating undercooked food (especially meat and poultry), for example beef burgers which are still pink in the middle, or chicken where the juices are still pink
- not storing food correctly, especially **perishable foods** that need to be in the fridge at temperatures between 0°C and below 5°C
- not storing cooked foods in the fridge, or storing them in the wrong place, for example storing raw meat above high-risk food such as cooked ham
- eating food that has been touched by someone who has a septic cut or has **symptoms** of food poisoning at any stage of preparation, cooking or serving (see page 264)
- cross-contamination, where **pathogenic bacteria** from raw food, equipment and work surfaces spread onto food. For example, if raw vegetables are prepared on a work surface before high risk foods, bacteria from the raw vegetables may spread from the work surface onto the high risk food (ready-to-eat food) and may cause food poisoning.

Figure 4.1.26 Rubbish bins should always have a lid

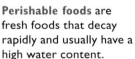

Key words

Perishable foods are fresh foods that decay rapidly and usually have a high water content.

Symptoms means the signs (of illness).

Pathogenic bacteria are bacteria that can cause food poisoning.

The general symptoms of food poisoning

The following symptoms may be a result of food poisoning. You may have one or more of these:

- vomiting
- diarrhoea
- nausea
- stomach pains
- vomiting and diarrhoea may lead to dehydration.

The symptoms of food poisoning may start within 2 hours of eating the food, but they can also begin after many days depending on the type of pathogenic bacteria that has caused the food poisoning.

The main types of food poisoning bacteria and methods of control

These bacteria are pathogenic, which means they can cause food poisoning.

Campylobacter

Campylobacter is the most common type of food poisoning bacteria in the UK. Most cases of campylobacter food poisoning in the UK are from contaminated poultry. This type of bacteria does not normally grow in food, but it only takes a few bacteria to cause food poisoning, and this type of bacteria spreads easily. The most likely way of getting it is from undercooked chicken or when the bacteria from raw chicken spreads onto other ready-to-eat food. To reduce the risk of this type of food poisoning, you should avoid storing raw and cooked foods together. Also, colour coding can help to separate the preparation of raw and cooked foods. Campylobacter can also be transmitted from domestic pets and other animals. This is why hand washing is so important after contact with any animals.

The Food Standards Agency has identified campylobacter in chicken as a particular problem and launched a campaign in 2015 to reduce food poisoning caused by it. The campaign emphasises the importance of not washing meat and poultry before cooking as this may spread bacteria around the kitchen.

It may also be spread by cattle, pigs, birds and pets, which carry campylobacter in their gut.

Activity

1 Use the link to watch the video on how campylobacter bacteria can spread around the kitchen: www.food.gov.uk/news-updates/campaigns/campylobacter/fsw-2014.
2 Produce a list of easy-to-understand bullet points for primary school children on how to prevent this type of food poisoning. If you have time, include diagrams and sketches to illustrate these points.

Figure 4.1.27 Raw chicken should not be washed as this can spread campylobacter bacteria, which may cause food poisoning

E. coli

E. coli is normally found in the intestines of people and animals. It is also found anywhere where **faecal contamination** occurs. If you get this type of food poisoning, it can have serious outcomes and may lead to death or untreatable illness. Only small numbers of the bacteria are needed which then produce a toxin which causes the illness. The bacteria can survive both refrigeration and freezer temperatures. Thorough cooking of food will destroy E. coli bacteria. People who work with animals or who handle raw meat should take special care when hand washing to ensure E.coli bacteria is not spread. Young children and the elderly are most at risk of serious outcomes.

Figure 4.1.28 Undercooked beef burgers can cause E. coli food poisoning

Salmonella

Salmonella bacteria live in the intestines of many farm animals and can contaminate meat, poultry, eggs and milk. Other foods such as vegetables, fruit and shellfish can also become contaminated due to contact with manure in the soil and sewage in water. It can be spread from one person to another or by not washing hands after going to the toilet, and if handling contaminated food such as raw meat.

To reduce the risks of infection, raw foods should be kept away from ready-to-eat foods in the refrigerator. All vegetables should be washed before preparation, special care should be taken if these are to be eaten raw. Salmonella is destroyed by cooking, so thorough cooking to a core temperature of 75°C is needed to destroy salmonella.

Most eggs sold in the UK are now produced within the **Lion Scheme**. The British Lion is one of the most recognised food safety marks in the UK. The stamp means that the eggs are guaranteed British and

Figure 4.1.29 Most eggs sold in the UK are stamped with the Lion Scheme stamp, which means the hens have been vaccinated against salmonella

that all hens have been **vaccinated** against salmonella bacteria. The 'best before' date is also stamped on the egg as well as the egg box. Since the British Lion stamp was introduced in 1998, cases of salmonella food poisoning have dropped dramatically.

Listeria

Listeria bacteria are found in many places in the environment, including in the soil, decaying vegetation and water.

It is most often found in **unpasteurised milk** and cheeses made from unpasteurised milk. It can also be found in food manufacturing environments, such as when cooked food is contaminated before packaging, on slicing machines in shops and also in the home.

Listeria is unusual as it multiplies below 5°C, so at fridge temperatures it can grow to harmful levels.

Around 1 in 20 people may carry listeria without knowing it, or showing any symptoms. These people are called **carriers**. If a carrier defecates and then fails to wash their hands before handling food, they may pass the bacteria on to other people.

Healthy adults usually only get mild symptoms from listeria, but it is dangerous to pregnant women who may miscarry or have a still-birth due to this bacteria.

Listeria is destroyed by thorough cooking, to a core temperature of 75°C and also by pasteurisation.

Staphylococcus aureus

Staphylococcus aureus is mainly transmitted by human handlers. It is found on the human skin and the mucus linings of the body. The bacteria produces a toxin which causes the symptoms of food poisoning.

The sources of the bacteria can be from person-to-person contact. It can be spread directly from the human carrier onto food. Cross-contamination can occur when an infected person handles high risk (ready-to-eat) food, such as cooked meat and cooked egg dishes. The storage of food contaminated with staphylococcus aureus can allow the bacteria to multiply and produce the toxin which causes food poisoning.

Name of pathogenic bacteria	Foods bacteria is found in	Source of bacteria (where bacteria comes from)
Campylobacter	Poultry, milk and milk products	Unclean water Unpasteurised milk Bottled milk pecked by birds Raw poultry Sewage
E. coli	Undercooked meat, especially burgers and mince Unwashed contaminated fruit	Raw and undercooked meat Dirty water Sewage
Salmonella	Undercooked or contaminated cooked meat Beansprouts Unpasteurised milk Foods made from imported poultry and eggs	Intestines of ill people Animals, birds Raw meat Unpasteurised milk Imported poultry and eggs
Listeria	Pâté, cooked chicken, prepared salads, soft cheeses	Sewage, decaying vegetation and unclean water
Staphylococcus aureus	Unpasteurised milk, meat and meat products	Human food handlers touching, coughing or sneezing onto food as well as human to human contact. An infected person may contaminate ready to eat food

Table 4.1.1 The main sources and methods of control of different food poisoning bacteria types

Key words

Listeria is a type of food poisoning bacteria that can multiply at fridge temperatures below 5°C.

Unpasteurised milk is milk that hasn't been heat-treated to destroy bacteria.

Carriers (of pathogenic bacteria) are people who carry these bacteria, but show no symptoms.

Check your knowledge and understanding

1 Describe how raw foods may cause food poisoning.
2 Discuss how the use of colour-coded equipment can prevent cross-contamination.
3 Explain why hand washing is so important in reducing the risk of food poisoning.
4 Describe how pests spread bacteria onto food.
5 Explain with examples why bins should always have a lid.
6 Name **two** 'at risk' groups for food poisoning and explain what 'at risk' means.

7 Food poisoning may be caused by eating undercooked poultry. Describe other possible causes of food poisoning.
8 What does 'pathogenic bacteria' mean?
9 Name **two** general symptoms of food poisoning.
10 Describe the most common type of food poisoning bacteria in the UK, its sources and methods of transmission.

Extension activity

Make separate mind maps of each type of food poisoning bacteria giving as much detail as you can. Revise the information on these in pairs and test each other on what you remember. Try to reconstruct each mind map without looking at your notes.

TOPIC 4.2 PRINCIPLES OF FOOD SAFETY

Buying and storing food

Learning objective

In this section you will learn about:
● the food safety principles when buying and storing food.

Temperature control when storing food

The correct temperature control of food is very important. Many outbreaks of food poisoning are caused by high-risk food being kept for too long within the **temperature danger zone**.

What is the temperature danger zone?

The temperature danger zone is the range of temperatures between 5°C and 63°C, where most bacteria can easily multiply.
● Bacteria grow very slowly, or do not grow at all at temperatures below 5°C.
● No bacteria grow at temperatures above 63°C.
● Bacteria will multiply the fastest at around body temperature of 37°C.

The temperature danger zone does not apply to non-perishable foods, which are normally stored in cupboards at around 17°C–20°C.

High-risk foods are the ready-to-eat foods that are most likely to cause food poisoning.

You will have learnt about the high-risk foods most likely to cause food poisoning in Topic 4.1 Food spoilage and contamination. See page 266.

Topic 4.1 Food spoilage and contamination. See page 266.

> **Key word**
>
> **Temperature danger zone** is the range of temperatures from **5°C to 63°C**, in which most bacteria can easily multiply.

The basic principle of temperature control of high-risk foods is to:
● keep hot food hot, at 63°C or above
● keep cold food cold, below 5°C
● keep prepared food out of the temperature danger zone of 5°C to 63°C.
● Fridge temperature = 0°C to below 5°C
● Temperature danger zone = 5°C to 63°C
● Safe reheating and cooking temperature = 75°C
● Boiling point of water = 100°C
● Freezing point of water = 0°C

Figure 4.2.1 Prawn cocktail is a high-risk food and should be kept out of the temperature danger zone

AQA GCSE Food Preparation and Nutrition

Perishable foods

Perishable foods are foods with a fairly short shelf life, which usually need to be stored in the fridge or freezer. Examples of perishable foods are:

- raw and cooked meat
- poultry and fish
- milk and eggs
- butter, low fat spread and yoghurts
- cheeses
- vegetables, fruits and salads.

All high-risk food should be stored in the fridge (or freezer) to ensure the food does not allow the growth of pathogenic bacteria.

When shopping and buying perishable foods you should store these in an **insulated cold bag** with ice packs to ensure the food stays out of the temperature danger zone until you get home after which they should go straight in the fridge.

Figure 4.2.2 Perishable foods usually need to be refrigerated or frozen and have a short shelf life

Ambient storage for non-perishable foods

Non-perishable foods are foods that have been processed in some way to prevent the growth of micro-organisms and to prolong their shelf life. These include canned foods, dried pasta and rice, breakfast cereals, flour, coffee powder and sugar. For example, dried pasta has had its moisture removed and is then packaged in a strong plastic bag to keep it free from contamination.

These foods are usually stored at **ambient** temperature, in food cupboards at home. Ambient storage is the temperature of the surroundings, also referred to as 'room temperature'. Some foods may be kept safely at ambient temperatures of around 17°C to 20°C. Foods stored at ambient temperature should, ideally, be in a dry, dark place to prolong their shelf life.

Non-perishable foods will have a 'best before' date, which indicates the recommended time in which the food should be eaten, but it can still be safely eaten after this date although the quality won't be as good as the product gets older.

Figure 4.2.3 Non-perishable foods are usually stored at ambient temperatures

Key words

Insulated cold bag is a padded bag used with ice packs to keep food cold.

Ambient refers to temperatures at 17°C to 20°C; also referred to as room temperature.

Correct use of refrigerators (fridges)

Fridges keep food chilled, usually between 0°C and below 5°C, which is a temperature where micro-organisms can only grow very slowly or not at all. This helps to prevent food poisoning. Once the food is taken out of the fridge, the micro-organisms will have warmth and will begin to grow again.

Some fridges have an ice box which can be used to make ice cubes or to store frozen food for a short amount of time. Ice boxes are not as cold as normal freezers; they often have a temperature of about −10°C.

The fridge temperature will vary in different shelves of the fridge. If there is no ice box, the top shelf of the fridge will usually be the warmest shelf. When you are checking the temperature of the fridge, put the thermometer here to make sure it isn't above 5°C. The door shelves are also warmer than other parts of the fridge and these may be used for storing butter and drinks.

Eggs carry bacteria on their shells, so it is better to store them in their box on the bottom shelf of the fridge near other raw foods. All raw foods on this bottom shelf (including raw meat and poultry) should be wrapped and covered so they do not make contact with the egg box.

Some foods, which do not have their own packaging, need to be wrapped before they are stored in the fridge. This will:

- stop the food drying out
- prevent cross-contamination with other foods
- stop flavours from stronger foods **tainting** other foods

Food inside the fridge needs to be packed so the air can circulate around it. The fridge relies on convection currents cooling the food and this can only happen if the air has room to circulate.

READY TO EAT FOODS
Such as dairy products, yoghurts, cream...

..cream cakes, butter/margarine, cooked meats, leftovers-covered, other packaged foods, e.g. coleslaw, tomato ketchup, jams etc.
TOP SHELVES AND MIDDLE SHELVES

RAW MEAT, POULTRY and FISH
Always cover and keep in sealed containers.
BOTTOM SHELVES

SALAD VEGETABLES, FRUIT & VEGETABLES
Keep ready to eat fruit and vegetables in sealed bagscontainers Always wash raw fruits and vegetables before use.
SALAD DRAWER

CORRECT FRIDGE TEMPERATURE 0 TO BELOW 5

Figure 4.2.4 Where to store food in a fridge

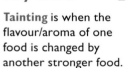

Key word

Tainting is when the flavour/aroma of one food is changed by another stronger food.

Most fridges purchased today are larder fridges, which means they do not have an ice box and they do not need to be defrosted. If fridges do need to be defrosted, this should be carried out about once a month following the manufacturer's instructions. It is important that the fridge is as frost-free as possible because if ice is allowed to build up, it will affect the efficiency of the fridge and it may become too warm, therefore increasing the chances of food poisoning. Some fridges have an alarm which sounds when its temperature rises too high. This usually happens if the door is left open for too long.

Fridges should be cleaned out regularly:
- The fridge should be switched off and unplugged; the food should be removed and stored in a cool place.
- It should be cleaned using a solution of bicarbonate of soda dissolved in hot water.
- Dry with a clean tea towel or kitchen roll.
- Switch back on, then replace the food.

Extra tips for storing food in a fridge
- Food should only be refrigerated for short periods of time, usually within 1–5 days. Food labels will have a date mark; 'use by' dates should be followed to prevent food poisoning.
- Remember to use older food before newer food to prevent food wastage.
- High-risk foods, raw poultry, meat, eggs, fish and seafood should always be kept in the fridge.
- Make sure that raw meat is covered on the bottom shelf of the fridge in a deep dish to prevent it dripping onto other foods.
- Allow hot food to cool to room temperature before putting it in the fridge. Hot food in the fridge will raise the temperature up into the temperature danger zone.
- Open and close the fridge door as little as possible to keep the cold air inside the fridge.

Correct use of freezers

Freezers store food for longer periods of time than a fridge. The food in a freezer is stored at −18°C or colder. At this temperature, bacteria do not have the warmth they need to grow and cannot multiply. As well as having no warmth, they have no water as it has turned into ice, which makes the water unavailable to the micro-organisms. However, enzymes may still be active at −18°C, which is why some fruit and vegetables need to be blanched before being frozen.

You will have learnt about blanching certain foods before freezing in Topic 4.1 Food spoilage and contamination. See page 248.

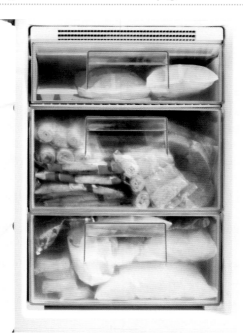

Figure 4.2.5 Freezers store perishable food at −18°C or below which prolongs their shelf life

Most bacteria survive the freezing process. While they are in the freezer, these bacteria become dormant, which means they are inactive. Once the food is defrosted (thawed), the bacteria can multiply again, and defrosted food should be treated as fresh food and consumed as soon as possible.

Foods may be stored in the freezer for up to one year, depending on the type of food it is. Foods that are frozen for too long are still safe to eat, but their flavour and texture will deteriorate over time. Shop-bought frozen food will have a 'best before' date, which should be followed.

If you are freezing your own food at home:

- You will need to use the 'fast freeze' button, which will take the freezer temperature down to as low as −25°C.
- Wrap, label and date food, so you know how long food has been in the freezer for. Wrappings should be strong and protect food from **freezer burn**. Freezer bags are ideal, they are like normal plastic bags but thicker and so they protect the food better during freezer storage.
- Do not overload the freezer and stack neatly with gaps, so the air can circulate and freeze the food properly.
- Rotate your stock, use the older foods first, but observe the 'best before' dates, or freezing dates if home-frozen.

Key word

Freezer burn is the excessive dehydration and oxidation on the surface of food while stored in the freezer. It is usually caused by inadequate packaging.

Defrosting (thawing food)

Some foods, such as peas, chips, burgers, vegetables and fish, do not need to be defrosted before cooking; they are best cooked from frozen.

With joints of meat, poultry and bulky food, you should defrost these foods first to ensure they cook in a reasonable time and evenly. If these foods are not properly defrosted, the core temperature may not reach the 75°C needed to kill harmful (pathogenic) bacteria.

You can tell if food is properly defrosted when there are no ice crystals and when the food is soft. With poultry, an extra check is to see if the legs and wings move fairly freely.

Checklist for defrosting raw frozen meat and poultry:
- Plan ahead, know how long it will take; for example, with large turkeys, this could take several days.
- Defrost in a container, so the liquid is contained as it defrosts.
- Cover the defrosting food.
- Once defrosted, cook straight away.
- Never re-freeze defrosted food.

Why shouldn't you re-freeze defrosted food?

When food is frozen and then defrosted, the food will pass into the temperature danger zone where pathogenic bacteria can begin to multiply. Defrosted food should be used straight away and should not be re-frozen as this will allow the food to pass through the temperature danger zone twice more, which will increase the risk of food poisoning.

Defrosting and cleaning a freezer

A freezer needs to be defrosted about once a year because if there is a build-up of ice it can stop the freezer working properly and cost more money to run. If you have a frost-free freezer, you will still need to empty it and clean it out at least once a year.

To defrost and clean a freezer:
1. Remove all food from the freezer, and store in an insulated cold bag or boxes wrapped in newspaper.
2. Remove the shelves.
3. Switch off and unplug the freezer.
4. Place bowls and towels inside the freezer and underneath it and leave the ice to melt. This will take several hours. You may need to empty the bowls if they fill up. Do not try to hack the ice off with sharp tools as you may damage the inside of the freezer. The freezer manufacturer may provide an ice scraper which will help you to remove the softened ice safely. Wait until all the ice is melted.
5. Wash inside the freezer with bicarbonate of soda dissolved in hot water.
6. Dry with a tea towel or kitchen towel and then switch back on for an hour before reloading the food back inside the freezer.
7. To clean a frost-free freezer follow the steps above, leaving out step 4.

Teacher's tips
- Bacteria, yeasts, moulds and enzymes can all cause food spoilage.
- Some bacteria (pathogenic bacteria) can cause food poisoning.

'Best before' and 'use by' dates

The date labels on food are either a **'best before'** date or a **'use by'** date. Other date marks such as 'display until' or 'sell by' dates are for shop staff, not for the customer.

'Best before' dates

These relate to the sensory quality of the food, colour, flavour and texture. It is considered safe to eat foods after the 'best before' date. Foods that carry a 'best before' date are usually non-perishable foods (see page 269). One exception is eggs, although these have a 'best before' date, they should be consumed by the date displayed on the box. 'Best before' dates appear on a wide range of mainly non-perishable foods, such as frozen foods, dried food and tinned food. Breakfast cereals also have a 'best before' date. Eating food past its 'best before' date is unlikely to be harmful.

'Use by' dates

'Use by' dates are on foods that may be unsafe to eat after this date. It is advised not to eat food after the 'use by' date, as there is a risk of food poisoning if you do. Foods with 'use by' dates are usually perishable and include fresh meat and poultry, cooked meat and poultry, milk, meat products and ready-prepared salads. You will see 'use by' dates on food that goes off quickly, such as fish, meat products and ready-prepared salads. **'Use by' dates are the most important date for people to consider, as these relate to food safety.**

While it is an offence to sell food after the 'use by' date, retailers can, with the exception of eggs, sell products after the 'best before' date, providing it is safe to eat.

Figure 4.2.6 A food umbrella protects food from pests

Covering food

All food stored in the fridge, freezer or cupboards should be wrapped or covered to keep it clean and prevent it from drying out.

When food is ready to serve after preparation and/or cooking, the food should be covered. This will prevent contamination from pests, especially flies, as well as dust and other foods. Suitable materials to cover food are:

- food umbrellas to keep flying insects off
- cling film
- foil
- a clean tea towel.

Although covering food does not prevent food poisoning bacteria from multiplying, it keeps flies, wasps, bees and other flying insects away from food.

Research activity

Buying and storing food safely is essential to help to prevent food poisoning. Describe the precautions you would take when buying these foods and where you would store them safely:

1 raw chicken
2 cooked prawns
3 carrots with soil on them
4 a cooked meat pie
5 apples
6 a bag of dried pasta
7 fresh fish for a meal to be eaten in 2 weeks' time.

Set your work out in a table as below, the first one has been done for you:

Type of food	Care when buying	Storage guidelines	Comments
Raw chicken	Check use by date. Keep away from cooked food. Put it in its own disposable bag Store in cool bag.	Store in the fridge or freezer at home.	The packaging of raw meat has bacteria on it, so take care to avoid cross contamination.
Cooked prawns			
Carrots (with soil on them)			

Extension activity

For each of the foods listed in the activity here, include the temperatures foods must be stored at once you get them home.

Check your knowledge and understanding

1 Give the correct range of temperatures for the danger zone.
2 Name **four** high-risk foods.
3 What are the correct temperatures of a fridge and a freezer?
4 What does ambient storage mean?
5 Give **four** tips for storing food in the fridge.
6 Name the best substance for cleaning a fridge or freezer.
7 Explain why some freezers need to be defrosted.
8 Explain why a frozen chicken needs to be fully defrosted before cooking.
9 Describe the differences between a 'best before' and a 'use by' date.
10 Explain why food should be covered if it is left out.

Preparing and cooking food

Learning objectives

In this section you will learn about:
- the food safety principles when preparing food
- the food safety principles when cooking food.

When preparing and cooking food, there are some basic rules that need to be followed to ensure conditions do not develop that allow the growth of bacteria that can cause food poisoning. The following sections detail the main situations when food could become contaminated with bacteria or have the opportunity to multiply. It is your responsibility to make sure you follow these rules to keep yourself and your family safe.

Personal hygiene

Personal hygiene is important for anyone preparing and cooking food. If high standards of personal hygiene are met, food poisoning is less likely to occur.

Your hands are the most likely way that you spread bacteria onto food. It is really important to wash your hands thoroughly with soap and hot water. When you are washing your hands, make sure you wash your fingertips and thumbs, as well as your wrists, because these will come into contact with food. Your hands should be dried with disposable paper towels to reduce the spread of bacteria.

Figure 4.2.7 How to wash your hands properly

Teacher's tip

You should wash your hands for at least 20 seconds to wash them properly!

You should wash your hands:

- before you start any food preparation
- after touching your hair or face
- after using the toilet
- after using a handkerchief or tissue to cough or blow your nose
- after cleaning or putting rubbish into the bin
- after handling raw meat, poultry, seafood, vegetables or eggs
- after eating or drinking.

Your nails should be kept short and you should not wear nail varnish when preparing food as it may flake off into the food.

Personal hygiene rules for the kitchen

- Don't cough or sneeze near food.
- Don't touch your head, especially your mouth, nose and ears.
- Don't brush your hair in the food room or with your apron on.
- Long hair should be tied back or covered.
- Wounds, such as cuts and scratches, should be covered with a coloured waterproof plaster/dressing.
- Wear a clean apron to protect the food from bacteria on your clothes.
- Don't prepare food if you are unwell with a tummy bug, or coughs and colds as you could spread bacteria onto food.

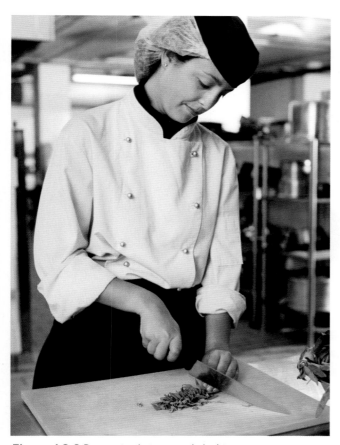

Figure 4.2.8 Protective hairnet and clothing

Clean work surfaces

Work surfaces in kitchens should be kept clean so they are free from bacteria. Work surfaces should be cleaned before any food preparation takes place, during food preparation and at the end of the practical session.

Work surfaces should be cleaned with hot, soapy water using a clean cloth. An **anti-bacterial spray** may be used afterwards, which will destroy virtually all the bacteria on the work surfaces. Anti-bacterial sprays should only be used after the work surface has been cleaned with hot soapy water, as they kill bacteria but are not designed to remove grease and dirt.

Separating raw and cooked food and the use of separate utensils

Colour coding in the kitchen helps to prevent the spread of bacteria from raw to cooked food.

You will have learnt about how colour-coded equipment helps to prevent the spread of bacteria from raw to cooked food in Topic 4.1 Food spoilage and contamination. See page 261.

Any food that is cooked and ready to eat should be protected from raw foods. There are normally lots of bacteria in raw food, but once it has been cooked, most of the bacteria are destroyed. If the cooked food comes into contact with raw food, it can become contaminated (this is called **cross-contamination**) and could lead to food poisoning.

If you are preparing food, for example at a barbecue, you need to have separate plates and utensils for raw and cooked food to avoid cross-contamination of bacteria from raw to cooked food.

> ### Key words
> **Anti-bacterial spray** is a clear spray that kills 99.9 per cent of bacteria; it should be used after surfaces have been wiped with hot, soapy water.
>
> **Cross-contamination** means bacteria spreading onto food from another place, for example hands, work surfaces, utensils.

Figure 4.2.9 Use separate utensils for raw and cooked food

Cooking food for the correct time

Some food can safely be eaten raw, for example most fruit and vegetables once they have been washed and or peeled.

Other foods, such as meat, poultry and most seafood, needs to be cooked, not just to improve the texture and flavour of the food, but to kill harmful (pathogenic) bacteria that may cause food poisoning. Although it is possible to eat some meats rare (for example, beef steak), some meat and all poultry must be cooked right through to the middle to ensure the bacteria are destroyed and the food is safe to eat.

Why can you eat a rare beef steak but not a rare beef burger?

Most bacteria is on the outside surface of meat, therefore, when the meat is cooked, the outside of the meat has most contact with the heat and is quickly destroyed. Inside the steak there are fewer bacteria.

With beef burgers, as the meat has been minced, the bacteria are mixed right through the meat to the centre of the burger. This means because the bacteria are inside the burger, the centre needs to be cooked as much as the outside to ensure thorough destruction of bacteria. Therefore, the only safe way to eat a burger is 'well done'. The inside temperature should reach at least 75°C.

Figure 4.2.10 Beef burgers should be thoroughly cooked

Serving food

Ideally, food should be served as soon as it has been cooked. This will ensure the bacteria have no time to grow. If this is not possible, it should be quickly cooled down and then chilled or frozen before being reheated (if applicable). Alternatively, it may be kept hot at 63°C or above before serving. Food should be served with clean utensils such as tongs or other implements to avoid cross-contamination. You should avoid touching food when you are serving it if this is possible. Plates should be the appropriate temperature for the food, so cold if being used for cold food and hot if being used for hot food; these will help to keep food out of the temperature danger zone.

Remember – hot food should never be put in the fridge – cool within 90 minutes to room temperature and then refrigerate. Alternatively, a blast chiller will cool your food down within a very short space of time

Temperature control of food

Temperature probes may be used for:
- checking to see whether food is properly **defrosted** before cooking, especially poultry and joints of meat
- checking to see whether cooked food has reached a safe temperature of 75°C or over
- checking to see whether ready-to-serve food is still hot (63°C or above)
- checking to see whether reheated food has reached at least 75°C; note only reheat food once.

As hot food should not be put straight in the fridge, it should be quickly cooled to room temperature first (about 20°C) within 90 minutes.

Key word

Defrosted means when frozen food has been removed from the freezer and left to stand in the fridge, until all ice crystals have melted.

How to use a food temperature probe

Figure 4.2.11 Using a food temperature probe

- Clean and **disinfect** the probe before and after each use (anti-bacterial wipes are useful for this, but should be used once only).
- Insert the probe into the thickest part of the food (where appropriate) and wait for the reading to settle before you take the temperature.
- Take care not to touch the baking tin or a meat bone with the tip of the probe.
- Leave the probe in place until the temperature stabilises.
- Temperature probes should not be put inside a fridge or on hot surfaces, as this can damage them.
- To check your temperature probe is working, crush some ice in a beaker with a little cold water, the temperature should be between –1°C and 1°C. Then test it with the steam of a boiling kettle, it should be between 99°C and 101°C.

Key word

Disinfect means to kill bacteria.

Teacher's tips

- Use a temperature probe to help keep food out of the temperature danger zone (5°C to 63°C).
- A temperature probe should be cleaned and disinfected each time it is used to avoid cross-contamination of bacteria.

Defrosting food

Frozen food should be defrosted before cooking in most cases, although some food can be cooked from frozen (see page 273). Once defrosted, the food should be treated as fresh and used as soon as possible to prevent the bacteria having time to multiply.

Some foods, for example chicken, should be thoroughly defrosted before cooking. Bacteria will be alive in the centre of the food. Unless the heat of the oven penetrates through to the centre of the chicken, bacteria may survive the cooking process. This is because, if the chicken is cooked without being fully defrosted, it will take much longer for the heat of the oven to penetrate to the centre of the chicken, which will give bacteria more time in the temperature danger zone and so time to grow. Also, it will extend the normal cooking time but the person cooking may not realise this. It could mean that the inside of the chicken is undercooked and more likely to carry food poisoning bacteria.

Defrosting should be planned – some large turkeys, for example, can take several days to defrost. The frozen food should be put in a large container with a lid. The defrosting food should be covered and put in the fridge on the correct shelf, to reduce the chance of cross-contamination.

Keep the defrosting food away from other foods, utensils and work surfaces.

Never re-freeze defrosted frozen food.

Reheating food

Reheated cooked food is a major cause of food poisoning. When reheating food, it needs more than just warming up.

When reheating food, it should reach an inside temperature of 75°C, which will destroy most bacteria in the food. If reheating in the microwave oven, make sure the food is evenly heated by stirring or turning the food during the reheating process. This will make sure the food is cooked properly, avoiding **'cold spots'** in the food.

Some **spore-forming bacteria** may not have been killed by the cooking process. Also, after cooking you could contaminate food with your hands or though cross-contamination (for example; using the same knife to cut raw and cooked chicken).

Other rules for reheating

- Keep food in the fridge (out of the **temperature danger zone**) until you are ready to reheat it.
- Keep food covered and handle it as little as possible.
- Divide food into smaller quantities so the reheating time is reduced.
- Heat food to at least 75°C.
- Serve reheated food straight away.
- Don't reheat cooked food more than once.
- Throw away any reheated food that is not eaten.

High-risk foods

High-risk foods are the most likely foods to cause food poisoning. Extra care should be taken when preparing and cooking foods that are high risk.

You will have learnt about high-risk foods in the section on micro-organisms and enzymes in Topic 4.1 Food spoilage and contamination. See page 251.

Washing fruit and vegetables

Some fruit and all vegetables should be washed in cold water before being eaten. Some fruit, such as bananas and oranges, are peeled, so these won't need washing. However, there are some fruit, such as melons, that are served in a dish with the skin on and these should still be washed as the melon and juice may come into contact with the skin while it is being eaten. Washing may be carried out in a colander under running water and then, for some vegetables such as lettuce, spun in a salad spinner. Some vegetables such as spinach should be washed in several changes of water to remove mud and other debris. The water should be changed until it runs clear to ensure it is clean. Fruit and vegetables may also be dried with paper kitchen towel.

Key words

Cold spots can be found in foods reheated in the microwave, if they are not stirred or turned during the reheating process.

Spore-forming bacteria refers to bacteria that can produce spores, which protect the bacteria from high temperatures, acids and disinfectants. Normal reheating doesn't destroy them.

Temperature danger zone is the range of temperatures between 5°C and 63°C, where most bacteria can easily multiply.

Key word

High-risk foods are ready to eat moist foods, usually high in protein that easily support the growth of pathogenic bacteria and do not require any further heat treatment or cooking.

Practical activity

Plan and make a two-course evening meal suitable for a family of one adult and two young children aged 2 and 4 years.

Figure 4.2.12 A fruit coulis is a thick fruit sauce

Main course

1 Find a recipe for falafels, meatballs or fishcakes.
2 Demonstrate your knife skills in the preparation of ingredients for these – for example, when finely chopping the onion and parsley.
3 Serve these with some fresh salad.
4 Suggest a starchy carbohydrate that could be served to complete the meal.

Dessert

1 Find a recipe for a baked dessert that includes a fruit coulis.
2 Use a jug or hand-held blender to make the coulis.
3 Evaluate your practical work, including information about how you prevented cross-contamination when making this meal. Describe how you safely used a temperature probe to check that the falafels, meatballs or fishcakes were cooked through and note what safe temperature was reached.

Use these sentence starters to help you write your evaluation, or you can write your own sentences:

For example: When I shaped the falafels I made sure I was hygienic by _____.

To check the falafels were cooked, I _____.

To prepare the salad safely I _____.

To prepare the fruit coulis hygienically I _____.

Evaluation

For the Practical activity above:
1 Include a time plan which includes a column for food hygiene and safety precautions from storing the food to serving the meal.
2 Describe how you carried out other tests for readiness on the dessert, including observation of the colour change and then using a skewer or 'poke' test.
3 Name the high-risk foods in your meal and how you prepared and served these safely to ensure they did not become contaminated with bacteria.

Check your knowledge and understanding

1 Suggest reasons why personal hygiene is important when preparing and cooking food.
2 Describe how to wash your hands properly.
3 Name **three** situations when you should wash your hands and explain why.
4 Give reasons why nail polish should not be worn when preparing and cooking food.
5 Explain why it is important to wear a clean apron.
6 Describe the ways you can avoid cross-contamination at a barbecue.
7 Explain why beef burgers should always be cooked until 'well done'.
8 Explain why it is important to disinfect a temperature probe before and after use.
9 Give reasons why chicken should be completely defrosted before cooking.
10 State the correct temperature for safe reheating of food and explain why it is important.
11 Describe what you should do with food that has been reheated once, but not eaten.

Section 4 Practice questions: Food safety

Multiple choice questions

1 Food poisoning is caused by: (1 mark)
   a) Spoilage bacteria
   b) Pathogenic bacteria
   c) Yeasts
   d) Enzymes

2 Which food below is a high-risk food?   (1 mark)
   a) Raw chicken
   b) Cheese salad
   c) Pickled onions
   d) Peanut butter sandwich

3 Which one of the following is the safest place to store raw meat
   in the fridge?   (1 mark)
   a) On the top shelf, near the ice box
   b) On the bottom shelf
   c) On the shelf above cooked food
   d) On the coldest shelf

4 How can ready-to-eat food be contaminated?   (1 mark)
   a) Using colour-coded chopping boards
   b) Using a clean dishcloth to wipe up spills
   c) Using the same tongs to pick up raw and cooked sausages at a barbecue
   d) Using a cover over food

5 The temperature of a fridge should be: (1 mark)
   a) 0 to below 5°C
   b) 2 to 11°C
   c) −4 to 1°C
   d) −5 to 1°C

Other question types

6 Name **three** micro-organisms that cause food to spoil. (3 marks)

7 List **three** conditions that micro-organisms need in order to multiply. (3 marks)

8 Name **two** foods on which moulds are most likely to grow. (2 marks)

9 Identify the different signs of food spoilage. (3 marks)

10 Micro-organisms are essential for the production of some foods. Name **one** of these foods. (1 mark)

11 Discuss ways to reduce the risk of food poisoning when buying and storing food. (9 marks)

12 Name **three** pathogenic bacteria that can cause food poisoning. (3 marks)

13 Suggest **two** ways to store dry food such as flour to prevent it from spoiling. (2 marks)

14 Explain how you can prevent food poisoning when storing and preparing food in the home. (9 marks)

15 Explain the difference between 'best before' and 'use by' dates. (4 marks)

16 Outline the advice that you would give someone on how to ensure the safe use of freezers and frozen foods. Give reasons for your answer. (9 marks)

17 Complete the following sentences about temperature control:
The temperature of a freezer should be below _____ °C.
The temperature danger zone is between _____ and _____ °C.
When reheating food the internal temperature should reach _____ °C. (4 marks)

18 Suggest some good advice to give somebody who is going to buy a new chopping board. (2 marks)

19 Explain the importance of good personal hygiene when preparing and cooking food. Make reference on ways to prevent cross-contamination in your answer. (6 marks)

SECTION 5
Food Choice

This section includes the following topics:

5.1 Factors affecting food choice

5.2 British and international cuisine

5.3 Sensory evaluation

5.4 Food labelling and marketing

Section 5 Practice questions

TOPIC 5.1 FACTORS AFFECTING FOOD CHOICE

Factors that influence food choice

Learning objectives

In this section you will learn about:

- the different factors that may influence food choice
- how to cost a recipe
- how to modify the cost of a recipe.

Activity

1 Draw a spider diagram of what you ate yesterday. Alongside each food identify a reason why you choose that food.
2 Compare your reasons with other students in your class.
3 In your groups make a list of how people choose food to eat.

There are many different factors that will influence what we choose to eat. Initially, we learn our food choices from our parents, but as we grow older the influence of friends and other factors in society become significant.

Figure 5.1.1 A family eating together

The factors that may influence us are shown in the diagram below.

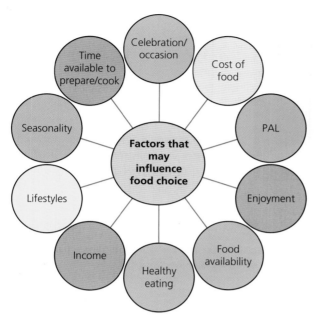

Figure 5.1.2 Factors that may influence food choice

Physical activity level (PAL)

How active we are may influence our choice of food. Our energy and nutrient requirements vary according to our age, sex, body size and levels of activity.

It is important that our food intake is balanced with our energy expenditure, so that we maintain a healthy weight.

- If you eat more food than you need, and you have a low **physical activity level (PAL)**, any excess energy is stored as fat.
- If you eat less food than you need, and have a high PAL, then the fat stores in the body are used up.

To maintain a healthy weight the energy taken in as food needs to balance the energy used up during activity.

Key words

Physical activity level (PAL) is the amount of physical activity you do each day, for example sitting, standing, running and exercise.

Figure 5.1.3 A celebration meal

Celebration/occasion

Food can play a vital role in any celebration or special occasion.

Some examples of celebrations where food plays a role include:
- birthdays and anniversaries
- weddings, christenings, funerals
- retirement parties
- special events or religious festivals in the year such as Easter and Christmas – these are often associated with specific foods (see Religious reasons for making food choices on page 299).

Activity

List six celebrations or special occasions in which food plays a part. Can you name any specific foods that are eaten on such occasions?

Many of us choose to eat out for special occasions and there is a wide variety of places to eat and prices to suit all budgets.

Cost of food

The cost of food can vary from shop to shop, and in different areas of the country. Supermarkets offer a range of food products at different costs.
- The popularity of value brands has grown considerably. Discount food retailers can offer very competitive pricing on selected products.
- Foods are often cheaper in a supermarket than in a corner shop where you are paying for convenience.
- The success of own-brand foods in supermarkets has meant that there are now different ranges offered at different costs. Shops now offer a wide variety of ranges from value ranges to premium.

Many people will look at ways in which they can save money when choosing food by:
- planning meals carefully so no food is wasted
- looking for the special offers in supermarkets
- shopping at the end of the day for reduced items, which have a shorter shelf life.

Practical activity

1 Protein foods, such as meat, fish and poultry, are generally more expensive foods. Mind-map a range of dishes, suitable for main meals for a family, that use protein from less expensive sources, such as eggs, cheese and pulses (lentils, chickpeas).
2 Make one of these dishes in your next practical lesson.

You will have learnt about costing when meal planning in Topic 2.3 Nutritional needs and health. See page 152.

AQA GCSE Food Preparation and Nutrition

Research activity

1. Use the internet or visit three different shops and compare the costs of the foods in the table below. Copy and complete the table with the cost of each item in the three different shops.

Foods	Cost: shop 1	Cost: shop 2	Cost: shop 3
1.5 kg own-brand self-raising flour			
250 g Cheddar cheese			
12 large eggs			
800 g white sliced bread			
1 pint of milk			
250 g soft margarine			
100 g instant coffee			
250 g teas bags			

2. Write a paragraph on your findings.

Extension activity

It is possible to budget for food with careful planning. Copy and complete the table below to show how it is possible to reduce costs when feeding a family.

Shopping for food	Choosing food	Preparing and cooking food

Enjoyment and preferences

For most people eating food is an enjoyable experience. We choose foods we like to eat because they provide enjoyment and meet an emotional need. The smell, taste, texture and appearance of food stimulate all of the senses.

There are some foods we enjoy eating and others we don't. Everyone has unique likes and dislikes. These preferences develop over time, and are often influenced by personal experiences. Parents usually feed their children the foods they enjoy, which can influence a child's eating preferences for the rest of their life.

Activity

1   Make a list of ten foods you like and identify a reason why you like them – think about appearance, taste and texture.
2   Make a list of ten foods you don't like and identify a reason why you dislike them.
3   Compare your answers with other members of the class. Make a list of the most common reasons for liking and disliking food.

Food availability

In the UK, we have access to a wide variety of foods, whereas people in developing countries often have access to a more limited variety and quantity of foods.

The choice of food available in the UK has increased greatly in recent years. This is because of new developments in transport, preservation and storage of foods. It is also because we import both foods that we cannot grow in this country and those we can. This means that much of our food is available all the year round, even when it is out of season. We can buy any food we want at any time of the year, but out of season it may be more expensive to buy.

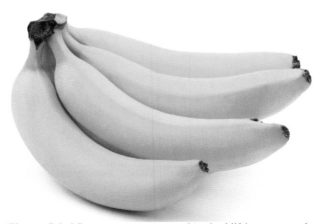

Figure 5.1.4 Bananas are consumed in the UK but grown abroad

Healthy eating

Eating healthily is an important consideration when choosing food. The range of 'healthy foods' offered for sale has increased.

Greater public awareness of the potential risks to health of a high-fat diet, and of eating a diet high in salt and sugar, has contributed to the rise in the availability of 'healthier' foods. A wide range of reduced-fat, fat-free, low-calorie, sugar-free and salt-free food products now exist. The increase in the number of consumers participating in slimming diets and following specialist, low-carbohydrate or high-protein diets has also widened the choice of products available.

Interest has grown in healthy convenience foods, as consumers become more concerned about health and diet and are increasingly lack the time to prepare healthy meals, and possibly also the knowledge to do so. Retailers and manufacturers make food products to meet this demand (for example, 'low-fat' ready meals).

Income

The choice of food purchased is affected by household income. Households with two wage earners may have more **disposable income** (this is the money left over for saving or spending after taxes are subtracted from income). Research suggests that more money is being spent on ready-to-eat 'premium' food products and some of those who have more disposable income want higher-quality food with minimal preparation.

The amount of money available affects both the quantity and variety of food that can be purchased. Research suggests more high-fat and high-sugar foods may be chosen if income is limited. Fruit and vegetables may not be purchased as they can be expensive. Most of the major food retailers offer their own brand of value ranges on key food products, which may be a less expensive option for those on lower incomes.

The Office for National Statistics (ONS) Family Spending Survey states that 11 per cent of income is spent on food. The average weekly expenditure on food and non-alcoholic drinks in 2013 was £58.80:

- £15.60 of this was spent on meat and fish.
- £4.30 was spent on fresh vegetables.
- £3.30 was spent on fresh fruit.

Key word

Disposable income is what money is left over for saving or spending after taxes are subtracted from income.

Lifestyles

Food choices have been affected by lifestyle and social changes. The main recent social changes include:

- both parents working
- an increase in people living alone
- people working longer hours and travelling longer distances to work.

People have busy lifestyles. More women and men are now both working full time, which can reduce the amount of time and motivation they have to cook meals every evening. Working parents can find preparing meals after working all day tiring and for convenience choose to eat outside the home, or purchase ready meals or part-prepared food products.

As the number of people living alone has increased, the number of single-portion ready meals purchased and consumed has grown tremendously.

Many people now travel greater distances to work. This means they have less time for breakfast and will often eat on the move. Increasingly, food products reflect our more flexible lifestyle (for example, protein shakes that can be consumed quickly and on the move). People who work longer hours may choose to eat more ready meals due to tiredness and a lack of motivation to cook a meal.

Due to busy lifestyles within families, there is often less emphasis on eating family meals together. Family members may have activities in the evenings, so quick snacks or ready meals are more convenient and family members may not all eat together every day.

Seasonality

Some foods are **seasonal**, which means they are only available at certain points in the year. People choose to eat seasonal foods because they can be:

- plentiful and therefore often cheaper
- locally produced
- fresher.

Figure 5.1.5 Strawberries growing in a field

In the UK, developments in preservation and storage of foods, and developments in transport allowing us to import out-of season foods mean that much of our food is available all the year round (although it may be more expensive to buy when it is out of season).

Time of day

The time of day can have an impact on the food choices we make. We tend to choose different foods to eat at breakfast, lunchtime and evening meal. Breakfast is an important meal of the day as blood sugar can be low in the morning. Students who eat breakfast have better levels of concentration in the morning.

Time available to prepare and cook

Due to people's lifestyles being so busy there is less time available to prepare and cook meals. Non-work time can be limited, so the time taken up by shopping for food, preparing meals, cooking and washing-up means ready meals are very appealing.

Consumers are demanding greater convenience from food products, and there are many products on the market designed to save us time. Grated cheese, prepared salads and pre-chopped vegetables are examples of foods designed to save time with meal preparation.

Other factors that may influence food choice

- **Peer pressure** plays a role in our food choices – we may choose certain foods to fit in or to be liked and accepted. Peer pressure can particularly have an impact on teenagers, who may be influenced by what their friends are eating.
- Information in the **media** will also influence food choices. Food scares, such as the discovery of horse meat in some processed foods, can have an impact on what we choose to eat. The media also uses advertising techniques to persuade us to make particular food choices. What celebrities choose to eat can have an impact on our choices; some young people may want to copy these celebrities – aspiring to look and be like them.
- There are always new **fashions and trends** emerging, which may influence our food choice. Examples of current food trends include an increase in the popularity of kale, juicing and the use of spiralisers to create starters.

Figure 5.1.6 Juicing

Research activity

Do some internet research into current food trends and write a report on what you think will be fashionable to eat in future years.

Activity

Summarise the factors that may influence food choice by copying and completing the table below.

Factor	Explanation
Physical activity level (PAL)	
Celebration/occasion	
Cost of food	
Enjoyment and preferences	
Food availability	
Healthy eating	
Income	
Lifestyles	
Seasonality	
Time available to prepare and cook	
Other factors	

Costing recipes

As explained earlier, cost is an important factor that may influence the foods we choose to eat and has an impact on our recipe choices.

It is an important skill when preparing and cooking food to know how much a recipe is going to cost to make.

You can use a table such as the example below to help you present information when costing a recipe.

Ingredient used	Total amount of ingredient used in grams/ millilitres	÷	Packet weight in gram/millilitres	X	Cost of ingredient to buy in pence	=	Cost of the amount of ingredient used in pence
Low fat spread	50		500		110		11
Flour	50		1500		80		3
Semi-skimmed milk	568 (1 pint)		568		45		45
Cheddar cheese	75		350		425		91
							Total cost: 150

Table 5.1.1 Costing a cheese sauce

When working out how much a recipe costs to make, you may need to do some calculations.

For example, in the recipe above for cheese sauce, 75 g of Cheddar cheese is needed. Cheddar cheese costs £4.25 for 350 g. To work out the cost of 75 g of Cheddar cheese:
- £4.25 is divided by 350 g to get the amount for 1 g.
- This is then multiplied by the amount used – 75g.

The cost of 75 g of Cheddar cheese is £0.91.

You may also need to work out the cost per portion. So, for example, if the sauce in the example above serves four people, and you need to work out the cost per portion, you need to divide the total cost (£1.50) by 4 – the cost per portion is £0.38.

To help you with recipe costing, you could use an Excel spreadsheet or computer software.

Making modifications to a recipe to decrease the cost

There are many ways in which recipes can be modified to reduce cost. For example:
- using cheaper protein foods, such as cheese, pulses, beans and eggs
- changing the method of cooking – for example, cooking vegetables in a microwave to save fuel costs
- buying loose produce not pre-packed – for example, loose onions and apples
- using value products rather than branded or premium-range products.

If we use the cheese sauce as an example, we could modify the cost of the recipe by buying value ingredients:
- Low fat spread – 500 g of branded low fat spread costs £1.10; supermarket own-brand low fat spread costs £0.89; supermarket value brand low fat spread costs £0.55.
- Flour – 1.5 kg of branded flour costs £0.80; supermarket own-brand flour costs £0.78; supermarket value brand flour costs £0.45.

- Milk – 568 ml of organic milk costs £0.58; non-organic milk costs £0.45.
- Cheese – 350 g of branded cheese costs £4.25; supermarket own-brand cheese costs £4.00; supermarket value brand cheese costs £2.50.

Research activity

1 Visit mysupermarket.co.uk and cost the recipe for a Victoria sandwich cake in the table below using:
   i) named brand ingredients
   ii) supermarket own brand ingredients
   iii) value products.
Identify the differences in cost.

2 Copy and complete the table, using the supermarket own brand prices to cost each ingredient used and the total cost of the recipe.

Ingredient used	Total amount of ingredient used	Cost of ingredient to buy	Cost of the amount of ingredient used
Low fat spread	150 g		
Flour	150 g		
Caster sugar	150 g		
Eggs	3		
Jam	50 g		
		Total cost:	

3 The Victoria sandwich cake will be cut into six portions. How much would it cost per portion?

Extension activity

The ONS Family Spending Survey (2016) states that £58.80 a week is the average amount spent on food by a household. This is about £8.40 a day.
1 Plan a day's menu for £8.40 for a single person.
2 Describe the ways in which you could make savings when buying and preparing the ingredients for the meal.
3 Show how you calculated the cost.

Check your knowledge and understanding

1 List **three** factors that may influence what we choose to eat.
2 Give **two** reasons why the choice of food in the UK has increased.
3 State how much the average family spends on food per week.
4 Name a social change that has had an impact on food choice.
5 State **one** advantage of eating foods in season.
6 Name **two** cheaper protein foods.

Food choices

Learning objectives

In this section you will learn about:
- how food choices are influenced by religion and culture
- how food choices are made for ethical reasons
- the medical conditions that affect food choices.

Cultural reasons for making food choices

Our food choices can be influenced by our **culture**. Culture includes our laws, morals, customs and habits – all of these have an influence on what we choose to eat and why. Many cultural groups have guidelines regarding acceptable foods, food combinations, eating patterns and eating behaviours. Following these guidelines creates a sense of identity for the individual and of belonging to the group.

Ethical and moral reasons for making food choices

Demand for ethically produced foods is increasing. More and more people are making decisions on what to eat based on ethical reasons. People want to have information on the production methods, the ingredients, the country of origin, and how far the foods they buy and eat have travelled (**food miles**).

Some ethical reasons for food choice include **not** buying food because:
- the animal has been killed (vegetarians)
- the food has been **intensively farmed** in poor welfare conditions
- the food has been **genetically modified**
- too many chemicals have been used in its production
- the food has high food miles and therefore a large **carbon footprint**.

CERTIFICATION MARK

Figure 5.1.7 RSPCA Assured logo

Religious reasons for making food choices

Food is very important for many different faiths. Many religions have specific rules relating to food, and have celebrations and festivals where specific foods are eaten at specific times.

Key word

Kosher refers to food that is allowed to be eaten because it is considered clean (in Judaism).

Jews (Judaism)

- Jews do not eat shellfish or pork.
- They do not eat dairy and meat in the same meal – for example, you cannot eat chicken and eggs together, or milk and beef.
- They only eat meat that has been slaughtered in a specific way in order to be called **kosher**. Kosher means that a food is allowed to be eaten because it is considered clean.

Jews have many major festivals where specific foods are eaten:

- Passover is celebrated by a special meal and the eating of matza, which is unleavened bread.
- Rosh Hashanah is the Jewish New Year, where a special meal is eaten and apples are dipped in honey.
- Yom Kippur is a day of fasting and prayers when families eat before the sun sets and then fast for 24 hours.
- Hanukkah is the festival of lights, where a lot of food is eaten to celebrate, including fried foods.

Figure 5.1.8 Apples dipped in honey celebrating Rosh Hashanah

Hindus

- Hindus do not eat beef or any beef products – this is because they consider the cow to be a sacred animal.
- They will use milk because no animal is killed during the process.
- Many Hindus are vegetarians, which comes from the principle of Ahimsa (not harming).
- Most Hindus don't drink alcohol.

Hindus celebrate Diwali – the festival of lights – by exchanging sweets.

Figure 5.1.9 Sweets used as gifts for Diwali, festival of lights

Sikhs

- Sikhs do not eat beef or any beef products because they also believe that the cow is a sacred animal.
- Many Sikhs are vegetarians.
- Many Sikhs will not eat **Halal** or Kosher meat, as they believe the animals are not killed humanely.
- Devout Sikhs do not drink alcohol.

Sikhs celebrate Guru Nanak's birthday, when Sikhs eat their sacred pudding Karah Parshad, made from equal parts butter, sugar and flour.

Muslims (Islam)

- Muslims do not eat pork.
- They will only eat Halal meat, which has been slaughtered in a very specific way.
- They won't eat seafood without fins or scales such as crab and prawns.
- Many Muslims do not drink alcohol.

Muslims have a month-long fast called Ramadam, during which they don't eat during daylight hours. To celebrate the end of Ramadam, they have a three-day festival called Eid where special food is eaten.

Buddhists

- Most Buddhists try to avoid intentionally killing animals and are vegetarians.
- Monks and nuns are usually very strict, and some monks fast in the afternoon.

Buddhists celebrate Wesak, where they eat only vegetarian food and don't drink any alcohol.

Rastafarians

- Rastafarians eat food which is natural, pure, clean or from the earth this is called I-tal. They try to avoid food which has been chemically modified or contains artificial additives.
- Rastafarians do not eat pork.
- Rastafarians eat fish, but will not eat fish more than twelve inches long.
- Rastafarians eat a large amount of vegetables, because they are from the earth.
- Food is prepared without salt.
- The oil used is coconut oil.
- They do not drink alcohol.
- They do not drink milk or coffee, but will drink herbal tea.
- Rastafarians eat and drink large amounts of fruit and fruit juice.

Figure 5.1.10 Christmas dinner

Christians

- Before Easter many Christians will observe Lent, where they give up certain foods for a period of 40 days and 40 nights.
- Some Catholics fast on Fridays and during the run-up to Lent.
- Christmas is a time of celebration where traditional foods are eaten, such as turkey and mince pies.
- At Easter, hot cross buns and Simmel cake are often eaten.

Research

Select one religious group (for example, Muslims, Jews or Hindus) and write a report on how religious belief can influence food choice and the celebration of festivals.

You could use these websites to help you:

- www.bbc.co.uk/religion/religions
- http://www.foodafactoflife.org.uk/

Practical activity

Plan and make a dish for a celebration in a religion with which you are familiar.

Activity

Copy and complete the table below.

Religion	Foods not eaten	Festivals and celebrations
Jews		
Hindus		
Sikhs		
Muslims		
Buddhists		
Rastafarians		
Christians		

Extension activity

Do some research into other cultures or religions not included in this book, and explain what people following these religions can and can't eat. Identify any festivals and celebrations these cultures or religions have.

Medical reasons for making food choices

Some people cannot eat certain foods without becoming ill. This can be either because they have a specific medical condition or because they experience a reaction to certain foods.

Food intolerances

Some people have a sensitivity to certain foods, which can give them symptoms such as nausea, abdominal pain, joint aches and pains, tiredness and weakness. This is called a **food intolerance**.

These are very general symptoms so it can be difficult to diagnose a food intolerance. The most effective way is for a person to stop eating the food they think they are intolerant to and see if they feel better. If they do feel better, they can then try eating the food again to see if they become unwell again.

Two examples of food intolerances are lactose intolerance and gluten intolerance.

Lactose intolerance

As already discussed in Section 2 (page 165), you read that **lactose** intolerance is fairly common in the UK. It means the body is unable to digest the sugar in milk. The sugar in milk and dairy products is called lactose.

An enzyme in the digestive system called **lactase** is needed to break down lactose. People with lactose intolerance don't produce enough lactase and so the milk sugar lactose stays in the digestive system, where it ferments and produces gases.

People with a lactose intolerance need to avoid all dairy products and foods that contain dairy products in their ingredients, including the following:
- milk, cheese, yoghurt, butter and cream
- processed foods that may contain milk
- pizza and lasagne
- ice cream and cheesecake
- chocolate, chocolate mousse, cakes and biscuits.

> **Key word**
> **Food intolerance** is a sensitivity to some foods.
> **Lactose** is the sugar naturally found in milk.

There are alternatives to dairy, which those who have a lactose intolerance can eat, including:
- soya milk and soya products
- dark chocolate
- lactose-free products.

Figure 5.1.11 Lactose-free products

Practical activity

Carry out a sensory analysis of some lactose-free products such as lactose-free yoghurt, cheese and milk. Carry out a comparison taste test of these products compared with ordinary milk, yoghurt and cheese.

Gluten sensitivity

Coeliac disease is a bowel disease; people with coeliac disease have a sensitivity of gluten. A person suffering from coeliac disease is called a **coeliac**. Gluten is a protein present in a number of cereals, including wheat, rye, oats and barley.

Symptoms of the disease include:
- weight loss (because a coeliac cannot absorb food properly)
- diarrhoea
- lack of energy, which may also leave people tired and weak
- loss of appetite and vomiting
- children may not gain weight or grow properly
- general malnutrition, as a coeliac cannot absorb enough nutrients.

Key words

Coeliac disease is a bowel disease; a sensitivity to gluten.

Coeliac is a person suffering from coeliac disease.

People with coeliac disease need to follow a strict gluten-free diet, which can be done with careful thought and planning.

Wheat is an important and nutritious staple in the UK diet and is found in a number of foods, including flour, baked products, bread, cakes, pasta and breakfast cereals, all of which must be avoided by coeliacs.

Many foods are naturally gluten-free, including fresh meat, fish, cheese, eggs, milk, all kinds of vegetables and fruit, rice, maize, potatoes, nuts, seeds, pulses and beans (as long as they are not cooked with wheat flour, batter, breadcrumbs or sauces). People with coeliac disease should check the labels on food products carefully to ensure they are safe for them to eat. Food products that have been certified gluten-free have the Crossed Grain symbol on them.

Figure 5.1.12 Crossed Grain symbol

Activity

List the foods that a coeliac can and cannot eat.

Gluten-free flour is now readily available in health food shops and in most supermarkets. It is possible to bake cakes, biscuits and bread using gluten-free flour.

There are also gluten-free baked products available to buy ready-made.

While it may sometimes be necessary to prepare separate meals if flour is being used, there are many occasions where everyone, including those with a gluten intolerance, can eat the same meal – for example a roast dinner, where the coeliac might just avoid the gravy if it is thickened with flour.

Practical activity

1 Prepare and make one of the following recipes using gluten-free flour in a practical session.

Gluten-free fairy cakes

75 g low fat spread

75 g caster sugar

2 eggs

1.5 ml $\left(\frac{1}{4}\text{ tsp}\right)$ vanilla essence

75 g gluten-free flour

1 tbsp milk

2.5 g $\left(\frac{1}{2}\text{ tsp}\right)$ baking powder

Figure 5.1.13

Method

1 Preheat the oven to 200°C.
2 Beat all ingredients together until smooth and creamy.
3 Divide into 12 cases.
4 Bake for 10–12 minutes.

Chocolate brownies

100 g low fat spread

100 g gluten-free flour

200 g caster sugar

1 tsp baking powder

3 eggs

75 g dark chocolate chips

Figure 5.1.14

Method

1 Preheat the oven to 180°C.
2 Gently melt the low fat spread.
3 In a separate bowl mix flour, sugar and baking powder.
4 Beat in eggs, low fat spread and chocolate chips.
5 Pour into a greased and lined tin, 15 cm by 20 cm.
6 Bake for 30 minutes.

2 Write up your results using the title 'Does gluten-free flour produce acceptable results?'.

Food allergies

A person has a **food allergy** when they experience an allergic reaction to a specific food. If the reaction is a bad one, it could give the following symptoms:

- a skin rash
- itchiness of skin, eyes, mouth
- swollen lips, face, eyes
- difficulties in breathing.

In severe cases, it can bring about **anaphylactic shock**. An anaphylactic shock is serious – the person will develop swelling in their throat and mouth, making it difficult to speak or breathe. This can lead to death if appropriate treatment such as an epi pen is not used quickly.

Figure 5.1.15 A person using an epi pen

There are 14 allergens which need to be emphasised on a food label, if they are used as ingredients in a pre-packaged food. They are:

- eggs
- milk
- fish
- crustaceans (for example crab, lobster, crayfish, shrimp, prawn)
- molluscs (for example mussels, oysters, squid)
- peanuts
- tree nuts (namely almonds, hazelnuts, walnuts, cashews, pecans, brazils, pistachios, macadamia nuts or Queensland nuts)
- sesame seeds
- cereals containing gluten such as wheat (spelt, Khorasan wheat/Kamut), rye, barley, oats, or their hybridised strains
- soya
- celery and celeriac
- mustard
- lupin
- sulphur dioxide and sulphites (at concentration of more than ten parts per million).

(https://www.food.gov.uk/science/allergy-intolerance/label/labelling-changes)

It is really important that, if you know you have an allergy or an intolerance, you manage your diet carefully. You need to:

- Read all food labels very carefully to check for any ingredients to which you may be allergic or intolerant.
- Check with the chef if you are eating out at a restaurant. Many menus are now clearly labelled with details of ingredients, but it is still important to check.
- Be aware of what those around you are eating – some people with nut allergies can be affected by being near someone eating peanuts, for instance.

Check your knowledge and understanding

1 State **two** ethical beliefs that need consideration when choosing food.

2 State **one** food that each of the following will not eat:
   i) Jews
   ii) Hindus
   iii) Muslims

3 Name some foods a person who is lactose intolerant must avoid.

4 Name a symptom of an allergic reaction.

5 State **two** foods that may cause an allergic reaction.

TOPIC 5.2 BRITISH AND INTERNATIONAL CUISINE

Traditional British cuisine

Learning objectives

In this section you will learn about:

- food and food products from British cuisine
- the distinctive features of British cooking, including equipment, methods of cooking, eating patterns and presentation styles.

Cuisine is a style of cooking characteristic of a particular country or region, where the food has developed historically using distinctive ingredients, specific preparation and cooking methods or equipment, and presentation or serving techniques.

Figure 5.2.1 A map of Britain

Traditional British cuisine

Although Britain imports many of the foods we eat today, we still produce crops such as barley, wheat and potatoes. Livestock farming is important too, with chickens, turkeys, beef and dairy cows, pigs and sheep reared for food.

The staple foods of Britain are meat, fish, poultry, potatoes, flour, butter and eggs. Many of our dishes are based on these foods. Other traditional British foods include bread, bacon, cheese and fruit such as apples, plums and pears.

Distinctive features and characteristics of cooking

The preparation techniques traditionally used in British cuisine are covered in Topic 1 Skills 2 and 3 on pages 12–27. They are: filleting, slicing, mashing, shredding, scissoring, snipping, scooping, crushing, grating, peeling, segmenting, de-skinning, de-seeding, blanching, shaping, piping, blending and juicing.

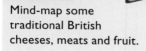

Activity

Mind-map some traditional British cheeses, meats and fruit.

The traditional foods grown in Britain are:
- vegetables, such as potatoes, onions, leeks, sprouts, peas, beans
- fruit, such as apples, strawberries, plums and rhubarb
- herbs, such as mint, chives and sage.

The traditional foods reared in Britain are:
- beef, lamb, poultry and game, pork, bacon and ham
- cheese, such as Cheddar, double Gloucester and Stilton
- milk.

The traditional foods caught in Britain are:
- fish, such as mackerel, cod, haddock and salmon.

Traditional dishes made in Britain

There are also many different variations of sweet puddings and cakes in Britain, but each of them usually begins with the same basic ingredients of milk, sugar, eggs, flour and butter.

Many of the desserts use home-grown fresh fruit, such as raspberries or strawberries, and custard and cream. Examples include:
- Pasties
- meat pies
- crème anglaise
- scones
- Victoria sandwich cake
- trifle
- Bakewell tart
- Lancashire hotpot
- shortbread
- custard
- bread and butter pudding
- mince pies
- Yorkshire pudding
- steamed puddings
- fruit crumbles and fruit pies.

Extension activity

Trace the outline of the map of Britain (Figure 5.2.1). Investigate some traditional British foods and research which area of Britain they come from, labelling them on the map (for example, asparagus is grown in Evesham in the Midlands).

Equipment and cooking methods used

The cooking techniques traditionally used in British cuisine are covered in Topic 1 Skills 4 and 6 on pages 28–55. They are: baking, roasting, casseroling, grilling, barbecuing, braising, steaming, boiling, poaching, simmering and frying.

The equipment commonly used in British cuisine includes:

- casserole dishes – deep round containers with lids, made of glass, ceramic or metal
- moulds and tins for baking pies and tart –round, oval or square in shape, with deep sloping sides, made of metal or glass
- Yorkshire pudding tins – tins very similar to patty (bun) tins, made of metal
- roasting tins for roasting large joints of meat, made of metal
- a variety of cake tins, usually made of metal.

Eating patterns

Breakfast

The classic 'full English breakfast' can include eggs, bacon, sausages, baked beans, fried tomatoes, black pudding and mushrooms. It is often accompanied by toast and butter or fried bread. Most people do not eat a full English breakfast every day – some have a full English breakfast as **brunch**, which is a combined breakfast-lunch meal, or as a weekend or holiday treat.

Most people in the UK will have cereals, yoghurt and fruit, toast or porridge for breakfast.

> **Key words**
>
> **Brunch** is a combined breakfast-lunch meal.
>
> **Elevenses** is an old-fashioned name for a mid-morning snack.

Figure 5.2.2 A full English breakfast

'Elevenses'

This is an old-fashioned name for a mid-morning snack. **Elevenses** usually consists of a cup of tea or coffee and some biscuits usually eaten around 11 am.

Lunch

On most days, people in the UK eat a light, quick lunch – such as a sandwich, soup or salad – usually between 12 and 2 p.m. Few people now eat a large cooked hot meal at lunchtime.

The exception is on a Sunday, when it is traditional to have a Sunday lunch – also called 'Sunday roast', because the main dish is roasted meat such as roast beef, pork or lamb.

Tea

Tea is an afternoon snack, a mid-afternoon version of 'elevenses'. Afternoon tea is popular in tearooms and cafés and is served in the afternoon. It consists of a pot of tea with a selection of small sandwiches, pastries and cakes. A 'cream tea' (which originally comes from Cornwall, Devon and Dorset) consists of a pot of tea, scones, jam and clotted cream.

Figure 5.2.3 Afternoon tea

Practical activity

In groups of four, plan, prepare and serve some dishes suitable for brunch. Present your dishes as a group.

Dinner

'Dinner' usually means an evening meal, which most people eat between 6 p.m. and 9 p.m. This meal is often a time to socialise with family or friends after work or school. Some of the traditional British dishes are typically served as the main evening meal (for example, Shepherd's pie, toad in the hole or sausage and mash).

Supper

Sometimes the evening meal is called supper. Supper tends to be served a bit later – usually between 7.30 p.m. and 9 p.m. – and is normally home-cooked. It is an old-fashioned term; most people now call it dinner.

Many people in the UK will have three meals a day – breakfast, lunch and an evening meal.

Practical activity

1 Plan, make and present a traditional British main meal that could serve a family of four. The meal should cost less than £10 to produce.
2 Suggest an accompaniment, sauce or gravy that would be suitable to serve with your meal.

Presentation styles

When plating up food to be served, particularly roast meals, then the classical plating style can be used. This method of styling uses the idea of a plate being a clock:

- between 12 and 3 are vegetables
- between 9 and 12 are starchy foods
- between 3 and 6 is the main component of the meal.

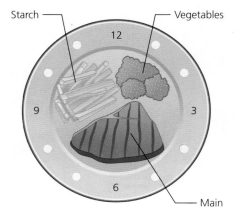

Figure 5.2.4 Plating food

Sauces can be used effectively to present food by pouring it over the food, drizzling it, dotting it or serving it in a small jug alongside the food.

Garnishes and decorations can be used successfully to enhance the dish.

You will have learnt more about garnishing and decorating dishes in Topic 1 Skill 3 Preparing fruit and vegetables. See page 25.

Savoury food is often served in oval dishes or on oval plates, and sweet food on round plates or in round dishes.

When serving cakes, biscuits or scones, the food is sometimes placed on a doily and then on a plate, or on a tiered cake stand.

International cuisine

Learning objectives

In this section you will learn about:
- food and food products from different international countries
- the distinctive features of different types of international cooking, including equipment, methods of cooking, eating patterns and presentation styles.

As more people from other countries are living in Britain, and there is also a greater opportunity for travel, our eating habits have changed. Many traditional British dishes are being replaced by ones that have originated from other countries and cultures. Some examples of these are discussed on the following pages.

Italy

There are different regions in Italy, each will have a different climate. This has an impact on what is grown and cooked there.

- The north of the country is cooler and mountainous; rice is grown and the land is mostly used to rear animals for cured meats.
- The south of the country is hotter, so more crops are grown, such as fruit and vegetables, most notably tomatoes, olives and lemons.

Women have played a huge role in Italian cuisine, with recipes being passed down the generations through mothers and grandmothers.

Family and food are very important to Italians.

Figure 5.2.5 A map of Italy

Distinctive features and characteristics of cooking

Italy has a long history of fine cooking dating back to Roman times, when the banquets were famous. Italian flavours are very simple and they often use only local ingredients. Vegetables are home-grown or from a market, and Italians are guided by the seasons and what is available at the time.

As with other Mediterranean diets (which include French, Greek and Spanish cuisines) the Italian diet is based on fresh vegetables, herbs and fish, as well as olive oil. Mediterranean diets are associated with good health, and people following a Mediterranean diet are thought to be at lower risk of heart disease and stroke.

The traditional foods grown in Italy are:
- bread, which is often baked every day
- olives, which are eaten fresh, preserved, or made into olive oil
- tomatoes, which are often sun-dried or cooked to make pasta sauces
- pasta – usually fresh and then filled or dried
- Arborio rice
- fruit and vegetables, such as lemons.

The traditional foods reared in Italy are:
- meat, which is then cured and made into products such as salami, pancetta, Parma ham and prosciutto
- cheeses, such as ricotta, mozzarella, Parmesan and pecorino.

The traditional foods caught in Italy are:
- fish – in plentiful supply from the coast, such as tuna, swordfish, shellfish and squid.

Traditional dishes made in Italy are:
- gnocchi – potato dough
- pizza
- risotto
- pasta dishes, such as lasagne, cannelloni, spaghetti Bolognese, spaghetti carbonara, ravioli
- tiramisu – an Italian trifle
- pannacotta – an Italian dessert made with cream and gelatine
- arancini – balls of rice coated in egg and breadcrumb
- minestrone soup
- biscotti
- ice cream
- espresso coffee – the Italians invented espresso, and a weaker version served with frothed milk – cappuccino.

Practical activity

In groups, make a batch of gnocchi dough. Shape it and cook it with a simple tomato sauce.

Figure 5.2.6 Traditional Italian dishes

Equipment and cooking methods used

Two main methods of cooking are boiling, especially for pasta and gnocchi, and baking. Pizza and bread are often cooked in a wood-fired oven, or in a traditional oven on metal trays.

Pasta and gnocchi are staple foods in Italy, so the right equipment is needed to make and cook them:
- a pasta machine
- a large saucepan for cooking the pasta
- a slotted spoon for removing it
- a gnocchi board – useful for shaping the gnocchi correctly.

Figure 5.2.7 A pasta machine

Eating patterns

The Italians take a huge amount of pleasure in their food, and enjoy social or family occasions where food can be shared.
- In Italy, the breakfast is usually light, consisting of coffee – either espresso or cappuccino – and some bread rolls.
- This is then followed by two main meals – one is served in the middle of the day; the other in the evening, usually quite late.
- The Italians love to have three or more courses for their meals over a long period of time.

Traditional meals consist of:
- starters – antipasto
- soup/pasta or risotto
- fish, meat or poultry, with accompaniments of either vegetables or salad
- dessert – fruit or cheese
- coffee at the end of a meal.

Presentation styles

The Italians often present their food very simply; the presentation style can be described as rustic. Large (wooden) bowls of food with serving spoons are often used; there is an emphasis on sharing.

Extension activity

Trace the outline of the map of Italy. Investigate some traditional Italian foods and research which area of Italy they come from, labelling them on the map (for example, lemons from Sorrento).

Spain

Spanish food is influenced by the fact that three sides of the country have a coastline, so seafood is one of its main ingredients.

● Northern Spain has a heavier rainfall so it is good for growing crops and rearing animals on the greener pastures.
● In the hotter south of the country, many types of fruit are grown, including grapes for making wine and sherry.

Figure 5.2.8 A map of Spain

Distinctive features and characteristics of cooking

Cooking is simple and rustic using plenty of fish and vegetables. Like the Italians, the Spanish like to use seasonal and local produce. Very little dairy foods are eaten, such as milk and cheese, and the fat used is olive oil. They also love their food and enjoy sharing it – tapas (as described below) is characteristic of this style of sharing food.

The traditional foods grown in Spain are:
● vegetables, such as tomatoes, fresh peppers, chillies called pimentos
● herbs and spices, such as saffron, cumin, coriander seeds, paprika and smoked paprika
● fruits, such as grapes, figs, melons, dates and apricots
● bread, such as pan de cebada
● olives – also made into olive oil.

The traditional foods reared in Spain are:
● meat, such as pork, poultry
● preserved meat, such as black, red and white sausages, chorizo, hams – jamon and Serrano

The traditional foods caught in Spain are:
● fish, for example, anchovies, shellfish and preserved fish: squid and calamari

Traditional dishes made in Spain are:

- paella – a dish made from rice, saffron, chorizo and shellfish
- frittata – similar to an omelette, with eggs, potatoes and vegetables such as onions and peppers
- gazpacho – a soup that is served cold
- bacalao – salted cod or preserved fish
- cocas – similar to pizza
- tapas and pinchos – a range of small snacks such as a bowl of olives, empanadas, prawns, slices of frittata, sausages, cured meats
- stews, such as bean and sausage stew, fish stew
- churros – like piped lengths of doughnut dipped in melted chocolate, often sprinkled with cinnamon and sugar
- magdalenas – small cakes like fairy cakes
- polvorones – almond biscuits.

Figure 5.2.9 Paella

Practical activity

In groups of four, plan, prepare and serve some items suitable for tapas. Present your dishes as a group.

Extension activity

Prepare and cook traditionally Spanish paella at home for your family.

Figure 5.2.10 Churros

Equipment and cooking methods used

Some common methods of cooking include: simmering, stewing and braising, deep-frying (for churros) and baking for bread, cakes and biscuits.

Specialist equipment includes:
- a **paellera** – the traditional large round pan with shallow sides used for cooking paella.
- a garlic crusher – very useful, particularly one where you don't have to peel the garlic first, because Spanish stews and soups tend to use a lot of garlic.
- ceramic and glazed pots – used for both cooking and serving food. A **cazeula** is a glazed terracotta dish that comes in different shapes and sizes.
- an espresso coffee pot – coffee is served after every meal so most people use one of these.
- a pestle and mortar – useful for grinding herbs and spices, to make dips for tapas and to grind saffron and salt together for paella.

Eating patterns
- Because of the hot climate, the Spanish have breakfast early – usually coffee and rolls.
- Lunch is around 2 p.m. to allow time in the afternoon for a 'siesta'. The meal is usually light, consisting of stew or soup, fruit and then coffee.
- The evening meal is eaten much later and is often meat, potatoes, salad, fruit and coffee.
- Before the evening meal, the Spanish may eat tapas.

Presentation styles

Very much like the Italians, the Spanish often present their food very simply, in terracotta bowls to share.

China

China has a rugged, quite barren landscape. In China, they grow potatoes, tomatoes and aubergines as these work well in poor-quality soil. In the north of the country, wheat and millet is grown. The wheat is used to make noodles. In the south of the country, rice and soya beans are grown. There are very few cattle because there is little grazing land.

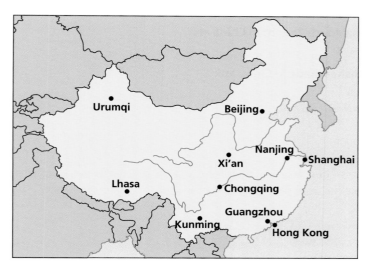

Figure 5.2.11 A map of China

Distinctive features and characteristics of cooking

Chinese food is traditionally quick to make, with an emphasis on colour, flavour and texture. Much of the food is stir-fried in a wok, or steamed in a bamboo steamer – both healthy ways of cooking.

Figure 5.2.12 Chinese-style stir-fried vegetables

The traditional foods grown in China are:

- noodles and rice – the staple carbohydrate foods of China
- grains
- vegetables, such as Chinese leaves, water chestnuts, bamboo shoots and beansprouts
- fruit, such as lychees and kiwi fruit.

The traditional foods reared in China are:

- pork, duck and chicken.

The traditional foods caught in China are:

- fish and seafood.

Traditional dishes made in China are:

- Almond jelly
- almond cookies
- egg tarts
- red bean buns
- spring rolls
- soups/broths – generally extremely light, with meat, vegetables and sometimes noodles added to a clear broth, for example Wonton soup
- dumplings
- prawn toasts
- beef/prawn chop suey
- Szechuan pork or beef
- crispy duck/Peking duck
- fried rice
- sweet and sour noodles.

Chinese food is often flavoured with ginger, garlic and soy sauce.

Equipment and cooking methods used

The cooking methods used are: stir-frying, steaming and deep-frying. In a very traditional Chinese kitchen there is no oven. Essential equipment includes:

- a wok – so food can be stir-fried quickly
- a bamboo steamer – often placed on top of a wok with boiling water in it
- a steel, spider meshed scoop – used to scoop out deep-fried foods from a wok half-filled with oil
- clay pots with lids – used to braise foods.

Activity

List ingredients suitable for using in a stir-fry.

Figure 5.2.13 Chinese serving dish and cutlery

Eating patterns

- Soups are an important part of the Chinese diet. They are not often eaten at the start of a meal but throughout or at the end. Soups are also eaten for breakfast.
- At meal times, the Chinese family will have four or five dishes at the same time. Each person has a small bowl with rice in it.
- Sweet foods are known as desserts; they are often eaten separately or as part of a meal. They are also eaten as snacks. Foods such as fruit or rice-based puddings are popular and will end the meal.
- The traditional drink with a meal is tea. This is usually green tea and is drunk without milk, sugar or lemon.

Presentation styles

The Chinese consider cooking to be an art, and they like to present their food beautifully using a range of colourful foods. They prepare vegetables to make them look as attractive as possible – they cut vegetables into julienne strips, and cut on the diagonal. The Chinese tend to have several dishes of food served in small bowls. You would then eat a little of everything, with chopsticks and large rounded spoons.

Practical activity

Make a traditional Chinese dish.

Figure 5.2.14 Chinese food is usually colourful and beautifully presented

India

India is a vast country made up of several states. There are huge variations in climate, religion and therefore foods. It is a mainly agricultural country, primarily growing crops.

- In the north of India, wheat is the staple food used to make chapatis.
- In the south, rice is the staple food and curries with plenty of sauce are served. There is more rainfall in the south, so many vegetables are grown there.

India has a coastline, so fish is also a major industry.

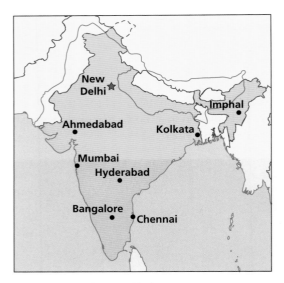

Figure 5.2.15 A map of India

Distinctive features and characteristics of cooking

A traditional oven is rarely used in India; food is cooked on hobs. Indian food is often fried, and a variety of spices are blended and used to enhance the flavour of the food cooked.

Activity

Name as many spices as you can that are used in Indian cooking.

Research activity

Investigate the different flavours used in Indian cooking. Find out which spices are used to give a korma or tikka flavour to make garam masala.

The traditional foods grown in India are:
- wheat, maize and basmati rice
- lentils
- spices, such as cumin, turmeric, chilli, cardamom
- tea, such as Darjeeling, Assam
- vegetables, such as aubergines, okra and peppers.

The traditional foods reared in India are:
- goat, lamb and chicken.

Traditional dishes made in India are:
- tandoori – fish, meat or chicken marinated in yoghurt and spices and then cooked in an oven
- naan bread
- tikkas
- kormas
- biryanis
- parathas
- poppadoms
- samosas
- onion bhajis
- lentil dahl
- kulfi – a sweet dish made from boiled milk
- lassi – a non-alcoholic drink
- mango, mango syllabub.

Equipment and cooking methods used

- In northern India, food is often cooked in a **tandoor**, which is a clay oven heated by charcoal. The tandoor is used to cook naan bread and tandoori dishes.
- Food is fried, often in ghee or oil. Ghee is made by heating butter, then leaving it to set.
- Food is stir-fried using a karhai, which is the Indian version of a wok. The karhai can also be used to simmer, deep-fry and steam.
- A flat griddle pan is useful for cooking chapatis and parathas.
- Many spices are blended or ground together to make Indian dishes, so a mortar and pestle or a small electric chopper/blender is useful.

Figure 5.2.16 Traditional Indian dishes

Eating patterns

- Entertaining in the home is very popular in India and, in a similar way to China, all the dishes are placed on the table at once and shared.
- About 80 per cent of Indians are Hindu, and around 18 per cent are Muslims. This influences what they choose to eat.
- Indians enjoy snacks – there are many street markets selling food. Snack food is also prepared in the home for any visitors.
- Desserts are not usually served every day. They are only served on special occasions, such as for the festival of Diwali.

Key word

Thali is a stainless-steel plate on which Indian food is served.

Figure 5.2.17 A thali

Presentation styles

In central India, small dishes of food are served on a tray or a **thali**. A thali is a stainless-steel plate, on which several small dishes are placed around the edge. In the centre, there are pickles, breads, rice and poppadoms.

Research activity

1 Find out about the cuisine of another country, for example Japan, France, Africa, Mexico or the USA.
2 Write a report on your findings. Use the following headings:
   i) Distinctive features and characteristics of cooking
   ii) Equipment and cooking methods used
   iii) Eating patterns
   iv) Presentation styles
   v) Give examples of a traditional recipe

Practical activity

Plan, prepare and serve a sweet and a savoury dish which originates from a country of your choice.

Check your knowledge and understanding

1 What is the definition of cuisine?
2 Name **two** sweet traditional British dishes.
3 Describe a traditional Italian meal.
4 Explain why Chinese food is considered healthy.
5 Copy out and complete the following table:

Country	Specialist equipment used for cooking	Foods grown/reared/caught/made	Traditional dishes
Britain			
Italy			
Spain			
China			
India			

TOPIC 5.3 SENSORY EVALUATION

Sensory evaluation techniques

Learning objectives

In this section you will learn about:

- the **reasons** why sensory testing is carried out on food products
- how **taste receptors** and **smell receptors** work when you eat food
- the different sensory testing **methods** that can be used
- how to **carry out** sensory testing.

Teacher's tip

Sensory testing is a crucial component of both the Non-Examined Assessments.

Sensory evaluation

The sensory evaluation of foods is very important. Food products (including fresh, processed and ready prepared foods) need to have many qualities if they are to be acceptable to a wide variety of people.

Reasons why sensory evaluation is carried out

Sensory evaluation is carried out on food products for a number of reasons. It aims to:

- ensure that a food product meets a consumer's expectations, for example to make sure a strawberry yoghurt has the appearance, taste, texture or mouthfeel and smell or aroma that is expected
- ensure that changes to an existing food product mean the product remains acceptable
- guarantee that food products remain consistent over time
- find out how a food product compares to other similar products, for example with a competitor's product
- ensure that a food product meets the original specification
- monitor the quality and shelf life of food products over time.

What is sensory evaluation?

When you eat food, you are judging the:

- appearance
- taste
- texture/mouthfeel
- consistency
- smell or aroma.

The characteristics of food that affect our organs or senses are known as **organoleptic qualities**. Judging food based on these characteristics is sensory evaluation.

Activity

Sensory vocabulary

Words are used to describe each of these features. Using the word bank below (and your own words) complete the table with the vocabulary that could describe each feature.

Appearance	Taste	Consistency	Smell

Word bank

burnt   crispy   sweet   creamy   golden brown   spicy

fruity   yellow   lumpy   salty   greasy   dry

sour   soft   chewy   fishy   rubbery   creamy

Key words

Organoleptic qualities are characteristics of food that affect our organs or senses.
Taste buds detect sweet, sour, salt and bitter tastes.

How the taste receptors work

Taste influences the selection of food to eat. Food must be dissolved in water, oil or saliva to have a taste.

Taste is detected by **taste buds**. There are about 10,000 taste buds on the surface of the tongue. Each taste bud is a pore, which contains very sensitive tiny hairs. When food dissolves in a pore the tiny hairs send messages to the brain about the food. The taste buds will tell the brain if the food is sweet, sour, bitter or salty.

The number of active taste buds in the mouth decreases with age. This means that people become less sensitive to the flavour of food as they get older and they may prefer more spice, sugar or salt in their food.

Basics of taste

There are **four** basic tastes that you can recognise: sweet, salt, sour and bitter. The tastes can be grouped as:

- **Sweet:** ingredients that produce a sweet taste include sugar, honey and artificial sweeteners.
- **Salt:** a salty taste comes from table salt or foods that have a high natural salt content, such as seafood.
- **Sour:** natural acids found in foods can give them a sour taste, such as Greek yoghurt, lemons, rhubarb. Foods preserved in the man-made acid vinegar also have a sour taste.
- **Bitter:** foods that offer a bitter taste are unsweetened coffee, dark chocolate and tea.

Umami or savouriness

A 'fifth' taste called **umami** has recently been found to have its own taste receptors. Umami literally means 'delicious flavour'. It is produced by glutamates. Glutamates are the main part of many proteins, found in protein-rich foods, such as meat, mushroom and fermented products (for example, soy sauce).

Umami provides food with a savoury or meaty flavour, which has been recognised in Asian cooking for a long time.

The tongue is covered in taste buds. The map below is only a guide to the most sensitive areas for a particular taste on the tongue. You can still taste bitterness on the tip of your tongue, but you are more sensitive to it at the back of the tongue.

> **Key word**
>
> **Umami** provides food with a savoury or meaty flavour.

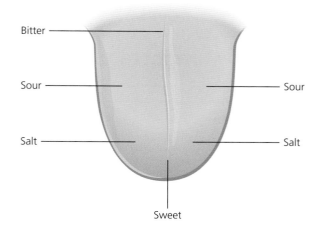

Bitter — Sour — Sour — Salt — Salt — Sweet

Figure 5.3.1 The tongue map

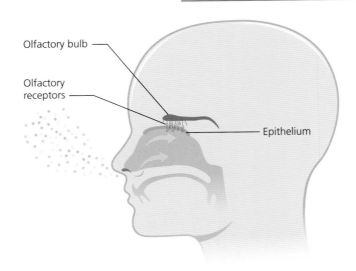

Olfactory bulb

Olfactory receptors

Epithelium

Figure 5.3.2 The olfactory system

How the smell receptors work

The nose is a vital organ for taste as well as smell. The **taste buds** on the tongue can only detect sweet, sour, bitter and salt. All the other 'tastes' are detected by the **olfactory system** in the nose.

The olfactory system is the 'smell device' and allows you to identify aromas and smells.

The smell or aroma of food makes a gas. When this gas enters the nose it passes over the **epithelium**. The epithelium contains more than 10 million receptors and is able to identify different smells. The **olfactory receptors** send messages to the brain about the smell. At this point, you will know whether you like the smell or not!

It is easier to smell hot food than cold food. This is because hot food produces more gas for the olfactory system to detect. This is why the smell from warm bread is stronger than the smell from ice cream.

The taste buds and olfactory system are absolutely crucial for ensuring food is enjoyable to eat. When we discuss food we often refer to its **flavour**. Flavour is the combined sense of taste, **mouthfeel** and aroma. Mouthfeel is the way a particular type of food feels in the mouth.

Key words

Taste buds detect sweet, sour, salt and bitter tastes.

Olfactory system is the body's 'smell device' and enables you to detect aromas and smells.

Epithelium contains scent receptors and can identify different smells.

Olfactory receptors send messages to the brain about the smells.

Flavour is the combined sense of taste, mouthfeel and aroma.

Mouthfeel is the way a particular type of food feels in the mouth.

Activity

Test to show how important smell is to the taste of food

Resources required

A small piece of peeled potato

A small piece of peeled apple (same shape as the potato so you can't tell the difference)

Process

1 Close your eyes and mix up the piece of potato and the piece of apple so you don't know which is which.
2 Hold your nose and eat each piece. Is it possible to identify the apple and potato without the sense of smell?

Check your knowledge and understanding

1 Explain why apple and raw potato are a good choice for this test.
2 Explain why it was difficult to detect the flavours without smell.

Sensory analysis tests

Sensory testing can be organised in different ways depending on what you are trying to find out. British Standards guidelines (BS5929) have been created, which the food industry has to follow when carrying out sensory testing.

The most frequently used sensory tests are:
- preference tests
- discrimination tests
- grading tests: ranking, rating and profiling.

Preference tests

Preference tests are sometimes called acceptance tests. Preference tests are used to find out if a food product is **acceptable** to the consumer.
- The information gathered from a preference test is very subjective because it involves asking for a personal opinion about a product.
- To ensure the results are reliable and valid, a large number of consumers are required to complete the test.

The main types of preference tests are **paired preference test** and **hedonic ranking**.

Key word

Preference test is used to find out if a product is acceptable to the consumer.

Paired preference test

The tester is given two samples of a food product and asked, Which sample do you prefer? A random number is assigned to each sample, and testers select the number of the sample they prefer. There are many uses for this test.

An example of a paired preference test

A school catering manager wants to introduce a new fruit drink.

Test objective: To find out which brand of soft drink should be sold in the school canteen.

Test design: 50 students, who buy fruit drinks, are invited to try two samples. The samples are served at the same temperature and at the same time. The students are asked to make a choice and complete a record sheet. The two different samples are given random numbers.

Paired preference test record sheet: This is an example of the record sheet.

Paired preference test record sheet
Taste the sample on the left first and then the sample on the right second.
Which sample to do you prefer?
Please circle one.
359   476

Test result: The catering manager will be able to find out which fruit drink is preferred by the students.

Activity

1   Complete a **paired preference test** in groups to find out your preferred fruit drink.
   - Make sure that the record sheets have two random numbers.
   - Serve the drinks in white plastic cups with a clear label.
2   Explain why the two drinks should be presented looking the same and at the same time.
3   It is a good idea to make sure that one sample isn't always tasted first. Why might this be important?

Hedonic ranking

Hedonic ranking is a preference test used to find out whether people like or dislike a product.

Hedonic ranking can be used for factory testing and for market research by finding out whether consumers like a product.

The tester is given one or more samples of a food product and is asked to rank them in order of preference. The test is used to establish the **best sample** from a group. A scale is used to rank the products.

Scales for hedonic tests can contain five, seven or nine ranks.

A five-point hedonic scale

Samples	Dislike very much	Dislike	Neither like or dislike	Like	Like very much
735					
451					
228					

Table 5.3.1 Example of a five-rank hedonic scale

A nine-point hedonic scale

A nine-point hedonic scale is often used in the food industry to find out consumer feelings about a food product. The nine-point scale is believed to be very reliable for showing consumer preferences.

These are the words used on the nine-point hedonic scale:

- Like extremely
- Like very much
- Like moderately
- Like slightly
- Neither like nor dislike
- Dislike slightly
- Dislike moderately
- Dislike very much
- Dislike extremely

Using the nine-point hedonic scale is too complicated for some consumers and alternatives have been developed. Symbols and very simple words can used.

Figure 5.3.3 A five-point hedonic ranking that can be used with young children

Discrimination tests

Discrimination tests are used to detect differences between two samples. They help a manufacturer to confirm the qualities of a product, for example testing whether reducing the fat content of a biscuit makes the biscuit harder.

Triangle test

The **triangle test** is a discrimination test. It is used to find out whether small differences between two products can be detected. Three samples are presented to the tester. Two of the samples are identical and one is different. The tester is asked to identify the **'odd one out'**.

An example of a triangle test

A café owner wants to change the fat spread they serve with their meals.

Test objective: To find out whether a full-fat spread is noticeably different from a lower-fat version.

Test design: Trained testers are used. Three samples are presented to each tester. Two are identical and one is different. Each sample is allocated a random number.

Triangle test record sheet: The actual number of testers who can correctly identify the odd sample are counted. This an example of the record sheet.

Triangle test record sheet
In front of you are three coded samples.
Two are the same and one is different.
Taste each sample in the order below.
Identify which sample is different.
Circle the code of the different sample.
819   390   736

Test result: If a significant number of testers can detect the low-fat spread the caterer may wish to try an alternative low-fat spread for testing and not risk making a noticeable change.

The triangle test is very useful for quality control and developing new food products. Newly developed products can be evaluated by finding out if a simple difference between the new and existing products can be identified.

Teacher's tip

This activity could be completed using a product made by the students. This could generate discussion on how to carry out sensory testing and to ensure **fair testing**.

Activity

1 Select **one** of the following food products to complete a triangle test or choose your own food product.
   - Fruit drink (full sugar and no added sugar)
   - Crisps (full fat and lower fat)
   - Digestive biscuit (original version and reduced fat)
   - Fruit yoghurt (original and fat-free)
   - Jam and plain cracker (original and reduced sugar)
   - Muffin (original and gluten-free)
   - Cheese spread (original and lactose-free)
   - Milk drink (full-fat and low-fat)
2 Design the record sheets and conduct the test. Remember that two samples are the same in each test.
3 Write up your findings. Could the testers detect the 'odd one out'?

Key word

Fair testing is when a test is carried out in carefully controlled conditions to ensure that the information gathered is reliable.

Grading tests

Grading tests are used to produce a ranking, rating and profiling of a product. These tests measure the strength of a specific sensory property, for example the sweetness of a fruit drink. Food samples are ranked in order of preference. Grading tests are useful because the results are easy to obtain and unskilled testers can be used.

The main types of grading tests are **ranking test**, **rating test** and **profiling**.

Ranking test

Ranking tests are used to measure the **strength** of a specific sensory property in a number of samples, for example the sweetness in biscuits. The tester will rank the samples in order. The sample that is strongest in the specified sensory property will be ranked first.

An example of a ranking test

A parent wishes to measure the saltiness of three cheeses before selecting one for their child's sandwiches.

Test objective: To find out which cheese is the saltiest.

Test design: Unskilled testers can be used as no specific skills are required. Each tester will taste the three different cheeses and rank them according to their saltiness. Each cheese is given a random number.

Ranking test record sheet: The most and least salty cheese can be identified. This is an example of the record sheet.

Ranking test
Please taste each of the coded samples in the order they are presented.
Rinse your mouth with water between each sample.
Rank the samples in order of saltiness. The most salty should be ranked at 1st.
Sample code _____   _____   _____
1st   2nd   3rd

Test result: The manufacturer may wish to reject a cheese thought to be very salty.

Rating test

Rating test allows people to rate the extent to which they either like or dislike **one aspect** in a number of similar food products. This could be the spiciness of a range of samosas. Alternatively, the tester could be asked to rate **different aspects** of one food product, for example the spiciness, aroma, colour and crispiness of one samosa.

An example of a rating test

A group of teenagers wishes to develop a new fruit smoothie. They are evaluating the smoothies already on the market.

Test objective: To find out which smoothie has the strongest fruit flavour.

Test design: Unskilled testers can be used as no specific skills are required. Each tester will taste the three different smoothies and rate them according to the strength of their fruitiness. Each drink is given a random number.

Rating test record sheet: This example shows how the results could be recorded. The tester will indicate where each sample sits on the scale. The fruit flavour in the smoothie could be rated on a scale of 1 (weak fruit flavour) to 9 (strong fruit flavour).

Fruit flavour									
Sample	1 weak	2	3	4	5	6	7	8	9 strong
106									
575									
761									

Test results: The manufacturer may try to replicate the drink with the strongest flavour or develop a new version.

The rating test is very useful to the food manufacturer because the extent of a particular sensory feature can be assessed, rather than just putting the products in order of preference.

Profiling

Sensory profiling tests are used to obtain a detailed description of the appearance, taste and texture of a food product.

Features such as mouthfeel, appearance, aroma, flavour and texture can be assessed separately or together in one profile. The results of the profiling test are plotted on a star diagram to give a visual profile of the product. This is called a **star profile**.

An example of a sensory profile test
A chef wishes to evaluate a new lemon-flavoured chicken.

Test objective: To find a detailed description of the chicken.

Test design: Trained testers must be used because judgements are difficult to make. Each tester will taste the chicken and rate it according to the strength of each descriptor on a scale of 1 to 10 or 1 to 5.

Profiling test record sheet: The example on the next page shows how the results could be recorded.

Sensory properties	Tester 1	Tester 2
Attractive	4	2
Crispy	6	5
Sweet	3	5
Moist	2	4
Fatty	8	9
Sour	9	9
Sharp	4	7
Chewy	8	2

Test results: The results are plotted to give a star profile for the chicken. If many testers have completed the evaluation, an average score of their judgements may be plotted on the graph.

This **star profile** shows that there is some disagreement over the chewiness of the chicken.

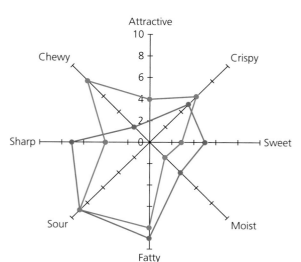

Figure 5.3.4 Star profile of lemon-flavoured chicken

Profiling test

1 Select **one** of the following foods:
   — Banana
   — Crispbread
   — Grapes
   — Bread
   — Dried apricots
2 Identify the sensory qualities you wish to measure.
3 Devise a profiling record sheet for your judgements.
4 Produce a star profile.

How to carry out a sensory evaluation

To make sure that a sensory evaluation produces reliable results, it is important to spend time setting up controlled conditions for the test. The guidelines below suggest how you can control the conditions for a sensory evaluation and ensure **fair testing**.

The testing environment

It is useful to have a testing room available for the sensory evaluation. The testing room should be a controlled environment, where distractions – including smells – should be removed.

● The lighting should be controlled. Coloured lighting is used to hide any visual differences between samples.
● The seating should isolate the testers from each other because they could communicate their reactions to the samples.

Individual testing cubicles are ideal for sensory evaluation.

The food testers

● A sensory evaluation can be carried out by untrained consumers or trained food tasters.
   — **Untrained consumer testers** can be used to taste-test foods. They are usually volunteers who belong to the target group at which the food product is aimed.
   — **Trained food tasters** can be used when it is necessary to identify subtle differences between food products. This requires special training before the sensory evaluation begins.
● All food testers should be in good health and free from any illness such as colds. Food testers should be non-smokers. Smoking and illness can dull the taste buds.
● The testers must not have strong likes or dislikes for the food being tested. This could influence their opinion about the food product.

The food samples

- The samples should be the same size, this is usually enough for two bites or sips. This ensures 'fairness' between the samples.
- Samples should be labelled with random three-digit numbers. The numbers 1, 2, 3, or A, B, C are not used because they could influence decision-making.
- The holding time before the sample is tested should be monitored. Some products can deteriorate if held for too long before testing, for example carbonated drinks can start to lose their fizziness once poured.

The testing equipment

- The plates, spoons or cups used to present the samples should be an identical shape, colour and size.
- **Food carriers** are sometimes used if the food product is usually eaten with another food. The food carrier should not interfere with the product being tested. Carriers can be bread, crackers or pasta. If cheese is being evaluated the carrier may be a cracker but the cracker must be completely neutral so it does not interfere with the flavour of the cheese.
- Water should be provided to cleanse the mouth in between each sample. The tester should also have a 30-second rest period between tasting each sample.

Practical activity

Comparison of homemade product and a ready-made product

1 Select a homemade product you can make that can also be purchased as a ready-made product. Possible ideas could include soups, falafels, pasta sauce and custard.
2 Make the homemade product and compare it with the ready-made product.
3 Use a sensory test of your choice to compare the outcomes. Conduct the sensory test and control the conditions as best you can in your school.

Check your knowledge and understanding

1 Name **four** types of tastes.
2 Explain **two** reasons why the food samples should look the same in a paired comparison test.
3 Name a test that requires trained food tasters.
4 Explain **two** reasons why testing should take place in a cubicle or in isolation from others.
5 Explain why it is important for the assessor to sip water between each sample.
6 Explain why random numbers are used to label the samples.
7 Discuss the importance of sensory testing for food manufacturers.
8 Discuss the advantages and disadvantages of **three** different types of sensory tests.

TOPIC 5.4 FOOD LABELLING AND MARKETING

Food labelling

Learning objectives

In this section you will learn about:
- how information about food is made available to the consumer
- the meaning of current food labelling
- the current nutritional labelling information
- how food marketing can influence food choice.

Food labelling is important to the consumer. It contains information provided by food businesses about their products and covers all food that is sold in shops, cafés, restaurants and other catering establishments.

Food labels provide information that will help us to:
- make informed decisions about the food we choose to buy
- store and cook the food we choose to buy correctly to prevent food poisoning
- establish the nutrient content of the food and how it contributes to our reference intake.

It is controlled by law to ensure that it is accurate, not misleading and safe.

Figure 5.4.1 Food labelling in a supermarket

The meaning of current food labelling

The mandatory and consumer information required on a label

New European regulations on food labelling came into force in December 2014. This new legislation provided controls on all the information on food labels.

Labels on food must be clear, easy to read and understand and must never mislead. Labels must show:

- the name of the food
- an ingredients list
- information on certain foods causing allergies or intolerances that are used in the manufacture or preparation of the food
- the net quantity of the food, weight or volume
- a date of minimum durability
- any special storage conditions
- the name or business name and address of the food manufacturer
- the country of origin
- instructions for use
- the alcoholic strength by volume (if required)
- a nutrition declaration – **mandatory** from 13 December 2016.

(Source: Food Standards Authority)

> **Key word**
> **Mandatory** means required by law.

The name of the food

- The name of the food cannot be false or misleading.
- The name should be precise enough that consumers know exactly what it is; for example, a quiche would be labelled with the main flavour (i.e. cheese and onion quiche).

An ingredients list

- Ingredients are listed in descending order, with the greatest quantity first.
- If any ingredient has been changed such as dried apricots, this must be indicated too.
- When ingredients are emphasised on the label, usually as part of the name of the product (for example, cheese and onion quiche), the quantity of the ingredient should be indicated.

Information on certain foods causing allergies or intolerances that are used in the manufacture or preparation of the food

It is really important that consumers read the label if they have an allergy or intolerance. An **allergen** is a substance that may cause an allergic reaction – in this case it is a food or ingredient.

The new legislation states that allergen information must now be highlighted in bold in the main ingredients list on the back of product packs. They were previously listed in a separate 'allergy information' box. All allergens – including gluten, milk and eggs – are now highlighted in bold, making them easier to identify. If there is a chance that allergens may come into contact with the ingredients then manufacturers should use an allergy advice warning.

Figure 5.4.2 Allergen label

The net quantity of the food

This is the weight or volume of the food.

A date of minimum durability

There can be some confusion about the difference between 'use by', 'sell by' and 'best before' dates. To clarify:

- **'Use by' dates** are usually given on high-risk foods such as soft cheeses, chilled meats, salads and sandwiches, which can go off quickly.
- The **'sell by' or 'display until' date** is aimed at shopkeepers not consumers, and is usually a few days before the 'use by' date, to allow some time for the customer to eat the food.
- **'Best before' dates** are given on foods that keep for longer, such as biscuits or canned foods. The food should be eaten before this date for quality purposes, but it is not usually harmful to eat it after the date.

Any special storage conditions

Storage conditions need to be given to ensure the food is stored safely. For example, a product may say 'once opened, store in the refrigerator and consume within three days'. It may say 'suitable for freezing'.

The name or business name and address of the food manufacturer

The name and address need to be provided on the food label in case a consumer wishes to contact them, particularly if they have a complaint about the food.

The country of origin

This must state clearly where the product has come from.

Instructions for use

The instructions for use must be detailed enough to make sure the food is correctly prepared or cooked. The time and temperature of cooking must be given in the case of raw poultry and meat.

The alcoholic strength by volume (if required)

When a product or drink contains more than 1.2 per cent alcohol it must be indicated on the label.

A nutrition declaration – mandatory from 13 December 2016

From December 2016, all foods must have the nutrient content of the product stated clearly.

Activity

1   Find a label from a ready meal package, stick it in the centre of a piece of paper and draw arrows to identify each piece of information.
2   Which ingredient is included in the greatest quantity and which in the smallest quantity?
3   How should the food be stored?
4   What are the preparation and cooking instructions?

The importance of food labelling

The information on a label is important to a consumer because:

- they may want to lose or maintain weight, so are looking for the fat or sugar content of the food.
- they may have a health condition, such as diabetes or high blood pressure, so they may want to check the carbohydrate content or the salt content of the food.
- they may have a severe allergy to certain ingredients (for example, nuts), so they need to check if the food contains those ingredients.
- if they need to complain about the food, they will need the manufacturer's name and address.
- they may have limited knowledge and experience of how to store, prepare and cook food so need these details.
- they may want to buy local produce, or be environmentally aware and will want to know where the food comes from.
- the information educates them about the food that they are buying.
- they can make more informed choices.

Activity

Copy and complete this table.

Information on a label	Reason why this information is important
The name of the food	
An ingredients list	
Information on certain foods causing allergies or intolerances that are used in the manufacture or preparation of the food	
The net quantity of the food, weight or volume	
A date of minimum durability	
Any special storage conditions	
The name or business name and address of the food manufacturer	
The country of origin or place of provenance of the food (if required)	
Instructions for use	
The alcoholic strength by volume (if required)	
A nutrition declaration – mandatory from 13 December 2016	

Current nutritional labelling information

From December 2016, nutritional labelling will be compulsory. Many supermarkets and food manufacturers are already following the new legislation. The labels on food must now contain precise and accurate information about the nutrients the food product contains.

Nutritional labels now include the following information:

- The energy content of food is stated in kilojoules (kJ) and kilocalories (kcal) per 100 g and per serving.
- Guideline daily amounts (GDAs) have been replaced by reference intakes (RIs). The percentage RI is used for fat, saturates, sugars and salt.
- There are new reference intakes for carbohydrate (260 g) and protein (50 g). (Previously, the old GDAs were carbohydrate 230 g and protein 45 g.)
- The RIs are expressed as a percentage that a serving provides. If there is space on the label, it also shows the actual RI figures for an average adult.
- There is no longer an RI for fibre.
- The new labels refer to 'saturates' instead of 'sat fat', 'sugars' not 'sugar' and 'salt' not 'sodium'.
- Energy values are not shown as a traffic light colour, but are shown in both kilojoules (kJ) and kilocalories (kcal).

The traffic light label

- Under the new legislation, on the front of the label, the 'wheel'-style traffic light system will change to a lozenge shape and include information on the percentage of the reference intake (RI), alongside the traffic light colours.
- The colours remain the same: high (red), medium (amber) or low (green) for amounts of fat, saturated fat, salt and sugar.
- The healthier choices are still the greens, followed by amber and fewer reds.
- Information is given on the types of fats, protein, fibre, carbohydrates and salt in the food or drink.
- This information is given per 100 g and per serving.

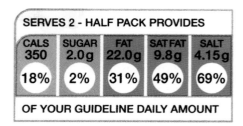

Figure 5.4.3 The traffic light label

List of nutrients

The legislation states how to provide the nutritional information on the back of the label. The nutrients/foods must be listed in the following specific order:

- energy
- fat
- saturates
- carbohydrate
- sugars
- fibre (not required by law)
- protein
- salt
- vitamins and minerals.

Manufacturers can state the nutrition information per portion, for example half a pie or one cracker, as long as this information is given in addition to the required per 100 g or per 100 ml information.

Nutrition claims

If the manufacturer wants to make a claim regarding nutrition or health there are now stringent rules about doing this, so as not to mislead the consumer. It is not possible to claim or make a suggestion that food can treat, prevent or cure any disease or medical condition.

These are some of the permitted nutrition claims:

- **Low energy** – the food product must not contain more than 40 kcal (170 kJ) per 100 g, or 20 kcal (80 kJ) per 100 ml for liquids.
- **Energy reduced** – the energy value is reduced by at least 30 per cent.
- **Energy free** – the food product does not contain more than 4 kcal (17 kJ) per 100 ml.
- **Low fat** – the food product contains no more than 3 g of fat per 100 g for solids or 1.5 g of fat per 100 ml for liquids .
- **Fat free** – the food product contains no more than 0.5 g of fat per 100 g or 100 ml. Manufacturers are also no longer allowed to state a product as 'x per cent fat-free'.
- **Low sugar** – the food product contains no more than 5 g of sugars per 100 g for solids or 2.5 g of sugars per 100 ml for liquids.
- **Sugar free** – the food product contains no more than 0.5 g of sugars per 100 g or 100 ml.
- **Low salt** – the food product contains no more than 0.12 g of sodium, or the equivalent value for salt, per 100 g or per 100 ml.
- **Salt free** – the food product contains no more than 0.005 g of sodium, or the equivalent value for salt, per 100 g.
- **High fibre** – the food product contains at least 6 g of fibre per 100 g.
- **High protein** – where 20 per cent of the energy value of the food is provided by protein.
- **Source of** vitamins or minerals – the food product must contain a significant amount of the vitamin or mineral for this claim to be made.
- **Light/Lite** – if the manufacturer states that products are 'light' or 'lite', it must meet the same requirements as for 'reduced'. There also has to be an explanation of what makes the food light or lite.

Health claims

Manufacturers can make a health claim to suggest there is a relationship between a food and health. Before a manufacturer can make a health claim, the claim is reviewed by the European Food Safety Authority, who will look at the scientific evidence and advise the manufacturer how to word the claim appropriately.

(Source: http://ec.europa.eu/food/safety/labelling_nutrition/labelling_legislation/index_en.htm)

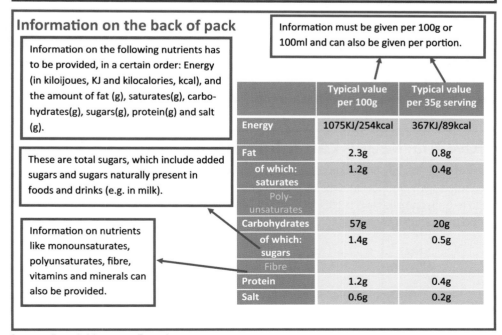

Source: British Nutrition Foundation

Figure 5.4.4 A quick guide to nutrition information on labels

How to interpret nutritional labelling

Food labels can be used to make healthier, safer and more informed food choices when choosing between products. For example, the consumer could choose:

- a sandwich with a higher fibre and lower salt content
- a pizza with a lower salt content
- cheese with a lower fat content
- cereal bars with a lower sugar content.

Food labels can help us to understand what nutrients food products contain. For example, teenage girls, who need fewer calories than teenage boys, may not get enough calcium and iron. They can use the label to help them choose foods that give a good supply of those nutrients.

The use of colour coding: red, amber, green on the front of packs, can help in the choice of foods with less fat, salt and sugars.

- A red label on the front of a pack means the food is high in something consumers should try to cut down on in their diet. It is acceptable to have the food occasionally, but these should be chosen less frequently and eaten in small amounts.
- An amber label means the food isn't high or low in the nutrient, so this is an acceptable choice for the majority of the time.
- A green label means the food is low in that nutrient. The more green, the healthier the choice.

Many foods with colour coding will have a combination of red, amber and green. When choosing between similar products, the consumer should choose foods with more greens and ambers and fewer reds, to ensure healthier choices.

The label also tells you the number of grams of fat, saturated fat, sugars and salt in what the manufacturer or retailer suggests is a 'serving' of the food.

Reference intakes (RIs) are on labels so that consumers can gain a better understanding of their daily intake of specific nutrients and in the process have a balanced diet.

Extension activity

Explain in detail the nutritional information that can be gained from the label in Figure 5.4.3.

How marketing can influence food choice

Marketing is identifying consumers' needs and wants, and using that information to supply consumers with products that match their needs and wants. In addition, the food products need to generate sales and profits for food retailers. There are many methods used to promote a food product to a consumer.

Media influences

People are strongly influenced by the media. Manufacturers spend millions every year on advertising food products through the media. It is expensive and usually involves advertising on television, the internet, radio, newspapers and magazines. It can be very effective, as the advertising may reach a wide audience.

Brand loyalty can be built upon and a carefully controlled image of the product can be created. Various promotional techniques are used by the media to build awareness of food retailers' and manufacturers' products and to influence shoppers to purchase. They can build loyalty to a particular brand or retailer. They can also make the consumer more aware of what is on offer and increase the likelihood of shopping around for a promotion seen on TV or online.

In-store marketing

All food retailers use some in-store methods to market and promote their products.

Buy one get one free (BOGOF) offers are an effective way of encouraging the consumer to try a new product or establish brand loyalty.

Price reductions and special offers are often used to attract consumers. For example, a discount off a purchase or a special introductory price can be used to attract the consumer. By printing coupons on the food product packaging offering a discount off a future purchase, customers may want to buy it at a later date. Retailers sometimes attract consumers by promoting a saving if two different products are purchased together, for example fresh pasta and a pasta sauce.

Figure 5.4.5 An in-store display of food products

Free samples to taste or try in store are another way of introducing a product to the consumer. These methods can sometimes be linked with money off coupons if a purchase is made.

Product placement is an important method of in-store promotion. Some retailers place more expensive items at eye level. Retailers also locate commonly purchased items, such as milk and eggs, at the back of the store so consumers have to walk through the entire store to access essential items. During this journey through the store, consumers are more likely to make other purchases.

In-store displays are particularly important when promoting seasonal items, such as Christmas party food and barbecue meats in the summer.

> ### Activity
>
> Look at a range of advertisements for snacks from magazines (free magazines from supermarkets are likely to have many advertisements and in-store promotions). Decide who the product is aimed at, and what nutritional claims the manufacturer states.
>
> Write a report on your findings and evaluate if this would influence whether you bought it or not.

Loyalty cards

Loyalty cards are available from many food retailers. Each time the card is used points are awarded to the consumer, which may be converted into 'money off' coupons for use in store or used to purchase goods and services from participating organisations.

The retailer is able to monitor consumer purchases. Retailers can identify a consumer's brand loyalties and preferences. The information can be used to increase sales and expand the range of products purchased.

Loyalty cards can be an effective way for a food retailer to target consumers with an established buying pattern into purchasing a more expensive alternative. They may post coupons to act as an incentive to try a more expensive but similar product.

Figure 5.4.6 A loyalty card

Meal deals

Some supermarkets offer meal deals where for a set amount of money you can choose from a combination of dishes for an evening meal (for example, a main course, side dish, dessert and a bottle of wine or non-alcoholic alternative for £10). Lunchtime meal deals are also available with sandwiches or alternatives, crisps, fruit and drinks. Careful choices by the consumer can mean they benefit from cost reductions in prices, when sandwiches, snacks and drinks are bought together instead of individually.

Check your knowledge and understanding

1 Give **two** reasons why labels are important to a consumer.
2 Name **three** items of information you would find on a label.
3 Explain the difference between a food labelled 'fat free' and a food labelled 'low fat'.
4 Name **three** ways in which a supermarket can promote new product ranges.
5 Suggest the advantages of buying a lunchtime meal deal.

Section 5 Practice questions: Food choice

Multiple choice questions

1 Which **one** of the following foods is **not** suitable for a Hindu? (1 mark)
   a) Beef
   b) Milk
   c) Carrots
   d) Apples

2 Which **one** of the following foods should a person with coeliac disease avoid eating? (1 mark)
   a) Fish
   b) Pasta
   c) Potatoes
   d) Cheese

3 Which **one** of the following foods is **not** a traditional dish in British cuisine? (1 mark)
   a) Roast beef and Yorkshire pudding
   b) Fish and chips
   c) Shepherd's pie
   d) Tapas

4 A preference test aims to find out: (1 mark)
   a) Whether consumers like or dislike a food product
   b) The sensory properties of a food product
   c) If small differences exist between two food products
   d) The strength of a sensory quality, for example sweetness

5 The ingredients list on a label is always in: (1 mark)
   a) Descending order, highest amount first
   b) Alphabetical order
   c) According to food groups
   d) Whatever way the manufacturer wants

6 A 'best before' date would normally appear on: (1 mark)
   a) A can of baked beans
   b) An egg sandwich
   c) A pack of ham
   d) Cheese

7 A red label on a food product means: (1 mark)
   a) Eat as much as you like.
   b) Don't eat it – it is harmful.
   c) You can eat it in moderation.
   d) Eat just once a week.

Extended questions

8   State **three** factors which may influence our choice of food.   (3 marks)

9   Takeaway foods are popular with many consumers.
    a) Explain why consumers choose to buy takeaway products
        instead of making the food themselves.   (4 marks)
    b) Explain some of the disadvantages of takeaway foods.   (4 marks)

10 Discuss a range of religious and cultural needs that manufacturers
    must consider when designing new food products. Include examples
    of different multicultural foods in your answer.   (10 marks)

11 Describe the distinctive features and characteristics of **one**
    international cuisine of your choice.   (8 marks)

12 Give **two** reasons why sensory testing is carried out on food products.   (2 marks)

13 Describe how you would carry out sensory analysis to compare
    a cook-chill lasagne with a homemade one.   (6 marks)

14 From 2016, food manufacturers must show the nutritional profile of a product.
    Explain how the traffic light system gives useful nutritional information to the consumer.   (6 marks)

15 Describe the methods used by retailers to promote new products.   (8 marks)

SECTION 6
Food Provenance

This section includes the following topics:

6.1 Environmental impact and sustainability of food

6.2 Food processing and production

Section 6 Practice questions

Food and the environment

Learning objectives

In this section you will learn about:
- the environmental issues associated with food
- seasonal foods
- sustainability and sustainable methods of farming
- transportation of food and food miles
- organic foods
- the reasons for buying locally produced food
- food waste in the home, during food production and retailing
- environmental issues relating to packaging.

Environmental issues associated with food

We should all be aware and concerned about the need to sustain our **environment**.

The **environment** includes the air, water and land on which people, animals and plants live.

To **sustain** our environment, we need to maintain and look after it by:
- using less energy
- reducing the consumption of water
- avoiding waste
- recycling and reusing as much as possible.

The management of waste (rubbish) is a huge issue. It is also important to think carefully about the way we shop, consume and live in order to sustain the environment.

Key words

Environment refers to the air, water and land in or on which people, animals and plants live. **Sustain** means to maintain and look after something, for example the environment.

Figure 6.1.1 Looking after the environment

The six Rs

There are six words beginning with 'R' – the six Rs – that are used when talking about sustainability and environmental issues. Some have more relevance than others when considering food choices, but they are useful to take into consideration when making the most environmentally friendly choices. The six Rs are:

- **Rethink** – how much of the ingredient do we need to buy? Think about the most energy-efficient cooking methods, and think about reducing air miles.
- **Refuse** – don't use a material or buy a product if you don't need it or if it's bad for people or the environment, for example buy loose products rather than those with excess packaging.
- **Reduce** – cut down the amount of packaging material on food, and conserve energy and water when you cook.
- **Reuse** – use leftover food to create another dish. Reuse packaging such as jars.
- **Recycle** – always recycle packaging, for example cans and plastic bottles, rather than throw them away, so waste products can be used to make something else.
- **Repair** – fix equipment used in preparation and cooking when it breaks down or doesn't work properly, rather than buy new equipment.

Activity

Copy this table and match the definition with the correct 'R'.

The six Rs	Explanation
Rethink	Always recycle packaging rather than throw them away.
Refuse	Fix equipment when it breaks down, rather than buy new equipment.
Reduce	Use leftover food to create another dish.
Recycle	How much of the ingredient do we need to buy?
Repair	Cut down the amount of packaging material on food, and conserve energy and water when you cook.
Reuse	Don't use a material or buy a product if you don't need it or if it's bad for people or the environment.

Activity

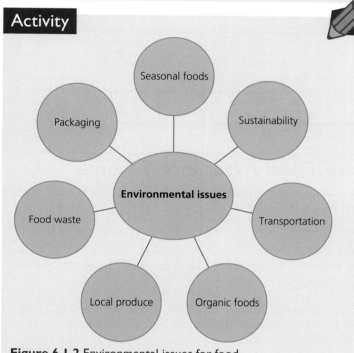

Figure 6.1.2 Environmental issues for food

Copy the diagram above. Identify the environmental impact for each factor; for example, buying local produce means you are supporting the local economy and local farmers.

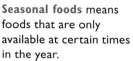

Figure 6.1.3 Seasonal foods

Seasonal foods

Some foods are **seasonal** – only available at certain points in the year. Many fruits and vegetables grown in the UK are seasonal. Choosing seasonal food has many advantages:

- It is more likely to be local or grown in the UK, so the food miles will be low and it will support local farms.
- It is often healthier because it is fresher – it has not travelled across the world spending time in transport and storage.
- Foods in season are often plentiful and therefore cheaper.
- Seasonal fruits, such as cooking apples, strawberries and plums, can be bought or grown in large quantities and preserved as chutneys, pickles or jam.

> **Key words**
>
> **Seasonal foods** means foods that are only available at certain times in the year.

Practical activity

Find a recipe which uses a seasonal food and make it in your next practical session.

Activity

Visit the website eattheseasons.co.uk to help you provide some examples of seasonal foods for each month in the table below.

Month	Seasonal foods	Recipe idea
January/February		
March/April		
May/June		
July/August		
September/October		
November/December		

The Red Tractor Food Assurance Scheme

The Red Tractor is a food assurance scheme which covers production standards such as safety, hygiene, animal welfare and the environment.

All suppliers in the Red Tractor food chain are inspected and certified to ensure that food has been produced to a set of standards across the food chain – from farm to pack. Red Tractor can only be used on food that has been produced, packed, stored and transported to Red Tractor standards.

By having the Red Tractor logo people will know that the food they are buying is safe, they will know where the raw ingredients come from and the standards to which the food has been produced, and they will know that the animals reared will have been raised according to high welfare standards.

Figure 6.1.4 Red Tractor

Sustainability and sustainable methods of farming

Many farmers now work in a sustainable way; this means that they grow crops, or rear animals in a way that maintains and improves the environment.

RSPCA Assured

RSPCA Assured, previously Freedom Food, is the RSPCA's food label. Foods that have this label mean that the animal has had a good life and it has been treated with compassion and respect.

If there is an RSPCA Assured label on the packaging of eggs, fish and meat, it means the farm, and everyone else involved in the animals' lives including hauliers and abattoirs, have been assessed and meet RSPCA animal welfare standards. The RSPCA welfare standards cover beef cattle, chickens reared for meat, dairy cows, egg-laying hens, pigs, sheep, salmon and trout, turkeys and veal calves.

Depending on the species, the RSPCA welfare standards include:
- more space
- natural lighting
- comfortable bedding
- environmental enrichment, for example objects for birds to peck at
- shade and shelter.

CERTIFICATION MARK
Figure 6.1.5 RSPCA Assured logo

Some packaging may still show the Freedom Food logo until May 2016 as companies have packaging to use up. From June 2016, all RSPCA Assured foods will have the new logo.

Egg production

There are different methods of egg production in the UK.

● Enriched cages – these have replaced battery cages. They have more space and height, a nesting area, litter for scratching and perches for the hens.

The more sustainable methods of egg production are:

● Barn eggs – these refer to the barns where the hens are kept, with plenty of space, perches and nest boxes.
● Free range – this means the hens also have access to an outside area.

Barn egg and free-range egg production is endorsed by the RSPCA Assured label.

Activity

Explain why people may choose food that has the RSPCA Assured logo on it.

Figure 6.1.6 MSC-certified sustainable seafood logo

Fish

There are over 20,000 fish and fish products with a Marine Stewardship Council (MSC) label. Fish with this label comes from a sustainable fishery, ensuring that appropriate fishing methods are used and that the supply is maintained and supported.

Some of the MSC sustainable fish are:

● cod
● crab
● haddock
● hake
● lobster
● mussels
● oyster
● plaice
● salmon
● shrimp/prawn
● tuna.

John West is a major producer of canned fish such as tuna. John West is committed to sustainable fishing. It assesses the sustainability of its fish through:

● the health of the stock
● the impact on the ecosystem
● the way fisheries are managed.

In addition, John West fish must be traceable from catch to consumer.

Figure 6.1.7 John West logo on a tin of tuna fish

John West has partnered with WWF-UK to improve sustainability which will help safeguard the marine environment, its wildlife and the livelihoods of the people who depend upon them. The initial phase of the partnership runs until 2018, after which it is intended to be renewed for another four years. By the end of the partnership, John West intends for all its tuna to be either Marine Stewardship Council certified or from a fishery in a Fishery Improvement Project or Conservation Project.

Transportation

Food miles are the distance that food is transported as it travels from producer to consumer. In the UK, our food travels by boat, air, lorries and cars.

Food transport is responsible for the UK adding carbon dioxide to the atmosphere each year. Some of this is produced by people travelling in cars to shop for food. This has an impact on global warming.

Food travels much further than it used to because of the demand for:
- seasonal food all year round; for example, it is now possible to buy strawberries throughout the year
- processed food
- cheap food
- a wider range of ingredients from different international cuisines and cultures, which are not produced or grown in the UK.

Organic food

Organic food means that at least 95 per cent of the ingredients come from organically produced plants and animals. Some ingredients are not available organically; up to 5 per cent of ingredients from a list of approved non-organic food ingredients are allowed.

All food sold as organic has followed very strict guidelines to ensure it has been produced in the correct way.

All organic food must be clearly labelled to show that it has met the necessary standards.
- The food must not have any artificial colourings and sweeteners, nor use artificial fertilisers. Pesticides are very restricted so the farmers have to make sure their soil is fertile soil. They do this by rotating crops and using compost, manure and clover which encourages natural wildlife to help control pests.
- For those farmers rearing animals, the animals' welfare is vital and they are always free range.
- The use of many drugs and antibiotics is banned.
- Animals raised as organic must have a 100 per cent organic diet.
- Genetically modified (GM) crops and ingredients are also banned.

Organic foods are thought to taste better because no artificial fertilisers are used and pesticides are very restricted.

Figure 6.1.8 Soil Association logo

Soil Association

The Soil Association promotes organic farming which includes using fewer pesticides and maintaining higher levels of animal welfare.

Any food products labelled as organic must meet a strict set of standards which define what farmers and food manufacturers can and cannot do in the production of organic food. Organic producers must be inspected by a certification body such as Soil Association Certification.

Taste testing

Aim: Is it possible to taste the difference between organic and non-organic produce? (You will have learnt about difference testing in Topic 5.3 Sensory evaluation techniques.)

1 Obtain a selection of non-organic and organic foods, such as carrots, crisps, chocolate and apples.
2 Carry out some difference testing. Use the table below as a guide, and complete one for each food tasted.

Sample A	◊	Δ	
Comment on: Appearance			
Flavour			
Texture			
Taste			

3 Which is the organic sample – is it ◊ or Δ? Why?

Evaluation

1 Carry out some research on the availability and cost of organic foods at a supermarket of your choice.
2 Write a report on your findings – evaluate whether organic foods are cost-effective for the average family?
3 Discuss the advantages and disadvantages of buying organic foods.
4 Evaluate your findings – can you tell the difference between organic and non-organic foods?

The reasons for buying locally produced food

● Shopping locally saves on fuel cost.
● Buying locally supports your local farmers and producers.
● Choosing food that is local and in season means that it does not have to travel so far. Reducing food miles can have a dramatic effect on reducing carbon dioxide emissions.
● The transport of live animals is an important animal welfare issue. The numbers of animals having to be moved around the country has grown, with the decline of local abattoirs and the increase in centralised abattoirs and meat-processing plants. Buying meat and poultry from a local butcher who uses the nearest abattoir means that the meat is fresher, it has not been packaged and it has not travelled as far, which is better for the animal's welfare.
● Freshly picked fruit and vegetables are better nutritionally because they are fresher and there has been less time for loss of vitamins; they will also have more taste.

Food waste in the home, during food production and retailing

There are two main reasons why we throw away good food: we cook or prepare too much; and we don't use food up in time.

The foods we waste the most are fresh vegetables and salad, drinks, fresh fruit and bakery items such as bread and cakes.

Almost 50% of the total amount of food thrown away in the UK comes from our homes.

We throw away 7 million tonnnes of food and drink from our homes every year in the UK, and more than half of this is the food and drink we could have eaten.

Wasting this food costs the average household £470 a year, rising to £700 for a family with children (the equivalent of arount £60 a month).

If we all stop wasting food that could have been eaten, the benefit to the planet would be the equivalent of taking one in four cars off the road.

(Source: www.lovefoodhatewaste.com)

Figure 6.1.9 Some waste statistics

Figure 6.1.10 Love food hate waste logo

Figure 6.1.11 How to reduce food waste

It is inevitable that there will be some food left over from meals. Any food which has been left over can be recycled as compost. Composting can be done at home. A number of things can be composted:

- vegetable peelings
- fruit peelings and waste
- teabags
- light cardboard such as toilet roll tubes, cereal boxes
- eggshells.

There are some foods that cannot be composted – cooked meat, fish, dairy products and vegetables.

Composting is great for the environment because little methane is produced and, after around nine months to a year, the compost can be used as fertiliser for the garden.

Any food that is left over can be reused to make another dish. Reusing not only saves money but it also saves on waste. There are so many recipes available today – on the internet, in books, newspapers and magazines – giving us new ways of using up any leftover ingredients bought for another recipe.

Some recycling ideas for food are:

- Use leftover cake to make a trifle.
- Use leftover meat in a shepherd's pie.
- Use leftover chicken in a curry.
- Mash leftover potato and use it in fishcakes, or use it in a frittata.
- Use leftover rice and pasta in salads.
- Fallen apples can be used to make pies, crumbles or preserves.
- Stale bread can be used to make breadcrumbs or a bread and butter pudding.

Food producers and retailers are also re-thinking their products and the way they are packaged and labelled to decrease food waste.

Many bread manufacturers have produced smaller loaves of bread at 600 g. There is now more of a range of different sized products so that the right amount can be bought and not wasted.

Date labels are now clearer as manufacturers are using the terms 'use by' and 'best before'. The dates are also much larger and clearer.

Some supermarkets provide storage advice on their free loose produce bags giving messages such as 'store fruit and vegetables in the fridge so they last longer'.

Heinz launched a Fridge Pack for baked beans; they can be kept in the fridge for up to five days after opening, and the snap packs are handy single person portions.

Manufacturers offer re-closable packs for products such as frozen peas, salad bags and fish-fingers, to help us reduce waste.

Some supermarkets have updated their guidance on freezing. It has been made clearer that you can freeze suitable foods before the 'use by' date, not just on the day you buy them.

Most products now have storage guidance. Storing food in the right way helps keep it fresh for longer, so there is less likelihood of waste.

Some packets now carry portion measuring marks on the side to help us cook the amount we need. In addition, supermarkets are varying the size of packets of food. It is now possible to buy smaller packets to save wasting food.

Research activity

Using the website www.lovefoodhatewaste.com, create a fact sheet on the issues relating to food waste, including:
- facts about food waste
- the cost of food waste
- types of food wasted
- how to avoid it.

Activity

Create a mind map of a range of dishes, both sweet and savoury, that use leftover food. Indicate clearly in each dish what the leftover ingredient is.

Practical activity

From the activity above, choose the most interesting idea to make in your next practical session.

Environmental issues related to packaging

Food packaging protects and preserves food. A range of materials can be used for packaging, some of which are environmentally friendly.

Sometimes there is excess packaging on foods, which contributes to waste. Aim to choose packaged products carefully to ensure food is kept fresh for as long as possible, and that the packaging can be recycled or reused.

Figure 6.1.12 Recyclable food packaging

Improvements in packaging

Some packaging has been improved to make the food stay fresher for longer:

● Some fruits such as strawberries are now in packaging that acts as an 'ethylene remover'. Ethylene is what causes fruit to ripen.
● Some meat such as steak is vacuum-packed, again extending shelf life.
● Milk is put into white plastic bottles to protect it from light, as light can have an impact on shelf life.
● Split packs, such as for ham and bacon, give us the option of not opening one half so it stays fresher, or freezing one half if we don't want to use it straight away.

How to reduce packaging waste

- Buy fruit and vegetables loose or with as little packaging as possible.
- Try to avoid disposable items.
- Either buy only what you need, or buy in bulk and store the excess carefully.
- Look for re-closeable packs; for example, cheese often has a zip lock at the top to reseal it when storing it opened.
- Avoid supermarket plastic carrier bags and take your own.
- Reuse jars and containers where possible or recycle them.
- Recycle as much packaging as you can, such as glass, paper, cardboard, plastics and cans.

Storing food correctly

Many products contain storage advice to help us make the right decision on where to store food to make sure it lasts and remains safe to eat, therefore preventing food waste.

Carbon footprint

Carbon footprint is a measure of the impact our activities have on the environment in terms of the amount of greenhouse gases produced through carbon dioxide emissions. This also has an impact on global warning.

Figure 6.1.13 Carbon footprint logo

We are advised to reduce our carbon footprint whereever possible by:

- Buying local produce and so reduce food miles
- Cooking fresh meals
- Using seasonal ingredients
- Cutting down on meat consumption

The carbon footprint symbol is used on products to show the carbon emissions in grams to enable people to make choices in reducing their carbon footprint.

Research activity

Create a fact sheet on how to reduce packaging waste when buying food and drink.

Check your knowledge and understanding

1 Give **three** advantages of buying seasonal ingredients.
2 Explain why consumers would choose to buy food with the RSPCA Assured label.
3 Name **one** sustainable method of egg production.
4 Name **two** types of fish that are sustainable.
5 Explain the advantages of buying locally produced fruit, vegetables and meat.

Food provenance and production methods

Free-range food production

Free-range food production is a method of farming where animals have access to outdoor spaces, rather than being restricted to an enclosure for 24 hours each day. Animals farmed using free-range production methods include pigs, grass-fed beef, laying hens, chicken and turkeys.

Figure 6.1.14 Free-range hens

Free range **does not** mean organic. In order to be classified as free range, animals must have access to the outdoors for at least part of their day.

The alternative to free-range production is **intensive farming**. Intensive production is a farming system that aims to produce as much yield as possible, usually with the use of chemicals and in a restricted space.

- Intensive farming can be used with crops and animals.
- Intensive production means that animals can suffer from isolation or overcrowding and cannot move around or behave naturally. Animals can be restricted from natural behaviours like grazing, rooting, scratching, foraging, mud wallowing, running and nesting.

The advantages of free-range production

- Free-range animals can graze and look for food. The animals are more likely to behave naturally and eat a more varied diet.
- Some consumers feel that animals produced by free-range production have had a better life and prefer to buy these products.
- Some consumers and chefs believe that the meat from free-range, grass-fed cows tastes better than the intensively farmed grain-fed cows.
- Free-range animals can roam around and are less likely to spread diseases between each other.

The drawbacks of free-range production

- Free-range animals can be at risk from being attacked by predators; for example, foxes will hunt chickens.
- Free-range animals can catch diseases from wild animals. Some people believe that badgers spread diseases to cows.
- Free-range animals can suffer discomfort during extreme weather. During heavy snowfall sheep can become trapped and die.
- More land is needed in free-range production and it needs to be carefully managed. This means that free-range foods can be more expensive to buy.

Extension activity

Visit the website www.foodafactoflife.org.uk and read about farming methods.

Egg farming

Enriched caged production is a type of intensive farming for hens. The cages contain space for hens to perch and nest, typically hold around 90 hens and are stacked on top of each other in tiers. The cages must provide 600 cm² of useable space per hen.

In barn systems, hens have freedom and space to move around but are still within a building. Perches and nest boxes are provided.

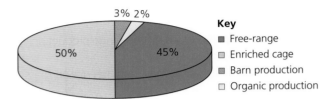

UK egg production

3% 2%

50%   45%

Key
■ Free-range
□ Enriched cage
■ Barn production
□ Organic production

Figure 6.1.15 UK egg production

Free-range egg production

The following **minimum conditions** are required for the label 'free range' to be used for eggs:

- Hens have continuous daytime access to open-air runs and perches.
- The open-air runs must be mainly covered with vegetation.
- Each hen has 4 m² of outside space at all times (about the size of two classroom doors).

Many food retailers have a policy of selling only free-range eggs, or not selling intensively farmed eggs. They apply this policy not just to eggs in their shells, but also to the eggs used in the baked goods and processed foods they sell, such as quiches, cakes and ice cream.

Activity

The table shows the price of medium eggs on sale in a large supermarket.

Egg production method	Price per egg (2016)
Free-range	25p
Enriched caged	8p
Organic	32p
Barn	10p

1   Which method produces the cheapest eggs? Explain **two** reasons why the price is low.
2   Give **two** reasons why organic and free-range eggs are more expensive.
3   What is barn egg production?

UK egg production methods

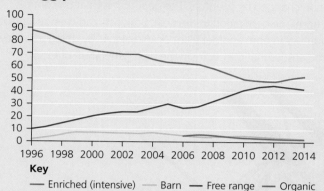

Figure 6.1.16 Egg production methods

Use Figure 6.1.16 to answer the following questions:

1 Which type of egg production is the most common in the UK?
2 Give **one** reason why the production of free-range eggs may have increased.
3 Which **two** methods of egg production have remained low?

In small groups, or as a whole class, discuss the advantages and disadvantages of each type of egg production method.

Copy each of the statements below onto small cards. In pairs, decide which type of egg production each statement describes. Divide your cards into two categories:

● Enriched cage production
● Free-range production

Hens have access to outside space and can perch.	Hens produce expensive eggs.	Hens have little personal space.
Hens are safe from predators.	Hens see daylight.	Hens can catch diseases in the soil.
Hens produce very cheap eggs.	Hens are exposed to the weather.	Hens are at risk from predators.
Hens are kept well-fed.	Hens are at risk of disease as they are living close together.	Hens are allowed to behave as they would in their natural environment.

The terms **'outdoor reared'** and **'outdoor bred'** are used to describe some food products.

1 Find some examples of foods that may carry this label.
2 Explain what these terms mean.

Genetically modified foods

Genetically modified foods (or GM foods) are foods produced from plants or animals that have had their genetic information changed by scientists. The genetic information controls the features that are passed on from one generation to the next. Scientists can change a plant or animal by adding genetic information from another plant or animal to it. By doing this, they are able to precisely select characteristics that they want in the next generation of foods.

Figure 6.1.17 Genetically modified wheat

Genetically modified foods could have:
- better resistance to insects, pests or disease
- increased storage life when harvested
- resistance to low rainfall
- faster growth.

At present, the production of genetically modified food in Europe is restricted. Only one GM crop is grown in Europe – a type of maize used for animal feed. GM crops and food can enter Europe as food or animal feed but they must be labelled.

Nearly all the maize and soya beans grown in the USA are genetically modified. Other genetically modified foods are oilseed rape, tomatoes, kiwi fruit and potatoes. These crops are not accepted in Europe.

Benefits of genetically modified foods

- GM foods can be produced in large amounts. This could benefit people who live in areas where it is difficult to produce food or who live in the developing world.
- GM foods are cheaper in the long run. The cost of buying the seeds is expensive but GM foods need less **pesticides** and **herbicides**, and less people to grow them successfully.
- The storage life of a food can be improved. A tomato, for instance, can be produced to stay fresher for longer, so extending its shelf life in the supermarket.
- GM crops can be developed to survive poor weather conditions such as drought.
- GM foods can be developed to have a large amount of a specific nutrient in them. 'Golden rice' is an example of a GM food that has been produced to contain high levels of vitamin A.

Key word

Genetically modified foods are foods produced from plants or animals that have had their genetic information changed.

Herbicides are chemicals that destroy weeds.

Pesticides are chemicals that destroy creatures that are harmful to the crops.

Research activity

Figure 6.1.18 Golden rice compared with white rice

Bill Gates, the founder of Microsoft, has invested in the development of 'golden rice'. You can find out about 'golden rice' on the website: http://www.gatesfoundation.org/What-We-Do/Global-Development/Agricultural-Development/Golden-Rice.

1 What is 'golden rice'?
2 Explain why 'golden rice' is important.

Problems with GM foods

- The pollen from GM crops could mix with wild plants. This could affect the natural species in the long term.
- GM technology could affect animal habitats. The food source for an animal could change if a new plant is introduced and this could be harmful for their survival.
- Pests could be become resistant to the new crop and continue to thrive.
- Some GM foods are modified using bacteria and viruses, so there is a fear that new diseases will develop.
- The labelling of GM foods can cause confusion. Genetically modified ingredients in a food must be identified on the food or drink label. There are some exceptions to this rule. Labelling is not required where the total amount of GM ingredients in the food is **less than 1 per cent**. Products such as meat, milk and eggs from animals fed on GM animal feed do not need to be labelled.

Research activity

Quality Assurance Standards and food production

Standards for the protection of laying hens, meat, chickens, pigs and calves are set by European law. These standards are improved upon within the UK.

Investigate the four Quality Assurance Standards used in the UK and describe what they mean for animal welfare:

- Red Tractor
- The British Lion egg mark
- RSPCA Assured
- Soil Association

Check your knowledge and understanding

1 What is free-range production?
2 Discuss the advantages and disadvantages of free-range production.

3 Explain what is meant by the term genetically modified food.
4 Give **three** benefits of genetically modified food.

Sustainability of food

The food security problem

The world is facing a possible crisis in terms of **food security**. Food security is about ensuring that all people, at all times, have access to enough safe and nutritious food for them to lead an active, healthy life. It is about meeting the challenge to provide the world's growing population with a sustainable, secure supply of safe, nutritious and affordable high-quality food, without having a negative effect on the environment.

There are four features of food security:
- availability of food
- access to food
- use of food
- stability of the supply.

Food security requires all four features to be met at the same time.

Figure 6.1.19 Food security is about having access to enough food

The physical AVAILABILITY of food	Food availability is about the 'supply side' of food security. The amount of food available in a country depends upon how much food they produce, store and trade. Some people will suffer food shortages if they are affected.
ACCESS to food	The access to food is affected by the cost of food. High food prices can mean that people on low incomes will be unable to buy enough food. Issues like access to land to grow food and poor transport systems can also limit the access to food for some people.
The USE of food	The use of food is about how the body uses the nutrients in food. People need to know how to use food and eat a balanced diet.
The STABILITY of the food supply	Food stability is about the supply of food over time. Poor weather and economic factors (unemployment, rising food prices and environmental disasters earthquakes, global conflicts e.g. war, flooding) can have a harmful effect on long-term food supplies.

Table 6.1.1 The four features of food security

The types of food insecurity

There are **two** types of food insecurity: short-term and long-term.

Types of food insecurity	Happens when	Caused by	Can be prevented by
Short-term	People do not have enough to eat for a short period.	A sudden drop in the harvest due to poor weather, or lack of access to food due to price increases.	Careful planning for possible shortages and stepping in quickly when they happen.
Long-term	People do not have enough to eat for a long period of time.	People living in poverty and not having the resources to access food all the time.	Long-term action to tackle poverty, such as education and supplying resources.

Table 6.1.2 Causes and prevention of short-term and long-term food insecurity

Figure 6.1.20 A failed harvest caused by flooding could cause short-term food insecurity

The UK enjoys a high level of food security because it produces a lot of food. The amount of food produced by a country is called its **self-sufficiency**.

- The UK is self-sufficient for about 60 per cent of the food we need.
- The remaining 40 per cent of the food we need comes from imports.

Imported food is food that is brought into the UK from other countries for sale. Fruit and vegetables are the biggest group of foods imported in the UK. Consumer demand for fresh fruit and vegetables all year round means that imports are necessary.

Figure 6.1.21 Imported tropical fruit

Research activity

All these foods are imported to the UK:

- Lamb
- Pears
- Bananas
- Pineapple
- Sweet potatoes
- Mango
- Oranges
- Grapes
- Tuna fish
- Kiwi fruit

1   Find out where each food is coming from and which foods have travelled the longest distance. Why do you think these foods are imported?
2   Can you identify any other foods that are imported into the UK? Find out where they are from and suggest why they are imported.

The distribution of food

Enough food is produced globally to feed all the people in the world. However, nearly 1 billion people are suffering from hunger and food insecurity.

In some parts of the world, sometimes called the developed world, food tends to be available and fairly affordable. In other parts of the world, the poorer, less developed areas (the developing world), there are people who go hungry. This is because food is expensive and not always available. Typically, families in poor countries spend up to 80 per cent of their income on food.

- The **developed world** refers to nations of the world that are considered more economically and technologically advanced, such as Europe, the USA, Japan, Australia.
- The **developing world** refers to nations of the world that are less economically and technologically advanced, such as parts of Africa and Asia.

Key words

Imported foods are foods that are brought into the UK from abroad for sale.

Developed world refers to nations of the world that are considered more economically and technologically advanced, such as Europe, the USA, Japan and Australia.

Developing world refers to nations of the world that are less economically and technologically advanced, such as parts of Africa and Asia.

AQA GCSE Food Preparation and Nutrition

Hunger and food insecurity happen because of poor food distribution and increases in the price of food. The factors that affect the distribution of food and increases in food prices are:
- changes to the environment
- the world population
- global trade.

Figure 6.1.22 Farming in the developing world

Research activity

Under-nutrition is eating too little food or too little of a particular nutrient to meet dietary needs.

The Hunger Map can be downloaded from the World Food Programme website: www.wfp.org/hunger-map-2015

The map shows where under-nutrition is most likely.

Look at the Hunger Map and answer the following questions.
1 How many people in the world go to bed hungry each night?
2 Which countries have a very low risk of under-nutrition?
3 Which counties have a high risk of under-nutrition?
4 Explain why you think these differences exist.
5 The opposite of under-nutrition is over-nutrition. What is over-nutrition?

Key word

Under-nutrition is eating too little food or too little of a particular nutrient to meet dietary needs.

The challenge to provide a sustainable and secure food supply

Food security is affected by changes to the environment, the population and the way we trade.

Environmental changes

Ideally, food production should feed everyone now, as well as not restricting the chances of future generations to feed themselves. This is not happening and many of the current methods used to produce food are damaging the environment. In the long term, this will affect the availability of food, as natural resources disappear and are not replaced.

Figure 6.1.23 Removal of rainforest for food production

Key words

Fossil fuels are coal, oil or natural gas, formed in the earth from plant or animal remains.
Greenhouses gases are gases that trap heat in the atmosphere; this can cause climate change.
Carbon footprint is a measure of the impact human activities have on the environment in terms of the amount of greenhouse gases produced.

Food production uses energy. Energy is needed to operate machinery, produce fertilisers and supply water. Energy is also used to process, transport and package food. The energy to do all these things comes from **fossil fuels**. Fossil fuels are coal, oil or natural gas, and are formed in the earth from plant or animal remains. The supply of fossil fuels is limited and eventually they will disappear.

Carbon dioxide is produced by burning fossil fuels. Carbon dioxide is a **greenhouse gas**. Greenhouse gases trap heat in the atmosphere and this can cause climate change. Farm animals produce methane, another greenhouse gas, from their digestive systems. Trees absorb carbon dioxide so removing forests to grow crops or farm animals is harmful. It is estimated that farming adds 10 per cent to the total greenhouse gas emissions in the atmosphere.

Carbon footprint is a measure of the impact human activities have on the environment, in terms of the amount of greenhouse gases produced. This has an impact on global warming. Some farming activities have a big carbon footprint.

Carbon footprint

The graph below shows the amount of carbon dioxide released by producing each of the foods.

The carbon footprint of food KG CO_2/Kg

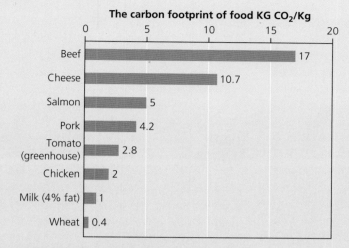

Beef	17
Cheese	10.7
Salmon	5
Pork	4.2
Tomato (greenhouse)	2.8
Chicken	2
Milk (4% fat)	1
Wheat	0.4

Figure 6.1.24 The carbon footprint of food

Use the graph to help you answer the following questions.

1 Which food has the biggest carbon footprint?
2 Explain why cheese production has a big carbon footprint.
3 Explain **three** farming activities that can contribute to carbon dioxide production.
4 Explain why tomato production generates more carbon dioxide than wheat production.

Key word

Global warming is a gradual increase in the overall temperature of the earth's atmosphere caused by increased levels of carbon dioxide and other chemicals in the atmosphere.

Many scientists believe that large amounts of carbon dioxide in the atmosphere are causing **global warming**. Global warming is a slow increase in the temperature of the earth's atmosphere caused by the release of too much carbon dioxide and other greenhouse gases.

Global warming will have a serious effect on food production:

● Droughts and floods will be more likely because rainfall patterns will change.
● An increase in temperature could also trigger more insect activity, which may damage crops.
● In some areas of the world food production might become difficult.

Global warming could affect the spread of animal and crop diseases:

● The bluetongue virus affects sheep and is transmitted by a biting midge.
● As global weather conditions have warmed, the range of the midge has spread to northern Europe. Affected animals are culled and meat prices increase as a result.

Figure 6.1.25 Land affected by poor rainfall

Industrial agriculture relies on chemicals, which can be harmful to the environment.

Pesticides are chemicals that destroy pests or creatures that are harmful to crops. Most sprayed pesticides do not reach the target pests and instead remain in the environment. Pesticides contribute to the removal of key species from the environment, for example bees.

Key words

Pesticides are chemicals that destroy pests, creatures that are harmful to crops.
Fertilisers are chemicals that enhance the soil by introducing nutrients.
Fish farming involves raising fish and shellfish in tanks or enclosures in the sea or lakes for food.

Figure 6.1.26 Crop spraying to kill pests

Teacher's tip

The Sustainable Food Trust has a selection of videos on their website in the 'Articles' tab covering a range of environmental issues linked to farming practices.

http://sustainablefoodtrust.org/

Soil is affected by growing the same crop over and over again. All the nutrients are removed from the soil. **Fertilisers** improve the soil by adding nutrients. Most fertilisers contain nitrates, which can have a harmful effect on water supplies. When a large amount of fertiliser enters a pond, lake or river, it kills the plants and fish.

Farming practices can exhaust natural resources. As populations grow, there is more pressure to produce more food.

Overfishing has depleted fish stocks to levels from which they may not be able to recover. The overfishing of cod and haddock has led to an increased use of more sustainable fish, for example coley, pollock, mackerel, salmon.

The increased demand for fish has led to the development of **fish farming** or aquaculture . Fish farming involves raising fish and shellfish in tanks or enclosures in the sea or lakes for food. In Scotland, the Scottish aquaculture industry produces significant quantities of salmon, rainbow trout and mussels.

In a similar way on land, the removal of vegetation and forests to grow crops or graze animals destroys natural habitats for many animals.

Figure 6.1.27 Fishing boats with full drag nets can contribute to overfishing

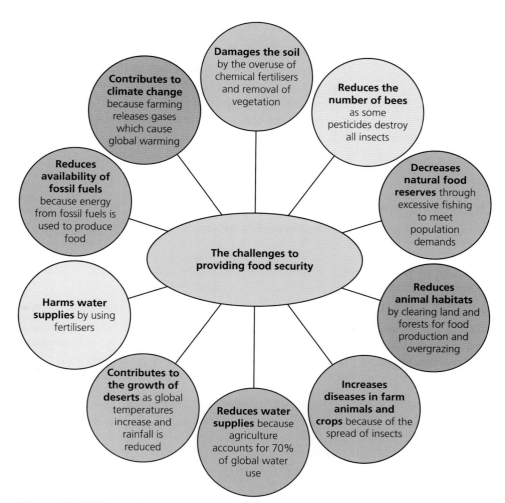

Figure 6.1.28 The challenges to providing a secure food supply

To reduce the effect of food production on the environment, the methods used will have to change. The aim is to create a sustainable environment.

A **sustainable environment** is one where the demands placed on the environment can be met without reducing its ability to allow all people to live well, now and in the future.

Population changes

More food is being grown now than in any other time in human history. It is expected that the world population will rise from about 7 billion in 2016 to 9 billion by 2050. This means that another 2 billion people will need to be fed in the next 35 years. World food production will need to rise by 70 per cent and food production in the developing world will need to double to meet demands. As a country develops, it needs more land for housing, which might have been used for growing or rearing animals.

Africa will suffer the greatest insecurity over its food supply if this trend continues, because it also suffers from the effects of climate change and conflicts over land.

Changes to global trade

Food is traded across the globe. It is an important resource.

Food prices will rise when:
- food supplies are limited
- demand for food increases.

People in Russia, Brazil and China are becoming richer. As they become richer, their diets are changing. The demand for meat and dairy products has increased. The production of meat and dairy products is expensive and affects the environment. Land is needed to grow crops to feed animals. Beef production is the most damaging to the environment and results in five times more climate warming gases than chicken or pork. It has a large carbon footprint.

Figure 6.1.29 Large-scale beef farming

Activity

Should we stop eating meat?

Investigate the impact of beef production on the environment. Consider the effect on the environment and on the health of people.

Produce a visual resource (for example, PowerPoint, infographic, Prezi, poster), which shows the concerns about global meat production.

Debate the issue in a whole class discussion.

These websites may be useful:
- Friends of the Earth (FoE): www.foe.co.uk
- World Wildlife Fund (WWF): www.worldwildlife.org
- People for the Ethical Treatment of Animals (PETA): www.peta.org.uk
- The Vegetarian Society: www.vegsoc.org/environment

Extension activity

Prepare for a debate on whether or not we should we stop eating meat.

Global trade is unfair on the poorest people in the poorest countries.

This is because:

- Unfair rules control global trade. Poor countries are encouraged to import food from rich countries but cannot easily export their foods to rich countries.
- Prices in the global food markets are very unstable. Farmers planting crops take a risk that the price may have fallen by the time they reach harvest.
- A few big companies control the trade of food. When prices go up they keep the profits rather than passing on any of the benefit to farmers.

The rising cost of grain to feed animals has increased the price of beef and pork. The pressure on food producers to provide meat at lower prices resulted in a food scare in 2013. During this food scare, horsemeat was discovered in beef ready meals sold in some supermarkets. This was food fraud because horsemeat is cheaper than beef in some countries.

The measures you can take to support local and global markets and communities

To feed the growing population and protect the environment, the production, processing and distribution of food must try to:

- use the same or less land
- use less water, fertiliser and energy
- produce less waste.

To achieve these goals and reduce your carbon footprint the following measures would help.

Use technology

Advances in technology can improve food security. Technology such as state of the art farming machinery helps more people to have access to a wider range of safe, nutritious foods at a reasonable price.

Precision farming uses technology to manage the environment and get the highest possible harvests from the land available. It is the use of satellite systems and unmanned aerial vehicles to check the growth of crops and use of fertilisers. Technology can also be used to make sure the correct crops are grown in the best location.

Key word

Precision farming uses technology to manage the environment and get the highest possible harvests from the land available.

Figure 6.1.30 Farming technology

The use of **genetically modified** crops could reduce the amount of food that is wasted and increase the amount of food grown. The advantages of genetically modified foods can be found on page 371. The main benefit of genetically modified food is its ability to help ease world hunger. High-producing and drought-resistant crops allow farmers to grow more food so less land needs to be used for production.

Reduce food waste

Too much food is wasted in the production, transport, storage, retailing and consumption of food. In the UK, households waste a large percentage of all the food they buy. Reducing food waste and packaging saves energy and natural resources used to produce food and packaging, and dispose of them, as well as saving money.

Change our diet

Food security is increased by reducing the amount of meat and dairy products eaten. Eating more vegetables, fruit, cereals and smaller amounts of animal products will to help reduce greenhouse gas emissions. By choosing fish only from sustainable sources future generations will be able to eat fish and seafood.

Change our food shopping

Food security is increased by buying local and seasonal foods. It makes no sense for a vegetable to be grown, harvested, packaged, stored and transported to cost less than a vegetable grown in the UK. The UK should produce more of its own fruit and vegetables and consumers should be encouraged to buy them. It reduces the energy used in food production, transport and storage and helps protect the local economy.

Buy food products from a trusted source

Global food security is increased if consumers buy food from trusted sources. The trusted sources offer disadvantaged producers a fair and stable price for their products and often protect the wildlife and ecosystems.

Figure 6.1.31 You may have seen the LEAF (Linking Environment and Farming) logo on vegetables, salad, fruit, crisps or cooking oil

Figure 6.1.32 You may have seen the Rainforest Alliance Certified seal on tea, coffee, fruit juice, chocolate, bananas or pineapples

Research activity

Sustainability in the food industry

Many food manufacturers are working towards the sustainable production of their food products. Working in groups, choose a food producer from the list below to investigate what actions they have taken. Produce a fact sheet of your findings.

● Coca-Cola: www.coca-cola.co.uk
● Birds Eye: www.birdseye.co.uk
● Nestlé: www.nestle.co.uk
● Starbucks: www.starbucks.co.uk
● Heinz: www.heinz.co.uk
● Fairtrade Foundation: schools.fairtrade.org.uk/resources/videos

Check your knowledge and understanding

1   What is food security?
2   List **five** different ways that food production affects the environment.
3   Explain how technology can support food security.
4   Describe how consumers can support food security.

5   Give a definition of a sustainable environment.
6   Evaluate the use of fish farms for providing a sustainable source of fish.
7   Name **three** problems associated with genetically modified food.

Food production

Learning objectives

In this topic you will learn about:
- the terms **primary** and **secondary** processing
- the **milling** of wheat
- the heat treatment of milk
- the secondary processing of **flour into bread** and **flour into pasta**
- the secondary processing of **milk into cheese** and **milk into yoghurt**
- the secondary processing of **fruit** into **jams**.

The process of food production

Our food supply comes from living plants and animals but only a small number of species are directly eaten as food.
- Most of our cereals, vegetables and fruits are grown on farms and in orchards.
- Meat is reared on cattle, sheep, poultry and pig farms.
- Eggs are laid by hens.
- Fish comes from the open ocean and rivers or is farmed in purpose-built facilities.
- Dairy foods come mainly from the milking of dairy cows, although a range of milks and milk products are supplied by other animals.

Most food undergoes some processing before it appears at the table. The whole process is referred to as 'field to fork'. **Field to fork** describes all the stages in the production of food from its source to the consumer. The food production process can be grouped into two stages according to the activities that are carried out on the food from its source to its sale.

The two stages of food production are **primary** and **secondary** food processing.

Primary processing is changing raw food materials into food that can be eaten immediately or be processed further into other food products. Primary processing includes the transporting, sorting, cleaning, blending, cooking, preserving, packing and storage of the raw food.

Figure 6.2.1 A combine harvester collecting wheat so that primary processing can begin

Secondary processing is when primary products are changed into other types of food products. Examples of secondary processing include:

- Wheat flour is transformed into breads, pasta, pastries and cakes.
- Milk is changed into cheese and yoghurt.
- Fruit can be processed into jams, jellies and marmalades.
- Vegetables can be chopped, sliced or shredded.
- Fish can be used as an ingredient in frozen meals.
- Meat can be processed and preserved in the form of salami and ham.

Activity

Discuss what you think are the main reasons for the increase in the number of processed foods available and their purchase by consumers.

Primary processing

Primary processing of meat

Meat and poultry are the muscle tissues of animals and birds. Meat is produced by the careful breeding of poultry and animals to produce lean, tender meat.

Types of meat	Examples of meat
Animal meats	Beef, lamb, pork, veal, venison, goat, rabbit.
Poultry meats	Chicken, turkey, duck, game birds e.g. pheasant
Offal (internal organs of animals)	Heart, liver, kidneys, oxtail, tongue

Table 6.2.1 Meat and poultry

Research activity

Identify a dish or recipe that uses each of the examples of meat listed above in Table 6.1.

The structure of meat

The muscle tissue in meat is made up of long, thin fibres. These fibres are held together in bundles by connective tissue. There are two types of connective tissue:

● **Collagen** which holds the bundles of muscle fibres together.
● **Elastin** which binds the muscle together or the fibre to the bone.

During long, slow, moist cooking methods collagen is softened in the cooking liquid and is converted to **gelatin**. Gelatin a soluble protein which is soft and tender and makes the meat easier to chew and digest.

Figure 6.2.2 Different types of meat

Cattle, sheep and pigs are the main animals reared for fresh meat in the UK. The flavour and tenderness of meat develops after slaughter. **Hanging** is the term used to describe the storage of meat after slaughter. Chemicals in the carcass develop the tenderness and flavour in the meat. Meat should be hung at 1°C. A minimum of seven days hanging from slaughter to consumption is recommended for beef, lamb and pork.

The primary processing of meat is carried out after animals are slaughtered and is the processing applied to prepare meat for consumption or to turn meat into other products. It includes transportation, jointing, cutting and the presentation for sale of raw meat.

The primary processing of beef involves the removal of the bones and jointing carcass.

The joints of meat produced are called the cuts of beef.

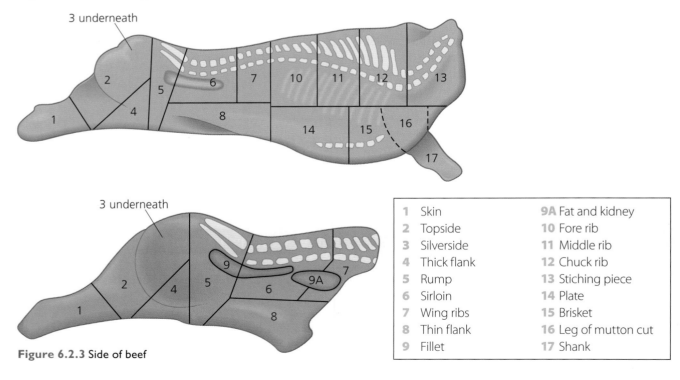

Figure 6.2.3 Side of beef

1	Skin	**9A**	Fat and kidney
2	Topside	**10**	Fore rib
3	Silverside	**11**	Middle rib
4	Thick flank	**12**	Chuck rib
5	Rump	**13**	Stiching piece
6	Sirloin	**14**	Plate
7	Wing ribs	**15**	Brisket
8	Thin flank	**16**	Leg of mutton cut
9	Fillet	**17**	Shank

The different cuts of meat produced from a side of beef have different features. The tender cuts of meat have very little connective tissue and can be cooked quickly and roasted. They include steaks, topside and rib. The tougher cuts of meat have more connective tissue and require slow, moist cooking methods. They are the shin, brisket, chuck and oxtail.

Salting and smoking	Meat can be soaked in brine (salting). This can be applied to brisket, topside and ox tongue. Salting, sometimes with smoking, is also used to produce bacon and ham.
Chilling	The meat is cut ready for cooking and stored in the refrigerator.
Freezing	The meat is cut, cooked and stored in the freezer. It will require defrosting before cooking.
Canning	Canned meats include corned beef. Pork is used to produce luncheon meats and canned ham.
Marinades and rubs	All meats can have seasoning rubbed into their surface or be soaked in a marinade. They can contain chemicals which will tenderise the meat and add flavour.
Mechanical action	The meat fibres can be beaten with a meat hammer to separate the fibres and tenderise the meat. Meat can also be minced or diced to reduce the length of the muscle fibres.

Table 6.2.2 Example of how meat is processed

Activity

Mincing   **gelatin**   **chickens**

Lambs   **beef cattle**   **brisket**

shin   **elastin**   **dicing**

Use the words above to complete the following:

Meat can come from .... and .... It contains two types of connective tissue, collagen and .... Collagen requires long, moist cooking methods to become .... Cuts of meat that require long slow cooking are .... and .... Meat can be processed by the mechanical actions of .... and ....

Practical activity

Plan and make a dish which contains meat. Identify the primary processing method used.

The primary processing of fish

There are over 200 types of fish eaten. Fish may be freshwater, for example trout or seafish, such as cod. The shellfish are another type of fish which can be found in seawater. Fish can be caught in the sea or reared on specially created fish farms. Commercial fishing boats will catch and process and preserve (usually by freezing) the fish at sea.

The types of fish are divided into three main groups:

Types of fish	Examples of fish
Oily fish	mackerel, salmon, tuna, trout
White fish	cod, haddock, plaice, coley
Shellfish	crab, oysters, mussels, lobster, shrimps, prawns

Table 6.2.3 Types of fish

Figure 6.2.4 Types of fish

The structure of fish

The flesh of fish is very similar to meat, except the muscle fibres are found in short blocks not long bundles. There is no elastin. They also only have a thin sheet of connective tissue surrounding them. This ensures that fish is relatively tender and only requires a short cooking time.

The basic cuts of fish are simple and related to the size of the fish. Fish are sold whole or cut into steaks, tail pieces, fillets and cutlets.

Salting	Salted fish is fresh fish that has been salt-cured and dried until all the moisture has been removed. In order to prepare salt fish for cooking, it needs to be soaked overnight.
Smoking	Fish can be smoked over burning wood to give it a unique flavour, for example kippers are smoked herrings.
Marinades or pickling	Fish can soaked in vinegar, this is called pickling. Pickling adds flavour and tenderises the muscles fibres, for example rollmops are pickled herrings.
Freezing	This most popular method of processing and often completed at sea or at port. Frozen fish is absolutely fresh and can be quickly defrosted.
Chilling	The fish is cut ready for cooking and stored in the refrigerator.
Canning	Oily fish like sardines, salmon, tuna and pilchards are usually canned in brine, oil, spring water or tomato sauce.

Table 6.2.4 Examples of how fish is processed

Figure 6.2.5 Smoked salmon is processed fish

Extension activity

The 'Big Five' refers to the five species of sea creatures which are the most commonly eaten in the UK. These are:

Cod   Haddock   Tuna   Salmon   Prawns

Produce a fact sheet about one of the Big Five. Include information about the preparation, use, cost and nutritional value in the diet.

Primary processing of fruit and vegetables

The types of fruit

There is a large range of fruit available. Fruits are usually eaten raw but on some occasions we cook fruit. Fruits are made up of cells which will soften when cooked.

Almost all fruits have a general structure that consists of a skin. The skin encloses the seed or seeds. Usually there is a space between the seed and the skin. The melon is a good example of this structure, with tough outer rind as the skin, the soft flesh within, and the seeds inside the flesh.

They can be classified according to their type.

Citrus fruit	All have a similar juicy texture. They have a hard skin which contains oils that can be used for flavouring food. Excellent source of vitamin C.	oranges, lemon, grapefruit, limes, satsumas
Tree fruit	Have a hard edible skin and have a firm crunchy texture.	apples and pears
Stone fruit	All have a hard stone at the centre and are usually fleshy fruits.	plums, peaches, cherries, mangos
Berries and soft fruit	Have small pips and a soft texture.	strawberries, raspberries, blackberries
Dried fruit	Have the water removed and have a long shelf life.	currants, dates, sultanas, raisins, figs
Exotic fruit	Exotic fruits are not naturally grown in the UK, are usually imported. Some exotic fruits are tropical.	bananas, passion fruit, kiwi fruit, melons, lychees, pineapple

Table 6.2.5 Types of fruit

Figure 6.2.6 Exotic fruit (clockwise from the top left: pineapple, papaya, coconut, kiwis and passion fruit)

The types of vegetables

Vegetables are very important in our diet. Vegetables can be organised into groups according to the part of the plant they come from. Those that grow above ground and are green are an excellent source of vitamin C. Seeds and pods contain protein, dietary fibre and some vitamin C. Vegetables that grow below ground contain carbohydrate, and fewer vitamins.

Plant part	Description	Examples
Roots	Roots are below ground and pass the water and minerals from the soil into the plant.	carrots, swedes, parsnips, radish
Tubers	Tubers are attached to the roots below ground and are the food store for new plants.	potatoes, sweet potatoes, yams
Bulbs	Bulbs found below ground are the food store of new plants.	onion, leeks, garlic, spring onions, shallots
Stems	The stems are above ground and support the plant.	celery, asparagus, rhubarb
Leaves	The leaves are above ground and make the food for the plant by using sunlight.	cabbage, lettuces, Brussel sprouts, watercress, spinach
Flower heads	The flower head is above ground and produces the seeds for the plant.	cauliflower, broccoli,
Fungi	Fungi grows above ground and is not a vegetable but an edible fungus.	mushrooms
Fruit	Fruit grows above ground and contain the seeds for the new plant.	tomatoes, peppers, pumpkins, aubergine, cucumber, squash, courgettes
Seeds and pods	Seeds and pods grow above ground and contain the new plant seeds within the pod.	peas, okra, fine beans, mange tout, sweetcorn

Table 6.2.6 Types of vegetables

Practical activity

Plan and prepare a snack suitable for a young child to eat which contains fruit.

Figure 6.2.7 Pods and seeds (clockwise from the top left: okra, sweetcorn, fine beans, mange tout, peas and beansprouts)

Harvesting

Fruit and vegetables must be harvested and processed quickly. Fruit and vegetables will continue to grow, ripen and decay after harvesting.

The processing after harvesting may include:
1. sorting the fruit and vegetables into different sizes
2. trimming off the excess leaves and roots
3. removing damaged and misshapen produce
4. washing to remove soil and any farming chemicals
5. wrapping to ensure safe transportation.

Peeling

Many fruit and vegetables are peeled before they processed into food products. A variety of mechanical methods are used. Tomatoes are scalded with boiling water or steam to loosen their skins and then brushed to remove it. Acid solutions are used to remove and destroy enzymes that will make the fruit turn brown.

Once peeled and in preparation for further processing fruit and vegetables can be mechanically cored, halved, sliced, chopped, mashed or pitted (stone removed).

Extracting juice

The fruit and vegetables are first finely chopped and then mashed into a pulp. The pulp is then pressed and the juices may be filtered to remove solid bits. Chemicals will be added to remove any cloudiness. The juice will then be pasteurised and sealed into cartons.

There are two routes that fruit and vegetables can take once harvested:
1 They can be packed for immediate sale.
2 They can be processed to slow down or stop the ripening and decay.

Figure 6.2.8 Fresh apples on for sale

Enzymes inside fruit and vegetables contribute to their ripening and decay. The action of enzymes in fruit and vegetables is explained in Topic 4.1 Food spoilage and contamination.

These processes will slow down the ripening and decay of fruit and vegetables:

Controlling the temperature	Different temperatures will slow down the ripening process. Refrigeration is ideal for most fruit and vegetables. Exceptions include potatoes, sweet potatoes, bananas, onions and squashes which keep well in cool places rather than cold storage.
Controlling the atmosphere	Adding carbon dioxide gas to the storage unit will slow down decay. A controlled atmosphere is used in bags of prepared salad to keep them fresh for days. Once opened and exposed to air the salad decays quickly.
Controlling the moisture	A general rule, vegetables require high moisture storage and fruits low moisture storage.
Coating with wax	Slows down the ripening process by preventing carbon dioxide from leaving the fruit and oxygen entering. This is used on lemons and oranges.
Blanching	Blanching is carried out before freezing, canning, or drying. Blanching destroys enzymes. It involves plunging the fruit or vegetable into boiling water, removed after a brief interval, and finally placing under cold running water.
Drying	Fruit and vegetables can be sun dried or tunnel dried by hot air. Drying removes moisture (preventing decay) and concentrates the nutrients.
Preserving in sugar	Many fruit are made into jams using sugar to preserve the fruit. Large amounts of sugar stop decay. Soaking fruit in sugar, followed by drying, will produce candid and crystalline fruit.
Freezing	Freezing retains the vitamin C content and allows storage for many months. Freezing fruit and vegetables to −18°C causes ice crystals to form which will cause the cell walls to collapse. Some soft fruits are not suitable for freezing because they become mushy when defrosted, e.g. strawberries
Preserving in an acid	The acid, usually vinegar, prevents decay. Pickled vegetables include cucumbers, green tomatoes, onions, radishes, and cabbages.
Canning	Fruit and vegetables can be canned in fruit juice, syrup, water, brine (salt) or a sauce to extend their shelf life. The cans are filled and sealed. The cans are placed in a large pressure cooker and the temperature is raised to 121°C. The fruit and vegetables are cook inside the can. Canning uses high temperatures so vitamins in the produce are reduced.

Table 6.2.7 Processing of fruit and vegetables

Primary processing of cereals

Cereals are the seeds or grains of cultivated grasses. They are often described as a staple food. A **staple food** is a food that is eaten regularly and is the main part of the diet for a group of people. Cereals provide people with the main source of energy in their diets.

Cereals are grown or cultivated around the world and the type of cereal which becomes the staple food depends on the local climate. In more economically developed countries the harvesting of wheat and other cereals is done by the **combine harvester**.

Cereals	Cultivation and use of the cereal
Wheat	Used to make many types of baked products including breads, pastries, cakes and biscuits. Durum wheat is used to make pasta. Couscous is steamed, dried and cracked grains of durum wheat. Wheat flakes are added to breakfast cereals. Wheat can be cultivated in a wide range of soils and can be successfully grown across the world.
Rye	Used to make bread. Has a higher fibre content than white bread and is often darker in colour and stronger in flavour. It is used to make crisp breads. Rye grows well in much poorer soils than those needed for most cereal grains. Rye is grown primarily in Russia and northern Europe.
Rice	Can be used in sweet and savoury dishes. Many types including basmati, long grain, pudding rice, brown rice. Rice flakes can be added to breakfast cereals. Rice flour and ground rice used for baking. Rice requires a hot, wet climate and is the staple cereal in India and China. Rice is an aquatic crop, which means that it is best grown in water. High rainfall and fresh water supplies are essential for its cultivation.
Maize (corn)	Used to make corn flour. Cornmeal is used to make tortillas, muffins and pancakes. Eaten as whole corn on the cob. Maize thrives best in a warm climate. It can be grown in Europe, China, North and South America.
Barley	Used for making beer and soft drinks, e.g. barley water. Pearl barley can be used to thicken soups and stews. Most of the barley grown is for animal feed. Barley can be grown in many climates but does not tolerate cold winters. It grows in Russia and Europe.
Oats	Available as oatmeal, porridge oats and jumbo oats. Added to breakfast cereals, snack bars and crackers. Oats are best grown in regions where the temperatures are neither very hot nor very cold. It grows in North America, Russia and Europe.

Table 6.2.8 Cultivation and use of cereals

For most cereal grains the main purpose of the primary processing is to separate the outer layers of the grain from the inner layers. To achieve this, the cereal must be milled. **Milling** is the process of grinding down the cereal grain.

All grains are **screened** for impurities, **sorted** by size and **scrubbed** to remove dirt and any brush hairs before processing. They are softened with water; this is called **conditioning**.

Wheat

Structure of wheat

All cereals have a similar structure inside. Figure 6.2.9 shows the basic structure of a grain of wheat.

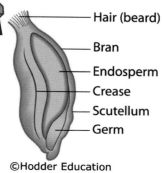

Hair (beard)
Bran
Endosperm
Crease
Scutellum
Germ

©Hodder Education

Figure 6.2.9 Inside a cereal grain

Milling of wheat

The **milling** of wheat into flour for the production of bread, cakes and biscuits is a huge industry. Cereal grains consist of three distinct parts. The purpose of milling is to separate the different parts of the grain. Three important parts of the wheat grain separated during the milling process are the:
- endosperm
- bran
- germ.

The floury, white endosperm needs to be separated from the outer bran and the germ.

Step 1: Breaking

The grain is broken between steel rollers, with grooved surfaces, working at different speeds. This is the first 'break' and the wheat grains are torn open.

Step 2: Sieving and reduction

The broken grain is sieved. Three main separations are made:
- Flour called the 'first break flour' is removed.
- Rough white flour called **semolina** is collected. Semolina is a coarse-ground flour produced from wheat.
- Large pieces of the wheat grain are collected.

After the 'first break flour' has been removed, the coarse semolina and large pieces of wheat grain are fed into a second reduction roll. The flour is sieved out after each reduction roll.

The semolina is repeatedly rolled between break rollers to produce a fine white flour. There are usually four or five more reduction rolls.

> ### Key words
>
> **Milling** is the process that separates the different parts of the grain.
>
> **Semolina** is a coarse-ground flour, which comes from wheat.

Milling stoneground flour

Flour made by a traditional milling process is still available to buy. The whole wheat grain is ground by passing it between two flat, round millstones. During the milling process, the bottom stone (the bed stone) remains fixed while the top stone (the runner stone) rotates. Grooves on the face of each stone help to grind the grain. This is a slow and gentle process, which generates warmth in the flour. It ensures that the wheatgerm oil, naturally present in the grain, is spread throughout the flour, which will improve the flavour of the bread.

Extraction rates

The **extraction rate** is the percentage of flour by weight that is taken from the whole grain to make flour.

Wholemeal or whole wheat flour	100% of the whole grain. The whole wheat grain, bran, endosperm and germ are milled and nothing is removed.
Brown flour	85% extraction. Some of the bran and germ are removed.
White flour	72% extraction. This means that every 100 kg of wheat produces 72 kg of endosperm-rich white flour. All the bran and wheat germ are removed.

Table 6.2.9 Extraction rates for flour

Bread and flour regulations

A 72 per cent extraction white flour is almost pure endosperm, as all the germ and outer layers of the grain are removed. The micronutrients are removed too. To rectify this, the flour is **fortified** during processing. Fortified means that micronutrients are added to the flour.

The Bread and Flour Regulations 1998 state that the following micronutrients must be added to white flour:
- calcium
- iron
- vitamin B1 (thiamin)
- vitamin B3 (niacin).

Types of flour

Besides the extraction rate, the amount of protein in the wheat grain can produce different flours. Some common types of wheat flour used in food products and baking are shown in Table 6.2.10.

Type	Description	Uses
Plain flour (soft flour)	Contains around 8% protein	Cakes, sauces, biscuits and pastries
Self-raising flour (soft flour)	Contains 10% protein and added raising agent (such as baking powder)	Sponge cakes, scones and puddings
Strong flour	Contains a maximum of 17% protein; can be wholemeal or white	Bread, Yorkshire pudding, puff pastry and choux pastry
Wheatgerm flour, e.g. Hovis bread	White or brown flour with at least 10% added wheatgerm	Bread-making
Brown flour	Similar to wholemeal but the coarse bits are removed; high in dietary fibre	Breads, pastries and biscuits
Stoneground flour	Wholemeal flour ground between two stones	Bread-making
Wholemeal flour	Contains the most dietary fibre	Breads, pastries and biscuits

Table 6.2.10 Common types of wheat flour

Figure 6.2.10 Bread made using stoneground flour has a dense texture

Practical activity

Prepare and make a dish using wholemeal flour, brown or stoneground flour.

How does it compare with white flour?

Key words

Extraction rate is the percentage of flour by weight that is taken from the whole grain to make flour.

Fortified means that micronutrients have been added to foods e.g. flour.

Organic flours

Organic flours are made from wheat grown and processed naturally without the use of chemicals. The Soil Association is an official body that approves the use of the term 'organic'. Producers must meet the organic certification standards to be able to claim that their product is 'organic'. Organic flours are available in many different types, including self-raising, plain and wholemeal.

Extension activity

Market research on flour

Find out the following:
1   Where can you buy the cheapest plain white flour? How much is it? How does it compare with an organic plain white flour?
2   What size bags is flour sold in?
3   Identify the names of **three** food manufacturers that make flour.
4   Identify **five** bread mixes that use different types of flour.

Activity

Table 6.2.11 shows the nutrients in different types of flour.

Nutrients	Wholemeal flour	White bread flour	White plain flour	Brown flour
Energy	327 kcal	353 kcal	352 kcal	339 kcal
Protein	11.6 g	11.3 g	9.1 g	12.2 g
Fat	2.0 g	1.2 g	1.4 g	2.0 g
Fibre	8.8 g	3.1 g	3.4 g	6.9 g
Calcium	32 mg	134 mg	96 mg	28 mg
Iron	2.47 mg	1.92 mg	1.94 mg	2.38 mg
Vitamin B1	0.36 mg	0.3 mg	0.28 mg	0.39 mg

Source: McCance and Widdowson, The Composition of Foods (2015)

Table 6.2.11 Nutrients found in 100 g of different flours

Answer the following questions using the table.
1   Which flour contains 301 kcals of energy?
2   Which flour contains the least amount of protein?
3   How much calcium is there in white bread flour?
4   Which flour contains 2.2 g of fat per 100 g?
5   Which flour contains the most iron per 100 g?
6   How much vitamin B1 does white plain flour contain?
7   Explain why wholemeal flour contains the most fibre and fat.
8   Explain why the amount of calcium present is higher in the white flours.

Secondary processing: flour into bread

Types of flour for bread-making

The types of flour used to make bread are rich in **gluten**. Gluten is a protein that is found naturally in flour. Bread dough needs a gluten network to support the gas bubbles of carbon dioxide that are created during the making process. The gas bubbles give bread a light texture. **Strong** flours have a large amount of gluten in them so they are ideal for bread-making.

You will have learnt about gluten formation in Topic 3.2 Functional and chemical properties of food. See page 216.

In the UK, nearly 12 million loaves of bread are sold each day. Bread made at home or at school follows a very similar process to the bread made in an industrial bakery.

All bread-making processes include four key steps:

1   Mixing
2   Proving and fermenting
3   Baking
4   Cooling

The ingredients required for bread-making are:

- strong flour to provide the gluten
- fat to keep the bread soft, fresh and lighter over time
- salt to add flavour
- water to produce a dough
- yeast to produce carbon dioxide gas, which enables the dough to rise
- ascorbic acid (vitamin C) to strengthen the dough
- acetic acid (vinegar) to preserve the bread.

Figure 6.2.11 Loaves produced by the Chorleywood Bread Process

Bread-making in an industrial bakery

The modern, commercial process used in large bakeries to make bread is called the **Chorleywood Bread Process**. More than 80 per cent of all the bread loaves in Britain are made using the Chorleywood Bread Process. The process makes the bread softer, reduces the cost and more than doubles its shelf life.

Steps	Process	Why
1 Sieving and checking	Flour arrives at the bakery from the flour mill. It is stored in large silos.	It is checked for metals or any other impurities.
2 Mixing and kneading	The ingredients are pumped into a giant mixer. The ingredients are mixed at high speed for 5 minutes.	Simply blending the ingredients is not enough to start gluten development; the dough needs to be worked.
3 Dividing	The dough is removed and divided into individual pieces by a machine.	All batches must be identical.
4 First rising	Dough circulates along a conveyor belt and the yeast becomes active. This is rising.	**Rising** is when the yeast fills the dough with gas (carbon dioxide), causing it to rise.
5 Knocking back	The dough is kneaded for about 2 minutes by a machine. The kneaded dough passes along another conveyor belt until it is dropped into pre-greased tins.	This stage ensures that the gas is distributed throughout the dough in small bubbles.
6 Proving	The tins pass along the conveyor belt into a warm area. The dough is placed at 45°C for about 50 minutes to allow the yeast to work.	The dough will be three times its original size. The dough has a fine texture.
7 Baking	The tins move slowly on a conveyor belt through a huge oven for about 20 minutes. Basic bread doughs are usually baked at about 200°C.	The dough rises rapidly as the gas (carbon dioxide) is produced. The yeast dies and rising stops. The dough sets and browns.
8 Cooling	The bread loaves are mechanically sucked out of their tins and cooled.	Long, slow cooling allows crust formation.
9 Slicing	The bread is sliced mechanically and bagged.	The label gives the weight and best before dates.

Table 6.2.12 The stages of the Chorleywood Bread Process

The key parts of the Chorleywood Bread Process are the use of **high-speed mixing** and the addition of **ascorbic acid** (vitamin C) to improve the quality of the dough.

Research activity

Visit the Flour Advisory Bureau website and watch the video showing how bread is made (www.fabflour.co.uk/fab-bread/how-bread-is-made/).

Answer the following questions:
- How many loaves are made and sold in the UK each day?
- What quality checks are carried out when the flour arrives at the bakery?
- What other ingredients are used to make bread?
- How long is the first rising?
- What conditions does the yeast need to grow?
- How long is the baking?
- How long is the cooling?
- Which parts of the process are controlled by computers?
- How long does the whole process take?

Key word

Chorleywood Bread Process is the name of the bread-making process used in large bakeries.

AQA GCSE Food Preparation and Nutrition

Secondary processing: flour into pasta

Pasta is made from a mixture of:
- water
- semolina flour made from durum wheat.

Durum wheat is a yellow-coloured, protein-rich wheat that is grown especially for making pasta.

In Italy flour is graded by using a 'zero' rating. This describes the amount of milling the grain has taken. A single zero flour rating '0' has a very gritty texture while a triple zero '000' has a very fine texture like cornflour. Flour for making pasta is usually classed as double zero or '00'.

Homemade pasta is made from same ingredients as the industrial process. The only difference is eggs. Eggs are usually used in all homemade pasta recipes. Eggs are not always used in manufactured pasta dough. Vegetable juices and herbs can also be added to pasta dough for colour and taste.

Key word

Durum wheat is a yellowy, high-protein wheat that is grown especially for making pasta.

	Process	Description
1	Mixing and kneading	The semolina is stored in silos. Pipes move it to a mixing machine fitted with rotating blades. Warm water is added to the mixing machine. The mixture is kneaded.
2	Flavouring and colouring	If the pasta is to be flavoured or coloured, vegetable juices are added. Tomato is added for red pasta, spinach for green pasta and carrot for orange pasta. Herbs and spices can also be folded in for additional flavouring.
3	Rolling	The mixture moves to a **laminator** where it is pressed into sheets by large rollers. The laminator flattens and presses air bubbles and excess water out of the pasta dough.
4	Pasteurisation	The flat dough moves through a steamer, which heats it to 104°C in order to kill any bacteria.
5	Cutting	Depending on the type of pasta to be produced, the dough is either cut or pushed through special cutters.
6	Drying	The pasta is placed in a drying tank in which heat, moisture and drying time are strictly controlled. The drying time differs for the various types of pasta.
7	Packaging	**Fresh pasta** is folded into clear plastic containers. As the containers move along a conveyer belt, a plastic sheet covers each container and is sealed with a hot press. A small tube sucks the air out of the container and replaces it with a mixture of carbon dioxide and nitrogen to prolong the shelf life.
		Dried pasta moves along a conveyer belt to the packaging station. The pasta is measured by machine into pre-printed boxes or packets.

Table 6.2.13 The manufacturing process for pasta

Research activity

Find out what types of pasta can be bought. Record your findings in a table.

Types of pasta – include a sketch	Cost/amount	Uses

Figure 6.2.12 Tagliatelle carbonara is made with pasta

The primary processing of milk

Milk is the natural food for all young mammals. All female mammals produce milk to feed their young. In the UK, milk is supplied by dairy cows but is also available from sheep and goats. The most popular breed of cow for producing milk is the Friesian cow.

Figure 6.2.13 A dairy herd is normally milked twice a day

Milk is used to make a number of products during secondary processing. These are known as **dairy products** and include butter, cheese, cream and yoghurt.

The structure of milk

Milk is a valuable part of the diet. Most of the milk sold in the UK is semi-skimmed milk.

Semi-skimmed milk contains:
- 88 per cent water
- 5 per cent carbohydrate
- 3.5 per cent protein
- 1.5 per cent vitamins and minerals
- 1.7 per cent fat

Pasteurisation

The milk collected from dairy herds goes through many processes before it reaches the consumer.

Most of the milk consumed is pasteurised. **Pasteurisation** is a process in which milk is heated to kill any potentially harmful bacteria that may be present in the milk.

Following pasteurisation, the milk is rapidly cooled and is then stored in a refrigerator in order to extend its shelf life. Milk is also homogenised as well as pasteurised.

Homogenisation

If milk is left to stand, the fat droplets in it will float to the top and form a layer of cream. To prevent this from happening most milk is homogenised. **Homogenisation** involves forcing the milk at high pressure through small holes. This breaks up the fat droplets and spreads them evenly throughout the milk to prevent separation of a cream layer.

Homogenisation means that processed milk has no cream layer. Homogenisation also increases the whiteness of milk because the fat droplets throughout the milk scatter the light more effectively.

Figure 6.2.14 Nutrient averages in semi-skimmed milk

- ▇ minerals 0.7%
- ▇ vitamins 0.8%
- ▇ protein 3.5%
- ▇ fat 3.8%
- ▇ carbohydrate 4.8%
- ▇ water 86.4%

Heat treatment of milk

Approximately 99 per cent of milk sold in the UK is heat-treated. Milk is the ideal substance for bacteria to grow in. To prevent food poisoning and extend the shelf life of milk, heat treatments are used. The heat treatment is carried out as soon as possible after the milk is collected.

Milk is also homogenised during the heat treatment.

Heat treatment	Process
Pasteurised milk is available in whole, semi-skimmed, 1% milk and skimmed varieties.	Pasteurisation is the most popular method of heat treatment. The process involves heating the milk to a temperature of no less than 72°C for a minimum of 15 seconds. Following heating, the milk is cooled rapidly to below 6°C. This is known as High Temperature Short Time (HTST). The milk will keep for 5 days.
Sterilised milk is available in whole, semi-skimmed and skimmed varieties.	**Sterilisation** is an intense heat treatment. The milk is heated in a steam chamber to a temperature of between 110°C and 130°C for approximately 10–30 minutes. Then it is cooled. Unopened bottles or cartons of sterilised milk keep for approximately 6 months without the need for refrigeration. Once opened, it must be treated as fresh milk and used within 5 days.
UHT milk (ultra heat treatment) is available in whole, semi-skimmed and skimmed varieties.	The milk is heated to a temperature of at least 135°C for 1 second. The milk is then packaged into sterile containers. UHT milks have a longer shelf life as a result of the higher temperatures used and the packaging used to store it.
Micro-filtered milks in whole, semi skimmed or skimmed milk varieties.	Filtered milk goes through an extra, fine filtration system, which prevents souring bacteria from passing through. This process is described as microfiltration. The milk is pasteurised. Microfiltration can extend the shelf life of milk up to 45 days when stored in a refrigerator and an average 7 days once opened.

Table 6.2.14 Heat treatment of milk

Research activity

Find out the prices/amount and uses of the different types of milk.

Complete a table like the one below.

Milk type	Price/amount	Uses

Key words

Sterilisation is a method of increasing the keeping quality of products by destroying all micro-organisms by heating food to a very high temperature.

Ultra heat treatment (UHT) is a process of sterilisation using a high temperature for a very short time.

Microfiltration removes the bacteria from milk using very fine filters.

Secondary processing: milk into cheese

Cheese is made from milk. Most cheese is made from cow's milk. Cheese can also be made from the milk of animals such as goats and sheep. Although there are many different types of cheeses, most cheese is made using the same process.

Figure 6.2.15 Lasagne is made with cheese

Research activity

Visit the website www.cheese.com and search the database of 1,775 cheeses. (You can search by names, by country of origin, by kind of milk that is used to produce it, or by texture.)

Find out some examples of:
- cheeses by type, for example soft, hard, semi soft, firm (there are eight groups on this website)
- cheeses by country
- cheeses by milk.

Teacher's tip

The British Nutrition Foundation website has produced a cheese-making video as part of a wide range of resources on farming and food processing.

http://www. foodafactoflife.org.uk

Practical activity

1 Plan and prepare a dish using a cheese of your choice. The choice of cheese could be part of a study into products from international cuisine, as suggested in section 3.5.2 British and international cuisines in the specification.
2 Research the cheese you have chosen:
   i)   How is it made?
   ii) Where is it made?
   iii) What nutrients does it contain?
   iv) Draw a colour coded diagram to show proportions of nutrients found in the cheese.
   v)   How much does it cost?

Process	Description
1 Pasteurise the milk	This destroys all the bacteria and makes the milk ready to accept the starter culture. The milk is cooled.
2 Add the starter culture and ripen	**Starter culture** is a special bacteria added to the milk. The bacteria grows and 'ripens' the milk. **Ripening** allows the **lactic acid bacteria** to change the **lactose** in the milk into **lactic acid**. The starter culture is added and the temperature is held at 32°C for 30 minutes.
3 Add the rennet	**Rennet** is a chemical which helps the milk to **coagulate** (set) and turns it into the **curd** (solid) and **whey** (liquid). This takes 30 minutes.
4 Cut curd and heat	The heating helps to separate the whey from the curd. The curd is then cut with cheese knives into small pieces. Different temperatures are used at this stage to make different types of cheese. Soft cheeses are made from soft curds at lower temperatures. Higher temperatures are used to make hard cheeses.
5 Drain whey	The whey is drained and the curd forms a mat.
6 Texture curd	The curd mats are cut into sections and piled on top of each other and flipped occasionally. This step is called cheddaring. **Cheddaring** helps to remove more whey and allows the mats to 'knit' together and form a tighter structure. The curd mats are then cut into smaller pieces.
7 Salt	Salt is added to produce the correct texture and flavour.
8 Forming the cheese into blocks	The salted curd pieces are placed in cheese hoops and pressed into blocks to form the cheese.
9 Store and age	The cheese is stored in coolers until the desired age is reached. Depending on the variety, cheese can be aged from several months up to several years.
10 Package	Cheese may be cut and packaged into blocks. Wax, foil, paper, plastic and cloth have all been used to protect cheeses.

Table 6.2.15 The manufacturing process for cheese

AQA GCSE Food Preparation and Nutrition

Secondary processing: milk into yoghurt

Milk from cows or ewes (sheep) can be used to make yoghurt. There are a vast range of yoghurts available to buy. Yoghurt is available in a variety of:

- textures, such as liquid, set, smooth
- fat contents, such as luxury, low-fat, virtually fat-free
- flavours, such as natural, fruit, cereal.

Yoghurt can be consumed for breakfast, as a snack or as a dessert. It can also be prepared and sold as:

- **Live yoghurt**, which contains harmless live bacteria and has a tangy flavour.
- **Probiotic yoghurt**, which contains live probiotic bacteria with potential benefits to health.
- **Bio yoghurt**, which has a milder, creamier flavour and is less acidic than some other varieties.
- **Greek yoghurt**, which is strained to make it thick, mild and creamy.

Process		Description
1	Pasteurise the milk	The pasteurised milk is **homogenised** to make sure that the fat droplets are dispersed throughout. The heat treatment reduces the amount of bacteria in the milk to provide a better environment for the **starter culture** to grow in.
2	Warm the milk	The milk is warmed to 42°C to bring the yoghurt to the ideal growth temperature for the starter culture.
3	Add the starter cultures	The starter culture is mixed into the milk. **Lactic acid bacteria** is used for the starter culture. **Ripening** allows the lactic acid bacteria to change the **lactose** in the milk into **lactic acid**.
4	Hold	The milk is held at 42°C. This allows the **fermentation** to start to form a soft gel as the protein sets. This process can take several hours.
5	Cool	The yoghurt is cooled to 7°C to stop the fermentation process.
6	Add fruit and flavours	Fruit and flavours are blended with the fermented, cooled yoghurt before packaging.
7	Package	The yoghurt is pumped from the fermentation vat and packaged. Yoghurt is chilled at 5°C for sale.

Table 6.2.16 The manufacturing process for yoghurt

Figure 6.2.16 Chicken salad uses a Greek yoghurt to bind the ingredients together

Practical activity

Make your own yoghurt

Ingredients

500 ml whole milk
10 g powdered milk
60 g natural full-fat yoghurt

Equipment

Saucepan
Large jam jar with a lid
Wooden spoon

Method

1 Wash and sterilise a large jam jar or a few smaller ones.
2 Place the milk in a saucepan and heat until a thermometer reads 80°C. Do not let it boil.
3 Take it off the heat and stir in the milk powder. Leave to cool.
4 When the temperature drops to 45°C, stir in the yogurt with a wooden spoon.
5 Pour into the jars and seal with the clean lid. Place somewhere slightly warm for 4 to 6 hours.

Secondary processing: fruit into jam

Key word

Gel is formed when a large amount of liquid is set by a small amount of solid.

Jam is made by boiling fruit with sugar until it forms a **gel** which will set on cooling. A gel is formed when a large amount of liquid is set by a small amount of solid.

Three essential ingredients are required to make a gel:

1 Pectin

Pectin is a complex carbohydrate and a natural gelling agent present in most fruit. Pectin is released from fruit cells when they are crushed and cooked at a very high temperature for a short period of time. Pectin requires acidic conditions to form a gel. In jam making pectin traps water, sugar and fruit together to make a gel.

The pectin content of fruit decreases as the fruit ripens, so even fruit traditionally high in natural pectin, so always choose slightly under ripe fruit for jam making .

Fruit high in natural pectin and acid, for gel formation only add sugar	Fruit low in natural pectin or acid, so require extra acid or pectin	Fruit which are very low in pectin, always require extra acid and pectin
Unripe plums	Apricots	Blueberries
Cooking apples	Plums	Figs
Gooseberries	Blackberries	Peaches
Oranges and other citrus fruits	Raspberries	Strawberries
Blackcurrants	Blueberries	Raspberries
Damsons	Ripe plums	Nectarines
		Cherries

Table 6.2.17 Pectin in fruit

Jam sugar is white granulated sugar with added pectin and citric acid.

Liquid pectin (usually brand name Certo) is made from pressed apples and can be added to the fruit during cooking.

2   Acid

Acid is needed to release the pectin from the fruit. Fruit is naturally acidic but sometimes lemon juice can be added to fruit to increase the acidity and release more pectin. Acid also improves the colour and flavour of the jam and prevents sugar crystals forming during storage.

3   Sugar

Sugar acts as the preservative in jam making. It must be measured carefully. The sugar should be about 60 per cent of the total finished weight of the jam.

Crystallisation is when sugar crystals appear on the top and sometimes throughout the jam. The jam is safe to eat but it will taste very sweet and gritty.

Crystallisation is caused by:

- too much sugar being added
- the sugar not being properly dissolved during the jam making
- the jam being overcooked
- a lack of acid in the mixture.

Jam making requires a large thick-based steel pan with sufficient space for the mixture to rise and boil. Special **preserving pans** can be used to make jam. Preserving pans are usually made of copper (an excellent conductor of heat), have a large handle, tall sides and a pouring lip. The tall sides easily contain any expansion and splashes when the jam is on a rolling boil.

Key words

Jam sugar is white granulated sugar with added pectin and citric acid.

Pectin is a complex carbohydrate and a natural gelling agent present in most fruit.

Crystallisation is when sugar crystals appear on top and sometimes through the jam

Setting point is when a jam reaches 105°C.

Preserving pan is a solid, heavy pan with and thick bottom used for jam making. It has a large handle, tall sides and a pouring lip.

Wrinkle test involves pushing your finger through a pool of jam on a plate to detect a wrinkle. If the jam wrinkles it is ready to pot.

Process	Description
1 Select suitable fruit	Select under ripe fruit because it has more natural pectin available than overripe fruit.
2 Wash and dry the fruit	Dip the fruit in cold water to remove any dust or insects. Drain thoroughly.
3 Prepare the fruit	Remove any bruised fruit, stalks, leaves or stones. Large fruit may require chopping.
4 Grease the preserving pan	Use margarine or butter to grease the preserving pan. This prevents a scum forming later, on the surface of the jam.
5 Add the water and acid, if required	The fruit needs to simmer at this stage until tender. The pectin is released from the fruit with the help of the fruit acid. Lemon juice can be added at this point, if the fruit is naturally low in acid. Different fruit require different lengths of simmering. Soft fruit requires about 10–20 minutes and hard fruit requires about 30–40 minutes.
6 Add the sugar	Add all the sugar at once. Stir gently to dissolve. The high concentration of sugar will prevent micro-organisms from spoiling the jam.
7 Add pectin, if required	Add the liquid pectin, if the fruit is low in natural pectin.
8 Bring the fruit mixture to a full rolling boil	A full, rolling boil is one where the bubbles do not stop or lessen when you stir it. Stir constantly and all the way to the bottom to avoid burning the fruit.
9 Test the set	The **setting point** for jam is 105°C. Use a sugar thermometer to take the reading in the centre of the pan. Use the wrinkle test to check the setting point has been reached. **Wrinkle test**: place half a teaspoon of hot jam on a very cold plate and leave to cool. Push the jam with your finger; if it wrinkles the jam has reached the setting point.
10 Pour into jars	When the setting point is reached pour the jam into sterilised jars. Fill to the top, seal with a wax or silicone disc and cover while still hot.

Table 6.2.18 The manufacturing process to fruit and jam

All the micro-organisms in the jam jars must be destroyed to prevent them from spoiling the jam. This can be achieved by placing the jam jars in a warm oven (160°C) for 15 minutes.

Practical activity

Make your own fruit jam

Students need to be reminded to take great care when making jam as they are working with very hot liquids.

This recipe is for soft fruit that is low in natural pectin so requires the use of jam sugar.

Strawberries, raspberries or blackberries would be suitable. A mixture of soft berries will also produce good results.

1 kg fresh or defrosted frozen soft fruit, washed, drained and hulled

1 kg jam sugar

Juice of 1 lemon

Equipment

Large stainless steel saucepan or preserving pan.
Wooden spoon
2–3 jam jars with lids (this makes about 1.5 kg of jam)
Waxed or silicone discs

Method

Figure 6.2.17

1   Wash, dry and sterilise the jars in a warm oven for 15 minutes.
2   Put the soft fruit and lemon juice into a large heavy saucepan, heat for a few minutes to soften.
3   Add the jam sugar and stir until dissolved.
4   Boil steadily for about 6 minutes, or until setting point is reached. Check using the wrinkle test.
5   Allow to stand for 15 minutes and remove the film from the surface with a slotted spoon.
6   Stir jam and carefully pour into sterilised jars, cover, label and date.

Check your knowledge and understanding

1   Outline the differences between primary and secondary processing of food.
2   Describe the process of milling.
3   Explain the process of pasteurisation used for milk.
4   Describe the Chorleywood Bread Process.
5   Explain why a starter culture is used to make yoghurt.
6   Discuss the importance of pectin, sugar and acid in jam making.
7   Explain why crystallisation occurs in jams.

Food processing

Learning objectives

In this topic you will learn about:
- the loss of vitamins through food processing
- the effect of heating on the sensory characteristics of milk.

Vitamins and food processing

Food processing affects the sensory and nutritional properties of ingredients. Vitamins are lost during every method of food processing. In fact, food processing is best avoided and food eaten raw to maximise the vitamin content. Contact with heat, sunlight, water or air will alter the vitamins found in food.

However, processing foods has advantages because it makes them safer to eat and offers more food choices.

Activity

Heat, air, sunlight and water can all have a harmful effect on vitamins. In the table below the ticks show which vitamins are sensitive to contact with which of these elements.

Vitamins	Heat	Air	Sunlight	Water
Vitamin A	✓		✓	
Vitamin D				
Vitamin E	✓	✓	✓	
Vitamin C	✓	✓	✓	✓
Thiamin	✓			✓
Riboflavin			✓	✓
Folic acid	✓	✓	✓	
Vitamin B12	✓		✓	✓

Table 6.2.19 The effect of heat, air, sunlight and water on different vitamins

Using the information in the table, answer these questions.

1 Which vitamin is the **most** sensitive?
2 Which vitamin is **not sensitive** to any of the factors?
3 What is vitamin B12 **not sensitive** to?
4 Which **two** factors is vitamin A sensitive to?
5 Which factor affects most of the vitamins?

The loss of vitamins through heating

Heating affects most vitamins. The food processing techniques that involve heat are **blanching**, **canning**, **pasteurisation** and **sterilisation**.

Blanching

Before food is canned or frozen, it is usually heated very quickly with steam or water. The water-soluble vitamins, including vitamin C and the B group, are sensitive to heat and are reduced by blanching.

Blanching is boiling fruit or vegetables for a short time to destroy enzymes, before plunging into iced water to stop the cooking process.

Canning

In the canning process, food and a small amount of water are heated inside a sealed can to a very high temperature. This kills any dangerous micro-organisms and extends the shelf life of the food.

The nutrients that are affected are:
- **Vitamin B1** (thiamin) is lost from canned meats.
- **Vitamin C** is lost from canned vegetables and fruit. The loss of vitamin C is large and can be as much as 80 per cent.

The water-soluble vitamins, vitamin B1, vitamin B2, vitamin C, folic acid and vitamin B12, will dissolve in water inside the can. They are lost if the canning liquid is thrown away.

Pasteurisation

Pasteurisation involves heating liquid foods such as milk and fruit juices to 72°C for 15 seconds to destroy micro-organisms.

The pasteurisation of milk leads to a loss of:
- 10 per cent of the vitamin B1 and vitamin B12
- 25 per cent of the **vitamin C**.

Pasteurised milk can be processed further into condensed milk and evaporated milk.

- **Condensed milk** is concentrated by boiling in a vacuum and adding sugar.
- **Evaporated milk** is made in a similar way to condensed milk but has no added sugar.
- Large amounts of **vitamins A**, **D**, **C** and **B1** are lost during the production of condensed and evaporated milk. These products will have vitamins added to replace those lost during processing.

Fruit juices may have added vitamin C, to replace the loss during processing. This must be indicated on the label.

Sterilisation

Sterilisation is used on milk and food products. Batch sterilisation used in milk production leads to a loss of:
- 30 per cent of the **vitamin B1**
- 50 per cent of the vitamin C, folic acid and vitamin B12.

Ultra heat treatment (UHT) is a type of 'quick' sterilisation and produces long-life milk. It is a continuous process and the food is packaged after processing into sterile containers. Vitamin loss on UHT milk is similar to pasteurisation due to the short processing time.

Figure 6.2.18 Heat-processed milks

Activity

Describe how heat processing affects the following:
- Vitamin C
- Vitamin B1.

Activity

Match up the food processing methods with the correct description.

Pasteurisation	Food is heated to boiling point (100°C) for a few seconds with steam or water
Sterilisation	Food is heated to a high temperature for minutes in a sealed, airtight can
Canning	Food is heated to 72°C for 15 seconds
Blanching	Food is heated to above boiling point (100°C) for 30 minutes

The loss of vitamins through drying

Drying food removes the water and the water-soluble vitamins. The water-soluble vitamins, which include vitamin C, vitamin B12 and vitamin B1, are lost during the processing.

All fruit can be effectively dried, and this can be done either by sun-drying, warm air-drying or through freeze-drying.

Vitamin A and E are not water-soluble and become concentrated in dried fruits. Dried apricots are an excellent source of these **antioxidant** vitamins. Antioxidants are very important for protecting the body against harmful substances and diseases.

Figure 6.2.19 Rock cakes made with dried fruit contain no water-soluble vitamins (such as the B vitamins or vitamin C)

For any packaged dried fruit that have a high vitamin C content on the nutrition label, this is because the vitamin has been added back into the product after processing.

Dried milk is usually made from skimmed milk. This means it will be low because the fat has been removed. When the fat is removed the fat-soluble **vitamins A** and **D** are taken out. Dried skimmed milk powder will have vitamins A and D added to replace the loss during processing.

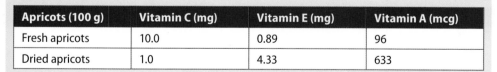

Activity

Apricots (100 g)	Vitamin C (mg)	Vitamin E (mg)	Vitamin A (mcg)
Fresh apricots	10.0	0.89	96
Dried apricots	1.0	4.33	633

Table 6.2.19 Antioxidant differences between fresh and dried apricots

1 Which type of apricot contains the least amount of vitamin C? Explain why.
2 Explain why the vitamin A and vitamin E content of the apricots increases by drying the fruit.
3 What is the function of an **antioxidant** in the body?
4 Identify some recipes that include apricots.

The effect of heating on the sensory characteristics of milk

The flavour of milk will change depending upon which type of heat treatment it has received.

The main methods of heat treatment applied to milk are **pasteurisation**, **sterilisation**, **drying** and **ultra heat treatment**. Milk can also be purchased as evaporated milk or condensed milk.

The flavour of milk after heating

The amount of time and the temperature that milk is processed at will affect the flavour. The sugar in milk is called **lactose**. Lactose will **caramelise** when heated to a high temperature. This will cause the milk to taste sweet.

Figure 6.2.20 Evaporated milk is a yellowy colour because heating causes caramelisation

The effects on milk flavour by processing:
- Heating milk for a short period of time at a temperature below boiling means a flavour change is difficult to notice.
- Cooking the milk for any period of time at a temperature above boiling means a flavour change is obvious and the milk will taste sweet or 'cooked'.

Type of milk	Effect of processing on flavour
Pasteurisation	Flavour change is not noticeable unless the pasteurisation was carried out incorrectly. Milk is heated below boiling point.
Sterilisation and UHT	Flavour is sweet or 'cooked' because the milk is heated to a high temperature. The heating causes the **caramelisation** of the milk sugar (lactose).
Dried milk	Flavour is slightly sweet or 'cooked' because the milk is heated to a high temperature to remove the water. The heating causes the **caramelisation** of the milk sugar (lactose).
Evaporated milk	Flavour is sweet or 'cooked' because the milk is heated to a high temperature using steam in a vacuum. The heating causes **caramelisation** of the milk sugar (lactose).
Condensed milk	Flavour is very sweet because sugar is added during the processing.

Table 6.2.20 How processing milk affects flavour

The colour of milk after heating

Most milk is **homogenised**. Homogenised milk has been forced at high pressure through small holes. This breaks up the fat in the milk and spreads it evenly throughout the milk. Homogenisation means that the milk has no cream layer. Homogenisation increases the whiteness of milk because the fat is distributed throughout the milk. The distributed fat will scatter the light better giving the appearance of whiteness.

Evaporated milk and condensed milk are a creamy yellow colour. This is because they have been heated for longer and a reaction has occurred between the protein in the milk and the sugar.

Key word

Homogenisation is the process of forcing the milk at high pressure through small holes to stop the layer of cream separating out.

Check your knowledge and understanding

1 Name the **three** processing methods that use heat.

2 Name the processing method that reduces vitamin C by 80 per cent.

3 Explain how drying affects the water-soluble vitamins in food.

4 Explain why heating milk to high temperatures changes the flavour.

5 Explain how heating can affect the colour of milk.

Figure 6.2.21 Benecol® is a cholesterol-lowering spread

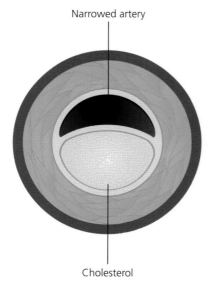

Narrowed artery

Cholesterol

Figure 6.2.22 Benecol® can help to prevent cholesterol building up in the arteries

Nutritional modification and the fortification of food

Some foods have added health benefits due to extra vitamins, minerals or other substances being added to them. These may be added to replace the nutrients that are lost during processing (**fortification**), or added to boost the overall nutritional value of the food (**nutritional modification**).

Foods that lower cholesterol

Some foods you eat can actually lower the amount of **cholesterol** in the blood. (See Figure 2.3.35 on page 180 to see how cholesterol can block your large blood vessels (**arteries**) and prevent blood from circulating properly.)

Benecol® and Flora pro.activ are types of **cholesterol-lowering spreads** that can be used instead of butter or other fat spreads. They contain natural extracts from plants, which have been proven to lower cholesterol. These are found naturally in corn, rye and other plants.

They work by stopping cholesterol from being absorbed into the bloodstream during digestion. This product is intended to be eaten by people who know they have high cholesterol and will help to prevent them developing cardiovascular disease (see page 181). These foods need to be eaten regularly to make sure cholesterol levels remain lower.

Key words

Fortification means adding micronutrients to food that were not originally in the food.

Nutritional modification means adding ingredients to foods that may improve health.

Cholesterol is a fatty substance found in the blood.

Arteries are large blood vessels that take blood away from the heart.

Cholesterol-lowering spreads are fat spreads that help to keep cholesterol levels low.

Fortified foods and enriched foods

Fortified foods are foods that have one or more micronutrients added to them. These nutrients are often ones that were never present in the original food.

Enriched foods are foods that have one or more micronutrients added to them. These nutrients are added to replace those lost during processing.

Flour

In the UK, all wheat flour (except **wholemeal** and **malted brown flour**) has to have vitamins and minerals added to it by law. This first started around the time of the Second World War to prevent important nutrient deficiencies. At this time, food was **rationed** and nutrients were scarce.

The four nutrients that must be added are the minerals **iron** and **calcium** and the vitamins **B1 (thiamin)** and **B3 (niacin)**.

- Calcium was originally added to reduce the number of cases of **rickets** in children.
- Iron is important to help to prevent iron deficiency anaemia.
- B vitamins allow the release of energy from carbohydrates.

It was decided to add these to flour as it is a basic commodity eaten regularly by most people in fairly large amounts. Also, it is easy to fortify flour during the final stages of milling of wheat flour (see page 397).

The iron, niacin and thiamin are added to **enrich** and replace the nutrients lost during milling, but the calcium is added to **fortify** the flour to levels that are higher than the natural levels in wholegrain wheat.

In 2013, the Department of the Environment, Food and Rural Affairs (Defra) held a consultation on whether flour still needed to be fortified and enriched or if the law could be changed. It was decided that the law should remain unchanged and that flour should continue to be fortified with these nutrients to avoid nutritional deficiencies.

Key words

Enriched foods are foods that have micronutrients added to them to replace those lost during processing.

Wholemeal means that the whole of the cereal grain (for example, wheat) has been used, nothing has been taken away.

Rationed refers to the controlled distribution of scarce resources (food).

Margarine is a butter substitute, usually made from vegetable oils/fats; it must contain 80 per cent fat.

Low-fat spread is a yellow fat spread for bread, which contains no more than 40 per cent fat.

Fat spread is a fatty yellow spread for bread, which contains no more than 60 per cent fat.

Figure 6.2.23 Most flour produced in the UK is fortified and enriched with vitamins and minerals

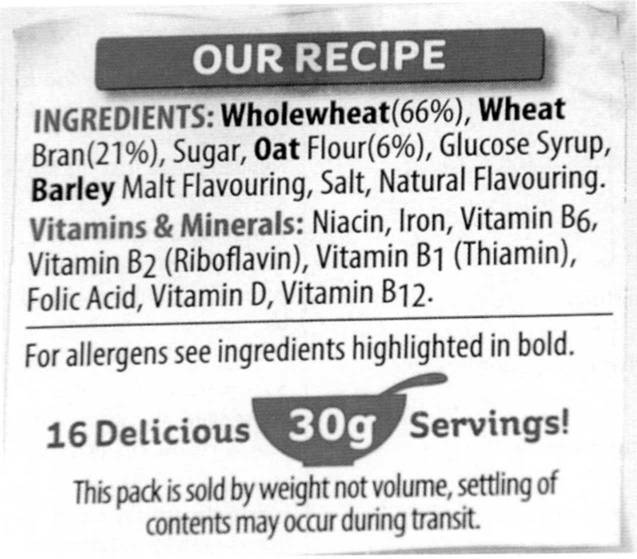

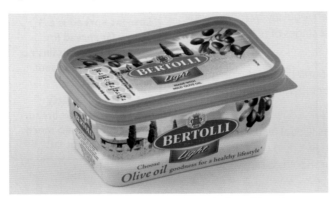

OUR RECIPE
INGREDIENTS: Wholewheat(66%), Wheat Bran(21%), Sugar, Oat Flour(6%), Glucose Syrup, Barley Malt Flavouring, Salt, Natural Flavouring.
Vitamins & Minerals: Niacin, Iron, Vitamin B6, Vitamin B2 (Riboflavin), Vitamin B1 (Thiamin), Folic Acid, Vitamin D, Vitamin B12.
For allergens see ingredients highlighted in bold.
16 Delicious 30g Servings!
This pack is sold by weight not volume, settling of contents may occur during transit.

Figure 6.2.24 Ingredients in Kellogg's Bran Flakes breakfast cereal

BERTOLLI
Light
BERTOLLI
Light
Choose Olive oil goodness for a healthy lifestyle

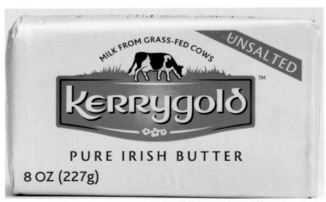

Figure 6.2.25 By law, margarine, fat spreads and low-fat spreads are fortified with vitamins A and D

MILK FROM GRASS-FED COWS
UNSALTED
TM
Kerrygold
PURE IRISH BUTTER
8 OZ (227g)

Figure 6.2.26 Butter naturally contains vitamins A and D

Fortified breakfast cereals

Many breakfast cereals are fortified and enriched with vitamins and minerals. These are added to make the cereals more appealing and to replace the vitamins and minerals lost during processing.

Research activity

Use the internet to find out which vitamins and minerals are used to fortify and enrich breakfast cereals. Which mineral is used to fortify cereals most frequently? Why do you think this is?

Fats and low-fat spreads

Butter is a dairy food made from milk. It concentrates the fat from the milk and is a good source of the fat-soluble vitamins A and D. During the Second World War, butter was rationed, so people used **margarine** instead as a cheaper alternative. The Government decided to make it law that vitamins A and D had to be added to margarine to bring these vitamin levels up to those present in butter.

- Vitamin A is important to ensure good eye sight, especially in dim light.
- Vitamin D is important to help the absorption of calcium, to prevent rickets for growing children and to prevent osteoporosis in adults.

If you look around shops and supermarkets today, you may find it difficult to spot a fat labelled 'margarine' as most are called spreads or **low-fat spreads**. This is because margarine, by law, must (like butter) contain 80 per cent fat, so food manufacturers make lower-fat spreads to appeal to consumers and also to make a bigger profit by increasing the water content of these spreads.

By law, all butter substitutes including **fat spreads** and low-fat spreads must have vitamins A and D added.

Activity

Carry out sensory analysis to find out which type of fat you prefer as a spread on bread or crackers. Choose from: butter, margarine and low-fat spread.

Use the **hedonic scale** chart below to record your results.

Type of fat	1. Dislike very much	2. Dislike	3. Neither like or dislike	4. Like	5. Like very much	Comments

Key word

Hedonic scale is a rating scale (scores) for testing/comparing food samples.

Extension activity

Investigate how plant stanols work to reduce cholesterol levels. In your write up include labelled diagrams.

Check your knowledge and understanding

1. Name **two** groups of nutrients which are commonly added to foods to fortify them.
2. What is the definition of a low-fat spread? And explain the health benefits of using low-fat spreads.
3. Describe the differences between fortified and enriched foods.
4. When did the fortification of flour begin?
5. Identify which nutrients must be added to most flour in the UK. Explain why.
6. State which **two** nutrients must be added to margarine and fat spreads by law. Suggest reasons why.

Food additives

All food additives used in the UK have to be tested for safety before they are allowed to be used. The **Food Standards Agency (FSA)** (see page 150) investigates food additives if any information they receive suggests there is a problem with the safety of food additives, and if necessary action is taken. European Union (EU) legislation means that most food additives are clearly labelled in the list of ingredients along with their function, followed by their E number or name. The E number means that a food additive has passed safety tests and has been approved for use in the UK and the rest of the EU.

Food additives are added to foods improve them in different ways, for example:

- To make foods last longer; **preservatives** can be added to bread to prevent it from going mouldy.
- To give us a wider range of food products; for example, instant whisk and serve custards, gravy granules and many ice cream contain food additives.
- To improve the flavour of a food product; for example, strawberry yoghurt with a strawberry flavour.
- To meet expectations about the colour of food by adding **food colouring**; for example, tinned salmon should be pink or red, tinned peas should be green.
- To promote the benefits of the product to the consumer; for example, vitamins added to baby foods.
- To replace nutrients lost during processing; for example, adding nutrients to bread or breakfast cereals.
- To maintain the texture of food products; for example, **emulsifiers** make sure that oil and water stay together in low-fat spreads, ice cream and salad dressings.
- To maintain the consistency of food products; for example, thickening agents, or **stabilisers**, are used to provide food with desirable consistency, for example, tinned custards.

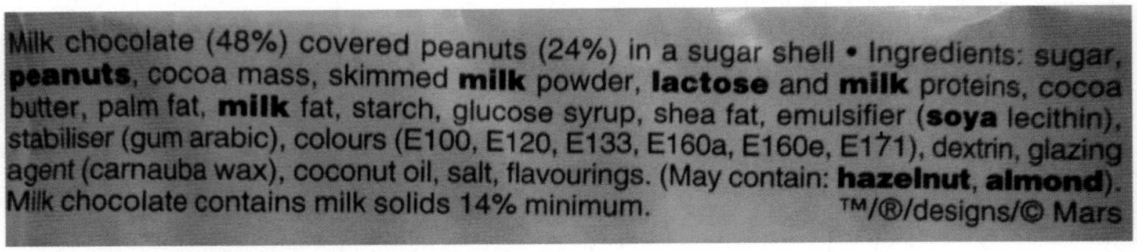

Milk chocolate (48%) covered peanuts (24%) in a sugar shell • Ingredients: sugar, **peanuts**, cocoa mass, skimmed **milk** powder, **lactose** and **milk** proteins, cocoa butter, palm fat, **milk** fat, starch, glucose syrup, shea fat, emulsifier (**soya** lecithin), stabiliser (gum arabic), colours (E100, E120, E133, E160a, E160e, E171), dextrin, glazing agent (carnauba wax), coconut oil, salt, flavourings. (May contain: **hazelnut**, **almond**). Milk chocolate contains milk solids 14% minimum. ™/®/designs/© Mars

Figure 6.2.27 Ingredients list showing E numbers

Preservatives

Positive aspects

These extend the shelf life of foods by preventing the growth of bacteria as well as yeasts and moulds, thereby reducing food waste.

Key words

Preservative is a food additive which keeps food for longer.

Food colouring is a food additive which changes the colour of the food.

Emulsifier is a food additive which enables oil and watery liquids to mix together.

Stabiliser is a food additive which prevents emulsified mixtures from separating.

Nitrates are preservatives used in processed meats which are linked to a higher risk of developing cancer.

Negative aspects

Cured meats such as ham, bacon and corned beef are preserved with **nitrates** which are a type of preservative linked to a higher risk of developing cancer.

Colourings

Positive aspects

Colourings are added to foods to improve their appearance. They are sometimes added to foods to replace the colours lost during food processing or to enhance the colour of foods, such as colours added to icing sugar when cake decorating.

Negative aspects

Food colourings can have a negative effect on children's behaviour and so some parents avoid buying foods which contain certain food colourings for this reason.

These food colourings are linked to **hyperactivity** in children:

- Sunset yellow (E110)
- Quinolone yellow (E104)
- Tartrazine (E102)
- Ponceau 4R (E124)
- Allura red (E129)

It is advised that parents should avoid these food additives if they suspect they trigger hyperactivity in their children.

Flavourings

Positive aspects

Flavourings are added to foods to enhance, improve or strengthen the flavour of foods. They can restore the flavours of food after processing or be used in home baking to add new flavours. For example, vanilla essence may be added to cakes to improve their flavour.

Negative aspects

Some flavour enhancers such as **monosodium glutamate** (E621) are reported to cause symptoms similar to an allergic reaction. These may show as itching, sweating and numbness as well as headaches.

Emulsifiers

Positive aspects

Emulsifiers are used to mix together ingredients which would not normally mix, such as water and oil. **Lecithin** is an example of a natural emulsifier and is found in egg yolk. It is used in mayonnaise to prevent the oil and watery vinegar or lemon juice from separating.

Negative aspects

There are few reported problems from emulsifiers, but flatulence and bloating have been experienced by some people.

Key word

Lecithin is a natural emulsifier found in egg yolk

Stabilisers

Positive aspects

Stabilisers are used to prevent oil and watery mixtures from separating once an emulsifier has allowed them to mix together. They are often used to keep salad dressing stable. They are also used to prevent ice crystals from forming in ice cream and to stop the fruit from sinking in jams and yoghurts.

Negative aspects

There are few reported problems reported from consuming stabilisers, although flatulence and bloating have been noted by some people.

Figure 6.2.28 Genetically modified tomatoes with extra vitamins were created in the UK

Genetically modified (GM) foods

All human and plant cells contain information carried in **genes**. Your genes affect your size, shape, colour of your hair and eyes. Genes also affect the shape and size of plants. These genes are passed on to the next generation when the plant or animal reproduces.

Genetic modification is when the genetic material is changed. Sometimes this can mean a different gene is transferred from another plant or animal with desirable characteristics. Foods which contain genetic material of more than 0.9 per cent must be labelled 'genetically modified'. At present few GM crops are grown in the UK, but since 2014 there have been calls for more UK trials to produce foods, such as tomatoes modified to contain extra antioxidant vitamins or rice (Golden Rice) with vitamin A added. In different parts of the world, where diets can be restricted, these extra nutrients could make a big difference, for example the extra vitamin A in Golden Rice could help to avoid blindness. It is claimed that Golden Rice can be developed which is also resistant to drought and heat. GM foods could improve food security to ensure there is enough food in the global food market. GM foods are reported to improve the yield of crops in a given area of land.

In contrast, the environmental group, Friends of the Earth have said that GM foods will not make food more affordable or sustainable. They argue that despite many years of research GM crops have failed to provide the food benefits that were promised. They want everyone to have access to healthy, affordable food that is kind to the planet. Guy Watson from Riverford Organic Farm asks whether the benefits of GM foods outweigh the risks. He suggests that the main people to benefit from GM crops are the biotech companies who trade in GM materials. He cites research from the USA that:

- GM crops have actually *increased* the use of pesticides and herbicides due to insects and weeds developing resistance to them.
- There is no evidence of an increased yield of crops.
- The promise of GM Golden Rice is, in fact, years from being ready to grow as a successful commercial crop, as the technology is not yet ready to make this work. In addition to this the side effects of eating Golden Rice over a long period of time are not known and so this is a concern.
- The loss of weeds in farmers' fields also means the loss of food and shelter sources for animals and insects.

Overall, it is likely that GM crops will have a role to play in how food is produced in the UK in the future, but both the positive and negative aspects of GM crops need to be considered so we do not put the health of consumers and farmers at risk.

Key words

Genes are found in all your body cells, these contain your genetic code that makes you who you are. Animals, plants and humans all have genes.

Pesticides are chemicals that destroy pests, for example aphids.

Herbicides are chemicals that destroy weeds.

Check your knowledge and understanding

1 Identify one type of food additive group do you believe is the most useful and explain why.
2 E numbers are listed on food labels. What is the definition of an E number?
3 Describe two other functions of food additives and justify when these should be used.
4 Contrast the differences between an emulsifier and a stabiliser.
5 What is the definition of genetically modified (GM) food?
6 Discuss the positive and negative aspects of growing GM crops. Give examples of GM foods in your answer.

Section 6 Practice questions: Food provenance

Multiple choice questions

1 Which one of these foods can be composted? (1 mark)
   a) An apple core
   b) Ham
   c) Cold chicken
   d) Yoghurt

2 What percentage of ingredients must come from organically produced plants and animals for a product to be labelled as organic? (1 mark)
   a) 10 per cent
   b) 50 per cent
   c) 95 per cent
   d) 100 per cent

3 The distance that food travels from producer to consumer is called: (1 mark)
   a) Food travelled
   b) Distance food
   c) Locally produced food
   d) Food miles

4 The method of farming where the animals can have access to outdoor spaces, rather than being restricted to an enclosure for 24 hours each day, is called: (1 mark)
   a) Free-range production
   b) Intensive farming
   c) Enriched cage production
   d) Genetic modification

5 Complete this sentence correctly. An advantage of genetically modified foods is that they could have: (1 mark)
   a) Better resistance to insects, pests or disease
   b) Slower growth
   c) Reduced storage life when harvested
   d) Resistance to high rainfall

6 Complete this sentence correctly. Global warming is caused by: (1 mark)
   a) too much oxygen in the atmosphere
   b) not enough oxygen in the atmosphere
   c) too much carbon dioxide in the atmosphere
   d) not enough carbon dioxide in the atmosphere

7 An example of a primary processed food is: (1 mark)
   a) pasta
   b) cheese
   c) milk
   d) jam

8 What is the extraction rate from the whole grain to make white flour? (1 mark)
   a) 50 per cent
   b) 72 per cent
   c) 100 per cent
   d) 85 per cent

9 Milling is: (1 mark)
   a) Grinding a cereal grain into a flour
   b) Adding nutrients to flour
   c) Washing the cereal grain before processing into flour
   d) Grading the flour

10 Identify a water-soluble vitamin lost during food processing: (1 mark)
   a) Vitamin E
   b) Vitamin D
   c) Vitamin A
   d) Vitamin C

11 The sweet flavour in cooked milk is caused by: (1 mark)
   a) Caramelisation
   b) Gelatinisation
   c) Coagulation
   d) Dextrinisation

12 Milk homogenisation is:

a) Heating milk using steam in a vacuum

b) Forcing milk at high pressure through small holes to scatter the fat

c) Removing the fat from milk

d) Heating milk to 72°C for 15 seconds

(1 mark)

Other question types

13 Explain how to reduce packaging waste. (6 marks)

14 Describe ways in which leftover food can be reused. Give some recipe examples in your answer. (8 marks)

15 Explain **three** advantages of free-range production. (3 marks)

16 State **one** disadvantage of free-range production. (2 marks)

17 What is meant by the term genetically modified food? (1 mark)

18 Give **three** benefits of genetically modified foods. (3 marks)

19 What is meant by the term carbon footprint? (1 mark)

20 Suggest **three** ways that families can reduce their carbon footprint when buying food. (3 marks)

21 Discuss the impact of food production on the environment. (9 marks)

22 Discuss ways consumers can make informed food choices which can sustain the environment. (9 marks)

23 Describe **one** advantage and **one** disadvantage of each of the following heat treatments. (6 marks)

Treatment	Advantage	Disadvantage
Pasteurisation		
UHT		
Sterilisation		

24 Explain how milk is made into cheese. (9 marks)

25 Explain how flour is made into bread. (9 marks)

26 Describe how heat affects the vitamin content of milk. (2 marks)

27 Describe **two** differences between pasteurisation and sterilisation. (4 marks)

SECTION 7
Preparing for assessment

This section includes the following topics:

Topic 7.1 Non-exam assessment

Topic 7.2 The written exam

Introduction to non-exam assessment (NEA)

The **non-exam assessment (NEA)** has been included as part of the assessment for this GCSE to allow practical skills to be assessed, which could not be examined by the written exam alone.

The NEA is assessed across two tasks:

- **Task 1 – Food investigation:** this is worth 30 marks (15 per cent of your total GCSE mark).
- **Task 2 – Food preparation assessment:** this is worth 70 marks (35 per cent of your total GCSE mark).

> **Student's tip**
>
> Non-exam assessment (NEA) makes up 50 per cent of the total mark for the GCSE.

When will the NEA be completed?

Both tasks must be completed in the academic year in which the qualification is awarded. So, for most students, this will be in Year 11.

There will be a choice of three tasks for both Task 1 and Task 2, which will be changed every year. Your teacher will give you information on each task and when you are expected to complete it.

Key word

Demonstrating technical skills means practising skills which you may use in the final dishes (section D) practical.

How long should I spend on the NEA?

- **Task 1** – The recommended time is a maximum of 10 hours.
- **Task 2** – The recommended time is a maximum of 20 hours, including the 3-hour period for the final three dishes. This allows 17 hours for the completion of the research, planning and **demonstrating technical skills** as well as the analysis and evaluation.

What format should the NEA take?

- **Task 1** should be a report between 1,500 and 2,000 words, this will be about 6–8 sides of A4 or A3 equivalent (including graphs and diagrams).
- **Task 2** should not exceed 20 sides of A4 or A3 equivalent paper. Work needs to be concise but contain sufficient information.

How will I be assessed?

There are four assessment objectives (AOs) shown below. These will be used to assess both the written exam and the NEA.

	Assessment objectives	Weightings for NEA
AO1	Demonstrate knowledge and understanding of nutrition, food, cooking and preparation	0%
AO2	Apply knowledge and understanding of nutrition, food, cooking and preparation	10%
AO3	Plan, prepare, cook and present dishes, combining appropriate techniques	30%
AO4	Analyse and evaluate different aspects of nutrition, food, cooking and preparation, including food made by themselves and others	10%

Table 7.1.1 Assessment objectives

Your teacher will mark your two tasks using the **marking criteria** in the specification; it will then be **moderated** by AQA.

Collecting background Information

For both Task 1 and Task 2 you will need to collect background information. It is important to be **selective** when doing this as credit is given for concise, detailed and relevant research.

Student tip

Be careful when choosing the methods of collecting background information as you have a word or page limit on each task.

Figure 7.1.1 Be selective when collecting background information

Figure 7.1.2 Interviewing is a primary method of research, which you may use for Task 2

Task 1: Food investigation

The food investigation task tests your knowledge, learning and understanding of the science of the preparation and cooking of food. It involves carrying out practical investigations.

What you investigate will depend on your chosen title. It may include investigating:
- ingredient choices
- preparation techniques
- cooking methods
- cooking conditions.

You will produce a report, which may be typed on the computer or handwritten. Your report should contain photographs of the experiments and investigations you carry out. It may also include other communication methods such as: charts, graphs and diagrams.

You should aim to write a report between 1,500 and 2,000 words – this is about 6–8 sides of A4 paper.

Student's tips

Presentation of your food investigation
- Try to present your task neatly. The language you use should be clear, using specialist words connected to the title of your task.
- Check your spelling, punctuation and grammar carefully. There are no extra marks for accurate spelling, punctuation and grammar, but this will help to improve the quality of your written communication.
- Use space available on the page wisely – quality is better than quantity!

Assessment of the food investigation

Your work will be marked in these three sections:

Section	Criteria	Maximum marks
A	Research	6
B	Investigation	15
C	Analysis and evaluation	9
Total		30

Table 7.1.2 Marks

The marks for the food investigation are awarded across two of the assessment objectives:
- **AO2** – apply knowledge and understanding of nutrition, food, cooking and preparation; this is worth 10 per cent of your NEA mark.
- **AO4** – analyse and evaluate different aspects of nutrition, food, cooking and preparation, including food made by themselves and others; this is worth 5 per cent of your NEA mark.

For this investigation, you will **research**, **investigate** and then **analyse** and **evaluate** your findings.

You will produce a report which is based on your research activities and outcomes and related to how ingredients work and why.

What you need to do for the food investigation: a summary

Content	Student tips	Assessment objective	Maximum marks available
A Research ● Background information on ingredients – finding out how these ingredients work and why. ● Write one or more aims for the **investigation** linked to the research findings. ● Plan the investigations and related practical work. ● Establish a **hypothesis** or predict an outcome.	It may be helpful to: ● Spend no more than 2 hours on background research, so you have more time for practical experiments. ● Have an aim for each investigation. ● Hypothesise or predict what will happen for each experiment.	A02	6
B Investigating ● Carry out the practical investigations, linked to hypothesis/**prediction**. ● Each investigation should have a clear aim. ● Results from one investigation should lead to the next. ● Record results using charts, graphs, tables and photographs. ● Explain your findings.	It may be helpful to: ● Record and explain your results clearly – link them to your hypothesis or prediction and make sure you photograph each experiment to show what you did.	A02	15
C Analysis and evaluation ● Analyse and interpret results of the investigative work, describing how these results can be used in other practical food preparation and cooking sessions. ● Evaluate the hypothesis/prediction with **justification**. ● Explain how the ingredients you used worked and why. ● Include a **bibliography** (this is not included in the word count).	It may be helpful to: ● Say if the hypothesis/prediction you made at the beginning came true. If so, why? If not, why not? ● Keep a note of the books and websites you used so that you can include these in your bibliography.	A04	9
Total			30

Table 7.1.3 Summary

Key words

Hypothesis is a statement which may be proved or disproved.

Prediction is a statement which says what you think will happen.

Justification means support to back up your findings

Investigation means examining carefully using different methods.

Bibliography is a list of books or other sources cited in a written text.

What you need to do for the food investigation: a closer look

Key words

Primary research is research you find out for yourself, for example a survey, an interview or dietary diary.

Secondary research is information previously researched, for example websites, books, leaflets, newspapers, labels and packaging.

Research for the food investigation

You should spend up to 2 hours on the research. You can find the information you need from **secondary** research. This *may* include:

- **Trusted websites** (for example, NHS, British Nutrition Foundation) – Use and discuss the information you find. Don't copy and paste large amounts of text. Be selective and make sure you list any websites in your bibliography.
- **Books** – Be selective and find key points on the topic you are investigating. You can quote some small sections, but make sure you write down the name of the book near the work or in the bibliography.
- **Leaflets, labels and packaging** – Some of these may be relevant to your investigation title and may give information that will be useful for your task(s).
- Magazine and newspaper articles.
- Multimedia – animations, YouTube clips etc.

All sources of secondary research you use need to be referenced in the bibliography.

An example food investigation task might be: **'Investigate what type of flour is best for bread-making'.**

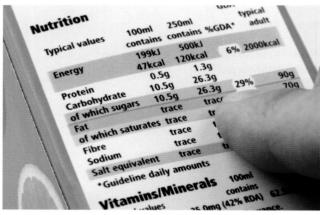

Figure 7.1.3 Carry out secondary research for your food investigation

For this investigation, you might consider carrying out the following research:

- What is flour made from?
- What does the wheat grain look like? (You may include diagrams of the wheat grain.)
- Find out the main types of flour available.
- What are the main ingredients, and what are their functions in bread-making?
- Find out about wholemeal flour, white flour, brown flour and their extraction rates.
- Find out how much protein each of these flours has: plain white, strong plain white, self-raising white flour.
- Find out what gluten is and the names of the two proteins that make gluten (include diagrams).
- Find out how to make gluten balls.
- Find a recipe for bread rolls.

Once you have completed your research, you will need to draw conclusions.

An example of how you might present the research and conclusions for this food investigation is shown on the opposite page.

(It is important that your research is focused on the task: for this example investigation the research is therefore focused on the choice of flours and not the other bread-making ingredients such as yeast).

Figure 7.1.4 Example of research for the Investigation

Investigate what type of flour is best for bread-making

What is flour made from?

What does a wheat grain look like?

What are the main types of wheat flour available?

What are the main ingredients and functions of these in bread-making?

What is gluten?

Conclusions from research

I have learnt that most flour is made from wheat and that if the whole wheat grain is crushed it makes wholemeal flour. The whole wheat grain includes the bran and wheatgerm, which gives the bread a brown colour and makes the bread higher in fibre. Other flours like brown flour and white flour have had some or all of the bran and wheatgerm sieved out.

The flour sold for bread-making is strong plain flour, which contains more protein than other types of flour. The names of the proteins in bread flour are glutenin and gliadin. When you knead these, they make gluten.

I found a bread recipe and saw that it contains yeast to make the bread rise and salt to flavour the bread and control the rate at which yeast grows. The flour is the main ingredient and gives the bread structure, volume and shape. Sugar is sometimes added to bread recipes to feed the yeast, but yeast can also use the natural sugars from the flour, so adding sugar is not essential in a bread recipe.

I found out how to make gluten balls and that once the dough has been kneaded the starch can be washed out under the cold tap. You are left with the gluten from the flour, which is a stretchy substance and looks to me like bubblegum. These gluten balls can be baked and compared to one another.

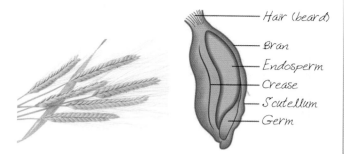

Wheat sheaves contain the grains of wheat

The structure of a grain of wheat

Different types of flour for bread-making

Ingredients for bread-making

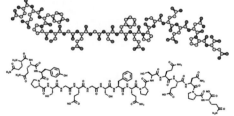

Gluten is the protein in wheat, made from glutenin and gliadin

You then need to decide what the aim of your investigation will be. For example, 'My aim is to find out how the gluten content of flour affects bread quality'.

Investigating

Once you have completed your research into how the ingredients work, you then need to decide on a hypothesis or predict an outcome.

Figure 7.1.5 **Example of hypothesis and prediction**

Hypothesis

My hypothesis is that the most successful flour for bread-making is strong plain flour because it has a high protein (gluten) content.

Prediction

I predict that the best flour for bread-making will be the strong plain flour because this flour is also called bread flour and is made from harder wheats suited to bread-making.

After deciding on a hypothesis and predicting an outcome, you can set your aims.

Aims

For example, if the aim for your first experiment is 'to find out how much gluten is in different flours', you could:

1 Investigate using three different types of flour to make gluten balls.
2 Bake these in a very hot oven.
3 Compare the baked gluten balls for size and texture and photograph the results.

Figure 7.1.6 **Example of a gluten ball experiment**

Gluten ball experiment

Gluten can be extracted from flour by washing away the starch in a muslin cloth

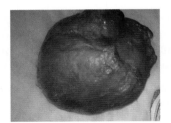

Gluten balls can be baked and compared to each other: they are strong and brittle

Using the results from the gluten ball experiment, you could then make different types of bread, each using a different type of flour. The aim of this experiment could be, 'Which flour makes bread with a good rise, flavour and texture?' You should record the results of these, and include photographs before and after baking.

Using the information from the bread-making experiment and the gluten ball experiment, you can then set your final aim, for example: 'to make the best bread using the most suitable flour(s)'. Plan and make bread using what you consider to be 'the best flour(s) for bread-making'.

Figure 7.1.7 Example of bread-making using different types of flour

Which flour makes food with a good rise, flavour and texture?

Bread rolls made with different flours, produce breads of varying colours, flavours and textures.

White bread dough

Wholemeal bread dough

Seeded bread dough

Baked wholemeal bread rolls

Baked white bread rolls

Baked seeded bread rolls

After bread-making, you could analyse the results of the investigations by:

- carrying out some initial **sensory analysis** to establish desired attributes for bread
- using a **star profile** to record which attributes the best bread should have
- setting up taste testing and asking four people to taste the bread, and then recording the results on your star profile
- deciding which types of flour would help you to make the best bread.

You should then discuss the results of your sensory analysis.

Figure 7.1.8 Bread made with the best flour for bread-making

You will have learnt how to carry out a sensory analysis in Topic 5.3 Sensory evaluation.

Figure 7.1.9 Example of sensory analysis results

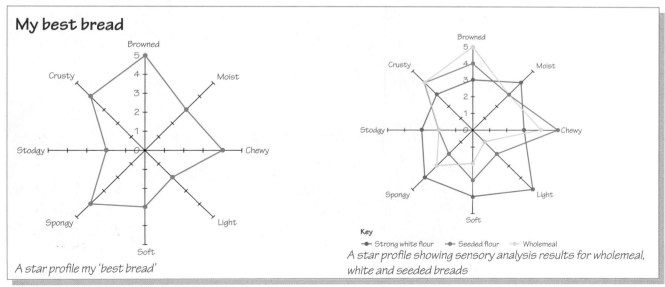

My best bread

A star profile my 'best bread'

Key
- Strong white flour
- Seeded flour
- Wholemeal

A star profile showing sensory analysis results for wholemeal, white and seeded breads

Analyse and evaluate

When you have completed your investigation and explained your findings, you then need to analyse and evaluate your results.

For the example investigation this would include:

- **analysis** of gluten ball experiments and discussion of the results
- sensory analysis of the breads made using different types of flour
- **evaluation** of the bread using the best type of flour(s) for bread-making
- explanation of how the results can be applied when preparing and making bread doughs in the future.

Figure 7.1.10 Example of analysis and investigation of gluten ball experiment

Analysis and evaluation of gluten ball experiment

Overall, the flour with the most gluten was the strong plain flour. This means it is the best of all the flours to make bread with.

Therefore I have learnt that high gluten flours are the best for bread-making. I learnt that bran, wheatgerm and seeds can break up the structure of the gluten, making it weaker, so although these breads have more flavour and a higher fibre content, the texture of the dough was not as consistent as the white strong plain flour.

I learnt that the dough must be kneaded for at least 5 minutes in order to develop the gluten from the gliadin and glutenin for it to give the bread strength and structure.

In future when I am making bread, I will always use strong plain flour so the gluten in the flour makes the dough stretchy and gives the bread a good chewy texture and a good crust. I will make it with a mixture of white and wholemeal flour. The wholemeal will give the bread a good colour and flavour as well as extra fibre in line with the new recommendation of 30 g per day for adults.

Figure 7.1.11 Bread samples for sensory analysis

Key words

Analysis means breaking down the results of a test and explaining them in more detail.

Evaluation is an overview of what went well and what went wrong, and a justification of conclusions – writing up what was learnt.

Figure 7.1.12 Example of analysis and evaulation of sensory analysis results

Sensory analysis results for different breads

I started off by making a star profile of what I thought the perfect bread should be like (Figure 7.1.9). I then asked four people to sample my three breads. They tasted the breads and gave each one a score from 0 to 5 depending on the intensity of each word (attribute) chosen. I took the average score for each bread to plot on the profile. I then compared the shapes and sizes of the star profiles to see which bread matched my 'perfect bread' profile the closest. From the charts I can see that the wholemeal bread matched my 'best bread' star profile the most.

Key word

Star profile is one method of recording sensory analysis results.

Figure 7.1.13 Example of evaluation of the bread using the best type of flour for bread-making

Evaluation of the bread using the best type of flour(s) for bread-making

During my research I experimented with the dough to see which type of flour produced the most gluten when kneaded. I discovered that the white strong plain flour produced the biggest gluten ball while the seeded gluten ball was smaller with the wholemeal being the smallest. This proved that white strong plain flour is well suited to bread-making as the larger amount gluten gives the dough strength and a good texture.

My results showed that the strong white flour produced the rolls with the biggest volume, as well as bread that was lighter than the other flours. The seeded rolls were smaller, but the texture was a combination of soft with the texture of the seeds adding some crunch. The wholemeal flour gave the smallest volume, but gave a solid texture and a good flavour and colour. The sensory analysis results of the baked rolls also showed that the white bread rolls and the wholemeal rolls were both enjoyed by most of the tasters with the seeded bread being less popular. It was less popular as it was too chewy and not spongy enough. For my best bread, I decided to use two parts strong white flour to one part strong wholemeal flour. Also by adding wholemeal flour I was increasing the fibre content of the bread. So to sum up, my best bread used a mixture of both strong white flour and strong wholemeal flour. The strong white flour gave the bread a lighter, but crusty texture and provided an elastic, but soft texture. The strong wholemeal flour gave the bread a good golden brown colour as well as a nutty flavour.

Figure 7.1.14 Example of explanation of how the results can be applied to future practical food preparation and cooking sessions

Explanation of how the results can be applied when preparing and making bread doughs in the future

When I am making bread doughs in the future, I will carefully think about which flour is the best to use. For pizza dough, I will need a strong base for the pizza topping and because I like my pizzas thin and crispy I will need to use a very strong flour. For bread rolls or loaves of bread, I do like to have lots of flavour and texture, so combining flours works well so I can get the best of textures and flavours from different flours.

Task 2: Food preparation assessment

The food preparation assessment is the second non-exam assessment you will carry out.

This food preparation assessment will allow you to show the food preparation skills you have learned during the course.

This will be a maximum of 20 sides of A4 paper and take no more than 20 hours which includes a 3-hour final practical assessment. It may be helpful to:

- You will research and analyse the life stage, dietary group or culinary tradition related to the chosen task.
- You will make three to four dishes to showcase a range of technical skills.
- You will then prepare, cook and present a final menu of three dishes, planning in advance how this will be achieved.
- You will prepare, cook and present your final dishes in one three-hour practical period and must include photographs of these within your task.
- Most of the marks for this task will be for your practical work.
- You must work safely and hygienically when carrying out practical work; this should be shown in your **time plan** and will also be assessed when making the final dishes (Section D)
- Your portfolio may be written or electronic.

Assessment of the food preparation assessment

Your task will be marked in these five sections:

Section	Criteria	Maximum marks available
A	Researching the task	6
B	Demonstrating technical skills	18
C	Planning for the final menu	8
D	Making the final dishes during the 3-hour practical session	30
E	Analyse and evaluate	8
Total		70

Table 7.1.4 Marks

The marks for the food preparation assessment are awarded across two of the assessment objectives:

- **AO3** – plan, prepare, cook and present dishes, combining appropriate techniques: this is worth 30 per cent of your total GCSE mark.
- **AO4** – analyse and evaluate different aspects of nutrition, food, cooking and preparation, including food made by yourself and others: this is worth 5 per cent of your total GCSE mark.

During this, you will:

- research the task
- demonstrate some technical skills which you may go on to use in the final practical session; photographic evidence will be needed to authenticate the technical skills.
- plan for the final menu
- make the final dishes
- analyse and evaluate: carry out **costing**, **nutritional analysis** and **sensory analysis** of your dishes.

Photographs of your three final dishes must be included in your folder.

Key words

Time plan is a step-by-step written timed plan of all the stages of making the final dishes, ideally showing dovetailing where appropriate.

Costing means working out the cost of the ingredients to make your dishes using software packages or manually with a calculator and a supermarket website.

Nutritional analysis means finding out the nutrients and energy in a recipe, meal or diet.

Sensory analysis means testing food samples by tasting, touching and visual methods.

What you need to do for the food preparation assessment: a summary

Content	Student tips	Assessment objective	Maximum marks available
A Researching the task ● Analyse the task, explain research requirement. ● Gather background information on the life stage/dietary group/culinary tradition followed by analysis of this information. ● Selection and justification of demonstrating your technical skills dishes, which reflect research and title chosen.	● Be selective in the methods of research you choose and record your results concisely.	A03	6
B Demonstrating your technical skills ● Consider ingredients and methods used. ● Demonstrate different technical skills to help decide which final menu to plan and make. ● Sensory analysis of all the dishes will be needed to help determine the final menu dishes.	● Make three to four dishes. ● The skills and dishes you choose should be relevant to your title. ● Try and include a wide variety of different skills and techniques within the dishes you choose. ● Use the correct equipment when necessary and make sure you know how to use this equipment before the practical session. ● List all the skills you have completed; these could be annotated on your photographs.	A03	18
C Planning for the final menu ● Choose the final dishes to make for the 3-hour session. The final dishes for Section D will be relevant to the task and will be different to the dishes made in Section B. ● Produce a 3-hour time plan (which includes food safety points) and completed sensory analysis sheets. ● Justification for the final dishes chosen, including skills, nutrition, ingredients, cooking methods, food provenance, sensory properties and portion size.	● You are not allowed to make the same dishes as you completed in the 'Demonstrating your technical skills' section again. ● Your time plan should include dovetailing of tasks to make the best use of your time. ● Try to include as many different skills as possible. You will need to demonstrate more complex dishes and be able to correct errors without any help. Remember to collect photographic evidence of skills used.	A03	8
D Making the final dishes ● In one 3-hour session, prepare, cook and present the three dishes. ● Show good food safety principles throughout.	● Demonstrate the skills accurately using the correct equipment. ● Follow your time plan carefully and be well organised. ● Take time to check flavours and present your final dishes well. ● Garnish and decorate the dishes that you make.	A03	30
E Analyse and evaluate ● Sensory analysis, costing and nutritional analysis of the final menu. ● Identify improvements for each of the final dishes.	● Comment on the dishes and analyse by identifying the key features from your results. ● Evaluate by discussing the good and bad parts of the completed work and give justified conclusions. ● Relevant and creative improvements for the final dishes should be linked to your task title.	A04	8
Total			70

Table 7.1.5 Summary

What you need to do for the food preparation assessment: a closer look

An example of a food preparation assessment task might be: **plan, prepare, cook and present a range of dishes that would be suitable for vegetarians, using a variety of skills. Present three final dishes.**

Collecting background information for the food preparation task

You may gather information for your background research by using both **primary** and **secondary** research.

Examples of primary research you may use include:

- **Surveys** – You can carry out a survey using the internet. For example, for the example food preparation assessment task, you could find out the different types of rice available in a large supermarket.
- **Dietary diary** – This is a record of the foods consumed. It could give information on the type of food and the approximate quantity. It can be recorded for a day or a few days.
- **Interview** – You may find someone who is an expert on the topic in your task who can give you more information on your task.

Examples of secondary research you may use include:

- **Trusted websites** – Use and discuss the information you find. Don't copy and paste large amounts of text. Be selective.
- **Books** – Be selective and find key points on the topic you are investigating. You can quote some small sections as long as you discuss them.
- **Newspaper and magazine articles** – Find up-to-date articles with relevant information and make sure you discuss the information linked to your title.
- **Leaflets, labels and packaging** – Some of these may be relevant to your title and may give information that will be useful for your task(s).
- Multimedia – for example, animations, YouTube clips etc.

Researching the task

Using some of the research methods listed above may be helpful when carrying out background research. For the example assessment task this may include, for example, finding out about the different types of vegetarians, their nutritional needs and alternative sources of foods supplying nutrients likely to be lacking in different types of vegetarian diets.

You will have learnt about different dietary groups and their nutritional needs in Topic 2.3 Nutritional needs and health.

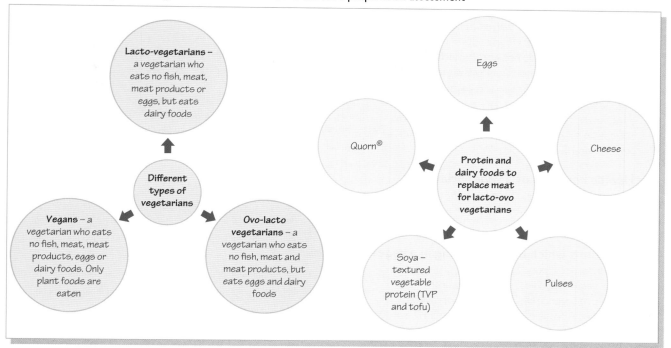

Figure 7.1.16 Example of background research

Background research

- Reasons why people become vegetarians
- The different types of vegetarian diets
- The health benefits of a vegetarian diet
- Which nutrients a vegetarian diet might be lacking in and plant foods which provide these
- Research into the range of meat substitutes
- Research into protein complementation

1 Reasons why people become vegetarians

There are different types of vegetarians depending on which animal foods are included in the diet. By interviewing someone who works in a vegetarian restaurant I found out that people may follow a vegetarian diet for different reasons:

- They do not like the thought of eating a dead animal, fish or bird.
- They think it is cruel to kill animals for food.
- They may follow a religion which does not allow them to eat meat, fish or poultry, for example many Hindus are vegetarians.
- They think it is healthier to eat a vegetarian diet than one that includes meat as this can lower the amount of saturated fat in the diet and help to lower cholesterol levels in the blood.
- They think it is wasteful to raise animals for food when the same land space could be used more economically to grow plants, which need less attention, less time spent producing them and less feeding and water compared with rearing animals.

Figure 7.1.16 **Continued**

2 Different types of vegetarians

From my *GCSE* textbook, I found out:

- Lacto-vegetarians do not eat animal foods such as meat, poultry and fish. They do not eat any animal products which involve the slaughter such as lard and gelatine. They will also not eat eggs, although they will eat dairy products such as milk, butter, cream, cheese and yoghurt.
- The lacto-ovo-vegetarian eats eggs as well as dairy products. Most UK vegetarians follow this type of diet.
- A vegan diet does not contain any animal foods. This means that no food that involves the slaughter or the use of animals in its production is included in the diet. All foods are plant-based so, as well as no meat or eggs, no dairy foods are included in a vegan diet.

3 Health benefits of a vegetarian diet

From my *GCSE* textbook, I found out that the health benefits of a vegetarian diet can include lowering cholesterol levels if suitable meat alternatives are eaten such as nuts, pulses and meat substitutes such as Quorn™ are eaten in place of meat.

4 Nutrients which may be lacking in a vegetarian diet:

From the internet I found out:

- Lacto-vegetarian diet – the mineral iron
- Lacto-ovo-vegetarian diet – the mineral iron
- Vegan diet – protein, calcium and vitamin D, iron, vitamin A and vitamin B12.

Iron from plant foods is not so easy for the body to absorb, but these plant foods are a good source of iron:

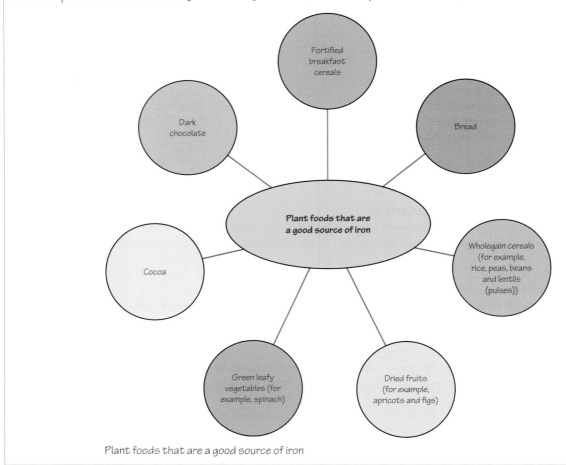

Plant foods that are a good source of iron

Figure 7.1.16 Continued

5 Meat substitutes

By asking a lacto-vegetarian to complete a food diary I found these foods were eaten in place of meat:

- Quorn™ – made from mycoprotein.
- TVP (textured vegetable protein) – made from soya beans.
- Tofu – made from soya beans. This is a bean curd.

6 Protein complementation

From my GCSE textbook, I found out that:

- Foods may be low biological value (LBV) or high biological value (HBV).
- Only HBV value proteins provide all of the essential amino acids.
- A combination of LBV plant proteins eaten together can provide all of the essential amino acids if this is planned properly.

Figure 7.1.17 **Example of analysis**

Analysis

People become vegetarians for many reasons, which include ethical, health, religious and economic reasons. Lacto-ovo-vegetarians exclude just meat, fish and poultry and any products which involve the slaughter of animals, but vegans exclude dairy foods and eggs as well. Lacto-vegetarians include dairy but exclude eggs. Including nutritious meat alternatives such as tofu and textured vegetable protein, made from soya in the diet would be better than relying too much on dairy foods such as cheese as these can be high in saturated fat. I found the nutrients a vegetarian may be lacking in are iron in a lacto-vegetarian and lacto-ovo-vegetarian diet. For vegans possible nutrients which may be lacking are protein, calcium and vitamin D, iron and vitamin C, vitamin A and vitamin B12.

With the findings of these results:

- Decide which type of vegetarian will be your target group and then select some recipes that will showcase your range of skills.
- Decide which equipment you will use to speed up or improve the quality of your chosen dishes.
- Justify why you have chosen these recipes and how these are relevant to the title and the target group – in the case of this example, vegetarians.

Figure 7.1.18 Example of ideas for selecting appropriate dishes

My target group will be ovo-lacto-vegetarians. This means they will eat all dairy foods as well as eggs. This target group are unlikely to have any nutritional deficiencies as a wide range of foods are eaten which will provide the nutrients instead of meat and meat products. Although I will need to ensure some high iron foods are included as the type of iron in plant foods (non-haem iron) is harder for the body to absorb than iron from meat (haem iron).

Selecting dishes

Ideas for suitable dishes:

I will now begin to consider which dishes will be suitable for ovo-lacto-vegetarians:

- Filled pasta dishes – for example, tortellini or ravioli.
- Soups – some soups are high in protein and iron as they contain pulses such as cannelloni beans. I can also show knife skills when preparing the vegetables.
- Breads – some bread, especially filled breads may contain cheese or herbs which give a good flavour and will also show my skills of bread making along with shaping bread rolls.
- Curries – these can be high in iron which is a nutrient which may be lacking in a vegetarian diet. By adding vegetables to the curry would mean vitamin C was also present which would aid the absorption of the iron.
- Rice dishes – some rice dishes also use pulses such as peas or kidney beans which show protein complementation.
- Vegetable quiches – these would be good for an ovo-lacto-vegetarian as I can use both eggs and milks which will supply useful nutrients such as iron and calcium.
- Sauces – sauces can be served with other main meal dishes. These may be vegetable based, such as a tomato, vegetables or a cheese based roux sauce.
- Vegetable lasagne – this could be made using handmade pasta and a sauce using pulses and vegetables. This would be an economical alternative to a meat lasagne.
- Salads – I can make salads using green leafy vegetables which are high in iron as well as seeds such as sunflower seeds which are high in protein.
- Fruit loaf – I can make a loaf such as a cranberry or banana loaf. In this I can include eggs which are a good source of iron as well as possibly using dried or fresh fruit.

Demonstrating your technical skills

The next stage is to make the dishes you have planned. Photographs will be needed to show the technical skills you have used, your candidate name and number should be visible in these photographs.

Write up the results, identify the skills you used and how you were organised and worked safely, especially when handling food and equipment. Carry out sensory analysis for each dish.

Figure 7.1.19 An example of skills trial write-up

Making fresh egg pasta dough demonstrates: Skill 5 Use of equipment (food processor and pasta machine) and Skill 10 Making, shaping and finishing a pasta dough

Spaghetti with tomato sauce demonstrates: Skill 8 Sauce making (reduction sauce)

Making vegetarian minestrone soup demonstrates: Skill 2 Knife skills (vegetables chopped into even-sized pieces), Skill 3 Preparing vegetables and Skill 6 Cooking methods (water-based using the hob)

Figure 7.1.19 Continued

Red onion and sage rolls demonstrates: Skill 2 Knife skills, Skill 3 Preparing vegetables and Skill 10 Making and shaping a bread dough

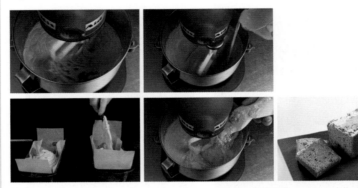

Making a banana loaf in a food mixer demonstrate: Skill 3 Preparing skills for fruit, Skill 4 Use of the cooker, Skill 5 Use of the food mixer, Skill 11 Use of chemical raising agents (baking powder) and Skill 12 Setting mixtures

Figure 7.1.20 Example of choices for demonstrating technical skills

Choices for demonstrating technical skills:

- Recipe 1 – Handmade spaghetti with tomato sauce
- Recipe 2 – Minestrone soup
- Recipe 3 – Red onion and sage rolls
- Recipe 4 – Banana bread

Initial reasons for choice of this menu

I have chosen these recipes as they are all suitable for ovo-lacto vegetarians. The dishes are colourful, attractive and nutritious. They also demonstrate a wide range of skills, some of which I can use in my final menu. I have made sure that I have included good sources of nutrients, especially iron and vitamin C which may otherwise be lacking in an ovo-lacto vegetarian diet.

Recipe 1

Pasta dough

Ingredients

225 g double 00 flour

3 g (½ tsp) of salt

18 ml (1 tbsp) of oil

2 eggs

18-35 ml (1-2 tbsp) of water

Figure 7.1.20 **Continued**

Tomato sauce

Ingredients

18 ml (1 tbsp) olive oil

1 small onion finely chopped

350 g passata

5 basil leaves

50 g parmesan cheese

Salt and pepper

Reasons for choice of Recipe 1

I chose to make spaghetti with tomato sauce as the egg pasta is a good source of protein and iron which are useful nutrients for a vegetarian diet and shows use of the pasta machine as well as knife skills and sauce making. I can also show the use of the food processor in making the dough.

Sensory analysis: Recipe 1 – Spaghetti and tomato sauce

Person	Appearance	Aroma	Flavour	Texture	Main comments
Louis	5	5	4	5	Good tangy sauce
Axel	4	5	4	5	Pasta cooked 'al dente'
Soraya	4	3	5	5	The smell was strong
Georgia	5	5	5	2	Tomato sauce – not smooth enough
Total	18	18	18	17	

Comment on sensory results above

The pasta was a popular choice with my taste panel, they liked the fresh pasta and how I had cooked it. The tomato sauce had mixed reviews, but both Soraya and Georgia didn't enjoy it due to its aroma and slightly chunky texture. I will need to change the flavouring of my pasta if I decide to make it for my final menu. I will need to consider vegetarian ingredients which are well flavoured and have a good aroma.

Planning for the final menu

Review the dishes you made at the demonstrating technical skills and select skills from these and choose three dishes (which may have accompaniments, for example curry and rice would be one dish), to make for your final menu. **This does not have to be a three-course meal, but it can be if you want.**

Give reasons for your choice, explaining why you have chosen these dishes linked to your background research findings.

Figure 7.1.21 Example of justification for the final dishes chosen

Reasons for my choice of ravioli with garden salad and dressing

In my skills trial I made fresh pasta using the pasta machine. I knew I wanted to make pasta in the final practical but I wanted to use more skills in the final practical as well, so I looked for more challenging recipes. I found recipes for tortellini and ravioli. I have decided to do giant ravioli as I can fit more filling in each one so that a bigger amount of cheese and spinach would be eaten per portion. This will mean that the vegetarian will have a higher protein and iron intake. I also want to show my skills of handling the pasta machine again and cutting and shaping the pasta into ravioli shapes by hand. The ravioli are cooked by simmering and I will show skills of handling large pans of boiling water and draining the pasta safely. In the skills trial I showed knife skills when preparing the minestrone soup. I will use these skills to prepare a garden salad and show how I can cut the vegetables into even-sized pieces. The textures of the soft and chewy ravioli and the crisp garden salad will complement each other and make the meal more interesting. I will make a French dressing for the salad to show an emulsion of lemon juice and olive oil and to add flavour and moistness to the salad. The salad will provide vitamins and minerals, especially the antioxidants vitamin A in the carrots, vitamin C in all the vegetables, but especially the red peppers, and vitamin E in the olive oil. The red cabbage and celery will provide iron which may be lacking in a vegetarian diet.

When you have chosen the final dishes and justified your choices, it may be helpful to make a **time plan** showing times, activities and points to remember, including food safety points (e.g. wash your hands).

Student's tips

Before you write your time plan you will need to:

- Collect the recipe(s) you are going to make and look at the cooking times, oven temperatures and chilling times. You will need to include the detail of these on your time plan.
- Decide which order you need to carry out the tasks, so that they will all be ready to serve at the end of the three-hour session. Remember: sometimes you can do more than one thing at once. For example, to save time, some tasks can be carried out while other dishes are cooking in the oven. We call this **dovetailing**.
- Allow time to garnish and decorate your dishes before they are presented and photographed.

Figure 7.1.22 Example of a time plan for a final menu

Time plan	Final menu Cream of tomato soup with croutons Giant ravioli with garden salad and French dressing Apple cake	
Time	Activity	Points to remember
9.00 am	Tie back hair, wash hands and put apron on. Wipe down work surfaces. Preheat oven to 180°C. Take the spinach out of the freezer and put in a colander over the sink to defrost. Butter and line a baking tin with parchment paper. Peel, core and thinly slice the apples, then squeeze lemon juice over. Set to one side.	Add lemon juice to prevent the apples browning.
9.10 am	Place the butter, caster sugar, eggs, vanilla and flour into a large bowl and mix with an electric hand mixer until smooth.	Wash hands after handling raw eggs. Make sure butter is softened. Mix for about 2 minutes.
9.20 am	Spread half the mixture into the prepared tin. Arrange half the apples on top of the mixture, then repeat the layers finishing with a layer of apple slices. Sprinkle with a little demerara sugar.	Before the cake tin goes into the oven, wipe off any spills on the sides of the tin with a clean, damp cloth, to avoid burnt-on mixture. Don't forget the sugar on the top, which will caramelise while baking.
9.30 am	Bake for 45–50 minutes until golden and springy to the touch. Wash up, dry up, put away dishes and wipe down work surfaces.	Use oven gloves when putting cake into oven to avoid burns. Keep area clean and tidy to prevent cross-contamination.
9.40 am	While the cake is baking, make the pasta sheets for the ravioli. Sieve the flour and salt. Make a well in the middle. Add the olive oil and water. Knead to a smooth dough. Rest for 30 minutes in a cool place.	Put the pasta dough in a bowl covered with cling film in the fridge to rest.
9.50 am	For the garden salad, wash and dry the lettuce and tear into pieces. Cut the carrots into julienne and finely slice the rest of the vegetables. Combine the ingredients in a large bowl with the peas. Put the kettle on to boil.	Make sure all the salad vegetables are washed and clean to prevent food poisoning. Cover salad with cling film and put in the fridge. Use the correct chopping board for vegetables.
10.00 am	Wash up, dry up and put away dishes. Wipe down work surfaces. For the tomato soup, make shallow cuts on the skin of the tomatoes before putting them in a large Pyrex bowl and pouring on the boiling water.	Leave the tomatoes in the boiling water so the skins loosen and will peel off more easily.
10.10 am	Check the apple cake. If it is golden brown, push with your finger to see if it springs back. When cooked, leave to cool for 10 minutes in the tin and then turn on to a cooling tray. Dice the onions and carrots for the tomato soup.	Test for readiness with a skewer if not sure – it should come out clean. Use the correct chopping board for vegetables.

Figure 7.1.22 Continued

10.20 am	Stir the defrosted spinach with the ricotta cheese, some grated nutmeg, salt and pepper in a small bowl.	Put the ravioli in the fridge until time to poach them.
	Take the pasta dough out of the fridge. Roll into a very long rectangle with a pasta machine. Eggwash the pasta and cut into large circles with a pastry cutter.	
	Put a spoonful of filling into the centre of each pasta circle and put another layer of pasta on top. Use a smaller pastry cutter to trim the edges neatly.	
10.40 am	Wash up, dry up and put away.	Chill the French dressing until needed. (Don't forget to shake again just before dressing the salad.)
	Put the ingredients for the French dressing into a jam jar with lid and shake together.	
	Tip the blanched tomatoes into a colander over the sink.	
10.50 am	Peel the skin off the tomatoes.	Add the mixed herbs or bouquet garni with a little salt and pepper once the soup is simmering.
	Begin to make the soup: melt the butter in a thick-bottomed pan. Add the onion and carrot and brown lightly. Mix in the flour and cook until a sandy texture. Gradually add the hot vegetable stock. Stir and bring to the boil. Then turn down the heat and simmer for 30 minutes.	
11.10 am	While the soup is simmering, wash up, dry up and put away dishes and equipment and wipe down the surfaces.	Use a pan stand to put the frying pan on once the croutons are golden brown.
	Make the croutons by shallow frying some stale bread cubes in a little vegetable oil in a small frying pan.	
	Boil the kettle for the ravioli.	
11.20 am	Prepare the pan to poach the ravioli.	Use a slotted spoon to remove the ravioli and put into an earthenware dish.
	Grate some Parmesan or Cheddar cheese.	
	Poach the ravioli in a large pan of simmering water about eight pieces at a time.	
11.40 am	Meanwhile, liquidise the soup with a handheld blender and taste and season as needed.	Leave in the pan with the lid on to keep warm.
	Sprinkle the cheese on the ravioli and grill before serving.	
11.50 am	Meanwhile, display the cake and serve one slice neatly.	Check final display and present neatly.
	Put ravioli and salad with dressing on a serving plate.	Photograph all dishes.
	Ladle the soup into a bowl.	
	Final washing up session and wipe-down of area.	
12.00 noon	End of practical.	Take dishes home for sensory analysis and bring results to next lesson.

Making the final dishes

You will need to make your three dishes within a three-hour session.

- You should follow your time plan.
- Try to be organised and tidy.
- Make sure that you follow the rules of food safety in your own personal hygiene and when handling food.
- Take time to garnish and decorate the dishes to your best standard.
- Photograph your final dishes. Your candidate name and number must be visible in these photographs. This is an essential requirement.

Figure 7.1.23 An example of final dishes

My final dishes

Cream of tomato soup with croutons

Giant ravioli stuffed with spinach and ricotta cheese

Garden salad

Apple cake

Analyse and evaluate

Carry out nutritional analysis and evaluation of your three final dishes. Using the information you found out at the investigation stage, you need to see if your dishes/meal match the nutritional needs of your target group – in this example vegetarians.

Figure 7.1.24 Nutritional analysis of a menu of tomato soup with croutons, spinach and ricotta ravioli, garden salad, apple cake

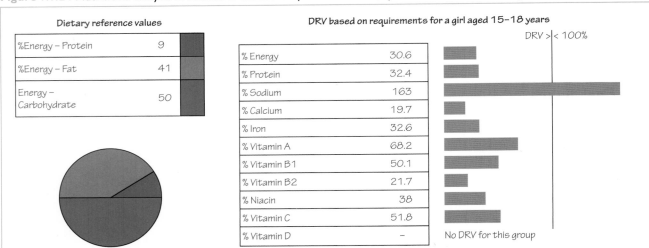

Dietary reference values	
%Energy – Protein	9
%Energy – Fat	41
Energy – Carbohydrate	50

DRV based on requirements for a girl aged 15–18 years

DRV >|< 100%

% Energy	30.6
% Protein	32.4
% Sodium	163
% Calcium	19.7
% Iron	32.6
% Vitamin A	68.2
% Vitamin B1	50.1
% Vitamin B2	21.7
% Niacin	38
% Vitamin C	51.8
% Vitamin D	–

No DRV for this group

My lacto-ovo vegetarian menu is actually a complete meal. I have analysed the menu together so I can see how all the nutrients add up for this meal. I have analysed this meal using 'Nutrients' software. To analyse the amount of nutrients the meal provides I have put myself (a teenage girl aged 15–18) as the target group so it is realistic for my needs. Although I am not a vegetarian myself, I do enjoy lots of vegetarian meals and often have days when I eat no meat or fish. This menu mainly meets the dietary needs of a teenage girl well. As it is one meal out of a day's meals, it would need to supply about one-third of the DRVs needed for the day. I can see that the meal provides the expected amounts of energy and protein. Of the nutrients that I found could be lacking in a vegetarian diet, the meal also provides about a third of the iron needed for the day, which is good as I found out teenage girls especially need extra iron due to menstruation. One nutrient which is rather low is calcium. To increase the calcium for this meal, I could serve the ravioli with extra cheese sprinkled on top and also serve the apple cake with some yoghurt, fromage frais or custard. One nutrient which is too high is the mineral sodium, which is present in the soup and ravioli. To reduce this I could use low-salt stock cubes and not add extra salt to the soup when making but use extra garlic and herbs to give it flavour. I would also not add salt to the ravioli as these have enough flavour without the extra salt.

The government-recommended per cent of energy from nutrients:
- Protein – 15 per cent
- Fat – 35 per cent
- Carbohydrate – 50 per cent (only 5 per cent from free-sugar, the rest should be from starchy carbohydrate and fruit sugars)

The per cent of energy from the three main nutrients does follow the recommended amount for carbohydrate at 50 per cent, and most of this comes from starches in the croutons, and the pasta for the ravioli. The apple cake is a low-sugar recipe. The per cent of energy from fat is rather high in my menu, I could reduce this by dressing the garden salad with lemon juice rather than French dressing and toast the croutons instead of frying them. The percentage of energy from protein is also rather low, but if I served the apple cake with low-fat yoghurt this would increase the protein as well.

You also need to carry out sensory analysis of all the dishes you have made.

You will have learnt how to carry out a sensory analysis in Topic 5.3 Sensory evaluation.

Figure 7.1.25 Example of sensory analysis of the final menu

Analysis of sensory testing

Sample	Dislike very much	Dislike	Neither like or dislike	Like	Like very much	Total (out of 4 people)
Tomato soup	0	0	0	3	1	4
Ravioli	0	0	2	1	1	4
Apple cake	0	0	0	3	1	4
Points	x 1 point	x 2 points	x 3 points	x 4 points	x 5 points	Total (out of a possible 20 points)
Tomato soup	0	0	0	12	5	17
Ravioli	0	0	6	4	5	15
Apple cake	0	0	0	12	5	17
Percentages						
Tomato soup						34.69%
Ravioli						30.61%
Apple cake						34.69%

Maximum score = 20 (the highest score for this test)

Minimum score = 4 (the lowest score for this test)

Hedonic ranking for the final menu

I asked four people to taste my dishes and record their scores using the hedonic scale. The tasters had a 5-point scale to score, with descriptors ranging from dislike very much to like very much. This scale was easy to use because everyone understood it as no complex words were needed to describe the food. The tomato soup and apple cake were the most popular of the three main dishes I made. The tomato soup was very tasty as I used fresh tomatoes and de-skinned these, which made the texture smooth. The ravioli was not quite so popular, I think this was because the texture of the ravioli was a bit slimy which some tasters did not like. They all enjoyed the flavour though and said they preferred it to meat ravioli. Next time, I would improve the texture of the ravioli by patting them dry with kitchen towel before serving, to make them feel less slimy in the mouth. The apple cake was very popular with the tasters and everyone liked it, but some did not like it very much as they said it was not sweet enough. I made it lower in sugar as I found out during my background research that our free sugar intake should only be about 5 per cent of our total energy intake, so most people need to get used to less sugar to stay healthy and to help prevent tooth decay and obesity. To improve the flavour of the apple cake I would use some cinnamon next time to make up for the loss of flavour from using less sugar.

Cost all the final dishes and discuss/analyse and evaluate the results.

You can work out the cost of your recipes by using a calculator and finding the prices of ingredients on a supermarket website using the method shown in the example below. However, there are also costing software packages available that you can use to work out the cost of your recipes and this will be quicker. Whichever method you use, make sure you discuss the final costs when drawing conclusions and whether they are appropriate for your task title.

You will have learnt about costing when meal planning in Topic 2.3 Nutritional needs and health.

Figure 7.1.26 Example of costing of the final dishes

Costing of the final dishes

I used a supermarket website to cost these ingredients and used the formula on this chart to calculate the cost for the entire recipe and then per serving. This recipe serves four people.

Food item	Packet price in pence	÷	Packet weight in grams/ millilitres	×	Amount used in recipe (grams/millilitres)	=	Cost in pence
Plain flour	50		500		200		20
Olive oil	350		1000		35		12.25
Water	N/A				105		0
Spinach, cooked	150		1000		200		30
Ricotta cheese	125		250		200		100
Butter	85		250		25		8.5
Nutmeg	100		30		2		6.7
Salt	35		750		2		0.1
Pepper	50		25		1		2
Total cost in pence							179.55
Cost per serving to nearest pence							45

Costing of ravioli

Analysis of costing

I have found out that the spinach and ricotta ravioli are very cheap to make. The whole recipe was only £1.80 and this is very good value for a recipe which serves four people. I bought frozen spinach as it was cheaper. I also bought value lines where these were available as I mainly needed basic ingredients and the value lines looked as good as the more expensive branded goods. Making vegetarian ravioli was cheaper than using meat. The cost of food was important to consider as most families have a budget for food and can't afford to waste money buying expensive food when cheaper food is available. By buying frozen spinach I didn't waste any of this as there was no washing, or trimming to do. Also, the spinach I didn't use was stored back in the freezer until I needed to use it again. However, I did waste the ricotta as I didn't need to use the whole tub; next time I use it I will just try to buy a smaller tub of ricotta or find another way of using the cheese in a different recipe.

Key word

Sensory qualities refers to the tastes, texture, aroma and appearance of the dishes/menu.

Suggesting improvements

After you have made the final dishes, you need to analyse and evaluate your practical work and identify improvements to the dishes. Suggest improvements for the final dishes linked to nutrition, **sensory qualities** and cost, and reasons for these improvements – try to do this as you go along.

Here are some examples from the vegetarian task:

- **Nutritional analysis**: Improvement: 'I could serve the ravioli with some cheese sprinkled on top, or serve the apple cake with custard, yogurt or fromage frais.' Reason: 'To increase the calcium content of these dishes.'
- **Sensory analysis**: Improvement: 'To improve the flavour of the apple cake I would add some cinnamon next time.' Reason: 'To make up for the loss of flavour from using less sugar.'
- **Costing**: Improvement: 'I will just try to buy a smaller tub of ricotta or find another way of using the cheese in a different recipe.' Reason: 'To avoid food waste.'

TOPIC 7.2 PAPER 1: FOOD PREPARATION AND NUTRITION (THE WRITTEN EXAM)

In the written exam you will be tested on five topics:
1   Food, nutrition and health
2   Food science
3   Food safety
4   Food choice
5   Food provenance

(These topics are covered in Sections 2–6 of this book.)

The written exam is worth **100 marks** (this is **50 per cent** of your total GCSE mark).

Your exam paper will be marked by AQA.

When will the exam be completed?

You must complete the written exam in May/June of the academic year in which the qualification is awarded. So, for most students, this will be in Year 11.

How long will I have to complete the exam?

The exam will last 1 hour and 45 minutes.

The assessment objectives

The GCSE exam in Food Preparation and Nutrition includes questions that will allow you to demonstrate your ability to:
● Recall information
● Bring together information from different areas of the specification
● Apply your knowledge and understanding in both practical and theory contexts.

What are the assessment objectives assessing?

The four assessment objectives (also called AO's) are examined across both the NEA and the written paper. In the written paper, just three of the AO's are assessed, these are:
● **AO1** – Demonstrate knowledge and understanding of nutrition, food, cooking and preparation
● **AO2** – Apply knowledge and understanding of nutrition, food, cooking and preparation
● **AO4** – Analyse and evaluate different aspects of nutrition, food, cooking and preparation including food made by yourself and others.

Different questions on the written paper will measure how you have achieved these AO's. The table below shows the weightings for the AO's examined in the written paper.

Assessment objective weightings for the written paper	
Assessment objectives (AO's)	Approx. % on the written paper
AO1	20
AO2	20
AO3	0
AO4	10
Total weighting for theory paper	50%

You can see that both demonstrating and applying knowledge and understanding of nutrition, cooking and food preparation are the main ways the written paper is assessed.

What format will the exam take?

The exam will be divided into two sections:

- **Section A** will include multiple choice questions. There will be 20 marks available for this section. You will need to answer **ALL** questions in this section.
- **Section B** will include five questions, with a number of sub-questions. There will be 80 marks available for this section. You will need to answer **ALL** questions in this section.

How will I be assessed?

There are three assessment objectives against which you will be assessed in the written exam. These are shown in the table below.

	Assessment objectives	Weightings for written exam
AO1	Demonstrate knowledge and understanding of nutrition, food, cooking and preparation.	20%
AO2	Apply knowledge and understanding of nutrition, food, cooking and preparation.	20%
AO3*	Plan, prepare, cook and present dishes, combining appropriate techniques.	0%
AO4	Analyse and evaluate different aspects of nutrition, food, cooking and preparation including food made by themselves and others.	10%

*(You will not be assessed against Assessment Objective 3 (AO3) in the written paper.)

The exam paper will be marked by AQA.

General advice on answering exam questions

- Read through the instructions on the front of the exam paper carefully.
- Read each question carefully (at least twice) before answering it and make sure you understand what you are being asked to do.
- Make sure that you understand what all of the command words in the question mean. You may find it useful to underline or highlight command words.
- Check how many marks are given for the question. This should tell you how many points or pieces of information you need to include in your answer.

State	Give only the bare facts, expressed clearly and fully.
	(For example: **State** three different religions which may affect food choice.)
Select	Carefully choose as being the best or most suitable.
	(For example: **Select** suitable recipes to make for demonstrating technical skills.)
Identify	Establish or indicate what (someone or something) is.
	(For example: **Identify** which drinks in the samples contain the most sugar.)
Suggest	Make a recommendation or suggestion.
	(For example: **Suggest** ways of reducing the fat content of your diet.)
Describe	Write out the main features. Write a picture in words.
	(For example: **Describe** a packed lunch which would supply a good source of iron and vitamin C for an ovo-lacto vegetarian.)
Outline	Write out the main points or a general plan, but omit minor details.
	(For example: **Outline** the main factors which influence food choice.)
Explain	Set out in facts and the reasons for them, make them known in detail and make them plain or clear.
	(For example: **Explain** why this recipe is not suitable for coeliacs.)
Consider	Think about in order to understand or decide.
	(For example: **Consider** which novel protein to use in your vegan meal.)
Justify	Show adequate grounds for decisions or conclusions. Prove to be right. Give a good reason.
	(For example: **Justify** why you have chosen this menu for young children.)
Compare	Point out the differences and similarities between the given items.
	(For example: **Compare** the wholemeal and white bread rolls.)
Contrast	Point out the differences between two or more given items.
	(For example: **Contrast** the two Victoria sandwich cakes made by both the all-in-one and the creaming method.)
Discuss	Write from more than one viewpoint, supporting and casting doubt. It is not always necessary to come to a conclusion.
	(For example: **Discuss** how leftover food may be safely used in meal preparation.)
Assess	Give your judgement of something. Put a value on it. Judge the worth of something.
	(For example: **Assess** the factors which may contribute to the risk of food poisoning when handling raw chicken.)
Evaluate	Judge the worth of something, sum up the good and bad parts and decide how improvements may be made.
	(For example: **Evaluate** your bread making skills.)
Draw conclusions from	Explain what you learnt.
	(For example: **Draw** conclusions from the yeast fermentation experiment you carried out.)

Table 7.2.1 Command words you may encounter in exam questions and their meanings

Section A: Multiple choice questions

Section A of the exam paper will include **20 multiple choice questions**

For each of the 20 multiple choice questions:
- You will be given a question and four possible answers.
- One answer will be the correct answer.
- You will need to decide which answer is correct and shade the box next to the correct answer.

For example:

I The ideal temperature for yeast to grow is
   A 100°C ☐
   B 45°C ☐
   C 25°C ☐
   D 10°C ☐   [1 mark]

- There will be **one mark** available for each correct answer.
- There will be **20 marks** in total available for Section A.

(There are examples of multiple-choice questions to help you practise at the end of Section 2-6 in this textbook.)

Section B: Other question types

Section B of the paper will include five questions, with a number of sub-questions.
- You will need to answer **ALL** questions in this section.
- There will be **80 marks** in total available for Section B.
- The number of marks available for each question will vary. Make sure you check how many marks are available for each question or sub-question, as this will tell you how many points or pieces of information you need to include, or how detailed your response needs to be.

A varied range of questions containing different command words are likely to be used in Section B. Each of these will require a different type of answer. Some examples of questions using these different words are included below, with some suggestions on how to approach answering them.

Short-answer questions

Question 1 is about Food, nutrition and health.

1.1 What is the difference between high biological value (HBV) protein foods and low
      biological value (LBV) protein foods?   [2 marks]

High biological value protein foods contain all of the essential amino acids and low biological value protein foods have some essential amino acids missing.

Relevant responses may include:
- **HBV proteins contain all of the essential amino acids**
- **LBV proteins are missing some of the essential amino acids.**

Commentary:

A detailed knowledge by recall is needed to be shown in the response. One mark could be gained by recalling the meaning of either HBV or LBV protein foods.

1.2 Complete the table below to show two different examples of each.

HBV foods – complete 3 examples of each below:	LBV foods – complete 3 examples of each below:
1.	1.
2.	2.
3.	3.

HBV foods – complete 3 examples of each below:	LBV foods – complete 3 examples of each below:
1. pork ✓	1. wheat flour ✓
2. meat ✗	2. kidney beans ✓
3. fish ✓	3. nuts ✓

Commentary:

This type of question just requires single word answers. Repetition of one type of food is not necessary. Fish would be marked correct.

Data response questions

Question 2 is about Food, nutrition and health.

The chart below shows Estimated Average Requirements (EAR) of energy for children aged 12–18 years.

Age (years)	PAL*	Boys' Daily Energy Requirements (Kcal)	Girls' Daily Energy Requirements (Kcal)
12	1.75	2247	2103
13	1.75	2414	2223
14	1.75	2629	2342
15	1.75	2820	2390
16	1.75	2964	2414
17	1.75	3083	2462
18	1.75	3155	2462

Table 7.2.1 Estimated Average Requirements (EAR) of energy for children aged 12–18 years

*PAL = physical activity level – a way to express a person's daily physical activity as a single number.

(Adapted from 'Dietary Reference Values for Energy', Scientific Advisory Committee on Nutrition, 2011)

2.1 What is the physical activity level number for teenagers? [1 mark]
2.2 How many kcal per day should a girl aged 16 years old consume? [1 mark]
2.3 How many kcal per day should a boy aged 16 years old consume? [1 mark]
2.4 Explain why the amount of energy needed by boys and girls is different. [2 marks]
2.5 What would happen if someone regularly consumed more energy than their body needed? [1 mark]
2.6 Name two health risks linked to a low physical activity level. [2 marks]

2.1   1.75

2.2   2414 Kcal

2.3   2964 Kcal

Marks are awarded as follows: 1 mark for each correct answer.

2.4   *Boys need more energy than girls as they are usually bigger than girls. Boys have a higher proportion of muscle than girls which requires more energy.*

1 mark for each correct response, or 1 mark for a correct response and 1 mark for an explanation or description of this reason.

Acceptable answers:
- **Boys are usually bigger than girls**
- **Boys have more muscle tissue**
- **Boys have a higher metabolic rate than girls.**

2.5   *You would put on weight.*

1 mark for a correct response. Acceptable answers:

You may:
- **put on weight**
- **become overweight**
- **become obese**
- **store surplus (body) fat**
- **increase body fat**
- **place health at risk.**

2.6   *If you have a low physical activity level, you are more at risk of becoming obese. This may lead to type 2 diabetes or coronary heart disease.*

1 mark for each correct answer. Answers include: obesity, coronary heart disease, type 2 diabetes, stroke, some cancers, arthritis and depression.

Commentary

This question is using data response to test your ability to understand and use information. In this case a chart is given and answers are based on this piece of information to examine your ability to use this information and decipher responses from it.

Answers to questions 2.1, 2.2 and 2.3 would be awarded full marks as each response is correct. Single-word answers are acceptable for single mark questions.

2.4: there are two marks available for this question and either two separate answers, or a single response with a reason are acceptable and could gain 2 marks.

2.5: this would gain the maximum mark of 1 mark, as the response is correct.

2.6: this response is very clear and concise. It would be awarded the full two marks as it firstly identifies that obesity is likely to be a consequence of a low physical activity level (PAL) and goes on to name two diseases which are linked to obesity.

Questions on recipes

Some questions present information such as a recipe to look and ask you to answer questions based on this information.

Question 3 is about Food science.

The information below shows a recipe for Braised Beef.

Braised beef

Ingredients

450 g shin of beef

30 ml vegetable oil

2 onions, finely chopped

2 cloves of garlic (crushed)

30 g seasoned flour

400 ml beef stock

200 g mushrooms (washed and sliced)

20g fresh parsley sprigs

Method

1 In a large saucepan, fry the beef in oil.
2 Add the onions, fry for 10 minutes.
3 Add the garlic fry for one minute, then stir in seasoned flour.
4 Gradually stir in the beef stock.
5 Braise gently for about 2 hours until the meat is tender. The mixture should just be gently simmering.
6 Add the mushrooms for the final 30 minutes of cooking.
7 Garnish with fresh parsley.

3.1 Which herb is used in this recipe?   [1 mark]

3.1 *Parsley.*

Commentary

This question asks you to extract information from the recipe and apply your knowledge and understanding of food and nutrition. There is just 1 mark available for this question and therefore you are only expected to give one fact or piece of information. You will get a mark for naming the correct food item (in this case parsley). If more than one answer is given, only the first answer will be marked.

3.2 Explain why this dish would not be suitable for Hindus. [2 marks]

A Hindu would not eat this dish because it contains beef and beef stock.

Hindus do not eat beef or any beef products because in the Hindu religion cows are holy, sacred animals so are not seen as a source of food.

1 mark for each relevant reason given, e.g.:
- Hindus do not eat beef or beef products for religious reasons
- Hindus consider the cow to be a sacred animal
- Many Hindus are vegetarians
- The principle of Ahimsa (not harming) is important to Hindus.

Commentary

This question is testing your understanding of the principles of how a religious diet (in this case Hinduism) affects food choice. It asks you to explain why the dish would be unsuitable for a Hindu. This means you need to show you understand why the dish would not be suitable for a Hindu by giving reasons.

3.3 This dish is cooked by braising. State which two methods of heat transfer are used during braising. [2 marks]

Heat is transferred in braising by conduction and convection currents.

1 mark for each relevant reason given, e.g.:
- By conduction
- By convection
- By convection currents.

Commentary

This question is asking you recall and relate your knowledge and understanding of how heat is transferred to food to the recipe.

3.4 Describe how heat is transferred during the braising of beef. [2 marks]

When the hob heats the base of the metal saucepan (metal is a very good conductor) the heat is conducted around the pan and into the food, which will cook the beef. Heat also travels through the cooking liquid (beef stock) through convection currents.

1 mark for each relevant reason given, e.g.:
- Heat is conducted through molecules in solids (the saucepan) or liquids (the beef stock)
- When a saucepan is placed on the hob the molecules in the pan start to vibrate
- Metal and water (in the beef stock) are good conductors of heat
- Convection currents move through the cooking liquid as the hot water rises and expands and cooler water takes its place at the bottom of the pan. The cooler water is then heated and rises and expands.

Commentary

You need to describe how conduction and convection transfer heat to the food during cooking. This answer has fully explained how the heat is transferred into the beef and also mentions that metal is a good conductor.

3.5 How does braising tenderise meat? [2 marks]

Cooking the meat at a low temperature in moist conditions for a long time causes the protein named 'collagen' in the meat to be converted to 'gelatine'. This increases the tenderness of the meat because gelatine is soluble and a much softer protein than collagen.

1 mark for each relevant reason given e.g.:
- Low temperature cooking
- Simmering (not boiling)
- Moist cooking method
- The protein collagen is converted to gelatine with the braising method as it is a longer cooking time with moist heat
- Meat fibres are softened during braising.

Commentary:

This question is asking you to apply your knowledge and understanding of working characteristics and functions of ingredients to the specified dish. You are asked to describe the function of tenderising the meat.

Open-ended questions

Open-ended responses require a different approach. An important skill is to understand what the question is asking. A question will begin with a command word (see page 441 to see what these command words mean).

Student's tips

The Word PEEL can help you to respond to open-ended questions it stands for:
- P – Point
- E – Explanation
- E – Example
- L – Linked

Question 4 is about food choice.

4.1 Suggest ways a family on a low income could save money when buying food.

[6 marks]

A family on a low income could use a price comparison site to compare costs of the ingredients at different shops and then buy the ingredients in the cheapest store. They could choose supermarket value range ingredients rather than branded products or luxury range products as these are often cheaper. They should avoid shopping in a convenience store such as corner shop, as these are often more expensive than supermarkets. They should buy the ingredients in a supermarket instead. They should aim to plan meals in advance so less food is wasted and see whether they could use any of the same ingredients in different recipes (for example, buying a large jar of passata for a tomato sauce recipe and for a pizza topping). The family could also see whether any special offers were available on any of the ingredients, such as 'buy one get one free'. They should shop at the end of the day as shops often reduce items which have a shorter shelf life then so they may be able to find cheaper ingredients.

Relevant reasons may include:
- Use price comparison sites
- Choose value range foods
- Shop in larger supermarkets as corner shops and convenience stores may be more expensive
- Plan meals in advance
- Use a shopping list
- Do not shop when you are hungry
- Shop at the end of the day when foods may be reduced
- Look out for offers e.g. buy one get one free, buy three for the price of two

Commentary

This question is asking you to apply your knowledge and understanding of factors which influence food choice and how to consider costing when meal planning. There are 6 marks available for this question and therefore you need to describe six different ways a family on a low income could save money, or give **three** different ways with specific reasons for each. The student has provided six different valid suggestions.

Open-ended, holistic responses are marked using level descriptors like the ones shown in the table below.

Mark band	Level descriptors	Marks
Upper	Response shows accurate application of relevant knowledge of saving money when buying food. Relevant examples will be given showing clarity of understanding. A range of specialist terminology is used correctly.	5–6
Middle	Response shows some application of relevant knowledge of saving money when buying food. Appropriate examples are given showing a grasp of most aspects, but some areas may lack clarity. Most specialist terminology will be used correctly.	3–4
Lower	Response shows limited application of knowledge with a few examples of saving money when buying food. The response may lack clarity with basic and few qualified answers.	1–2

Question 5 is about food safety.

5.1 A family re-heats a chicken curry the day after it was made, but later they develop the symptoms of food poisoning. Assess the factors that may have caused the food poisoning. Draw conclusions about how food poisoning could be avoided in the future. [9 marks]

After cooking the chicken curry, it should have been cooled down and put in the refrigerator. It is important that cooling is done quickly so that the dish does not stay in the temperature danger zone of 5°C to 63°C for too long as food poisoning bacteria may grow between these temperatures. The dish should have been cooled within 90 minutes and then put in the fridge at 0° to below 5°C. The chicken curry should not have been stored below raw meat in the refrigerator as this could drip onto and contaminate the cooked chicken which could have led to food poisoning.

When the chicken curry was re-heated, if it was re-heated in the microwave it may not have been re-heated thoroughly as microwaves can leave cold spots in the food which would not destroy the bacteria. Food re-heated in a microwave should be piping hot and steaming; if possible you need to again check the temperature is above 75°C with a temperature probe. If the chicken curry were re-heated on top of the cooker hob or in the oven, again it should reach a temperature of at least 75°C to ensure food poisoning bacteria were destroyed.

Once the chicken curry had been re-heated it should have been served straight away with clean utensils and eaten immediately. Care should be taken with personal hygiene when handling the food, ensuring hands are washed and a clean apron is worn. Any leftovers should have been thrown away as it is not safe to re-heat food more than once. This is because the chicken curry would pass through the temperature danger zone too many times and this would allow more bacteria to grow.

Relevant responses may include:
- Key temperatures – chilling 0°C to below 5°C, freezing – 18°C or below, temperature danger zone 5° to 63°C, cooking 75°C, re-heating 75°C
- Hot food should not be put in the refrigerator until cooled to room temperature
- Need to cool hot food within 90 minutes to minimise bacterial growth
- Correct storage of foods in the refrigerator raw foods underneath cooked foods to reduce the risk of cross contamination
- Correct use of a temperature probe
- Use of clean equipment and utensils
- Personal hygiene – mention of the following points, for example: hair tied back, hand washing, no nail varnish, wearing a clean apron, not handling food when ill
- Mention of piping hot or steaming hot food
- Re-heat curry in batches so the heat reaches the centre of the food quickly; this avoids temperatures in the danger zone
- Problems of cold spots when food re-heated in the microwave – need for stirring
- Throw away leftover food if not eaten after re-heating as food will have passed through the temperature danger zone four times at this stage.

Commentary:

Open-ended, holistic responses are marked using level descriptors as shown in the table below.

Mark band	Level descriptors	Marks
Upper	Response shows thorough application of knowledge and understanding of food safety issues and provides detailed examples of cooling food after cooking and how to safely re-heat the chicken curry. May include correct references to the type of food spoilage agents and the conditions needed for these to be active. Specialist terminology is used correctly.	7–9 marks
Middle	Response shows some knowledge and understanding of food safety issues. Responses will be qualified with some explanation of the need to safely cool, and store the chicken curry before re-heating safely. Most specialist terminology is used correctly.	4–6 marks
Lower	Response shows limited knowledge of food safety issues with less clarity in understanding. Response will show limited correct facts or extended answer showing limited understanding of food safety. Answer will be generic with simplistic terminology.	1–3 marks
No answer worthy of credit		0 marks

Question 6 is about Food provenance.

6.1 Organic food often costs more than non-organic food. Discuss why some people are prepared to pay more for organic food.
[6 marks]

Some people want a more natural diet and want to avoid foods grown with artificial fertilisers. Organic farmers rotate their crops and use natural compost to make sure their soil is naturally fertile and this avoids the need for artificial fertilisers. This method of production usually costs more and some people are prepared to pay more for what they consider better quality food, grown on natural soil.

Animals raised as organic have a good quality, natural diet, free from genetically modified ingredients. Their diet must be 100% organic and antibiotics are not given unless the animal is ill. These animals may produce foods such as milk and eggs which cost more as the animals are more expensive to keep as they need more space and must always have access to outdoor space. Animals which are raised for meat naturally grow more slowly as they are not given drugs to speed up their growth. For all of these reasons organic food usually costs more, but is still a popular choice for some people.

Relevant responses may include:

Some people:
- Choose organic food for its better taste
- Choose organic for a more natural diet
- Prefer foods with no artificial fertilisers
- Prefer foods with no chemical pesticides
- Understand the soil is naturally fertile which benefits the crops
- Prefer organic foods which may have an increased nutritional value as compared to conventional crops
- Choose organic to avoid genetically modified ingredients which are not allowed in organic foods
- Organic food often contains no or very few food additives
- Choose organic foods as they care about the environment and the natural wildlife that develops in organic farming
- Animals raised as organic must have a 100% organic diet
- Antibiotics are not routinely given to animals raised as organic
- Organic animals are more expensive to rear
- Most organic foods cost more than non-organic foods, because of the less intensive production methods
- Organic animals are all required to be free range and must have a larger land area to qualify as organic which is more costly
- Organic animals are not given growth hormones, so naturally grow more slowly; this costs time and money
- Organic food will not contain any genetically modified ingredients nor may animals being raised as organic be fed on any genetically modified foods.

Commentary:

This type of question requires a longer answer. For this reason it would be marked holistically using mark bands.

Mark band	Level descriptors	Marks
Upper	Response shows accurate application of relevant knowledge of organic farming methods. Relevant examples will be given related to cost, showing clarity of understanding. A range of specialist terminology is used correctly.	5–6
Middle	Response shows some application of relevant knowledge of organic farming methods. Appropriate examples are given showing a grasp of most aspects related to cost, but some areas may lack clarity. Most specialist terminology will be used correctly.	3–4
Lower	Response shows limited application of knowledge with a few examples of organic farming methods related to cost. The response may lack clarity with basic and few qualified answers.	1–2

Glossary

Aeration is when air is trapped in a mixture.

Aerobic means with oxygen.

Al dente means 'firm to the bite', a description of the texture of correctly cooked pasta.

Allergen is a substance that may cause an allergic reaction.

Ambient refers to temperatures at 17°C to 20°C; also referred to as room temperature.

Amino acids are the basic components of all proteins.

Amylopectin produces a clear gel when it thickens and has the same thickness hot or cold.

Amylose causes sauces to thicken, turn cloudy when cooked and get even thicker as they cool.

Anaerobic means without oxygen.

Analyse means to find out and discuss results.

Analysis means breaking down the results of a test and explaining them in more detail.

Anaphylactic shock is a serious condition in which a person develops swelling in their throat and mouth, making it difficult to speak or breathe.

Angina is when the blood supply to the heart is restricted.

Anti-bacterial spray is a clear spray that kills 99.9 per cent of bacteria; it should be used after surfaces have been wiped with hot, soapy water.

Antioxidants are vitamins A, C and E, which protect the cells from harmful substances.

Arteries are large blood vessels that take blood away from the heart.

Ascorbic acid is another word for vitamin C.

Au gratin refers to a dish sprinkled with breadcrumbs or cheese and breadcrumbs, browned under the grill.

Bacteria are single-celled micro-organisms; some types of bacteria can cause food poisoning.

Baking powder is a chemical raising agent that produces carbon dioxide.

Barbecue means to cook food over a grill over burning charcoal.

Basal metabolic rate (BMR) is how many kilocalories you need to stay alive for 24 hours when warm and resting.

Batter is a mixture of flour, milk or water, and usually an egg.

Beating a liquid or mixture adds air.

Beri beri is a lack of vitamin B1.

'Best before' date means that food is at its best quality before this date, although – with the exception of eggs – it may safely be eaten after this date.

Betacarotene is vitamin A from plant sources.

Beurre manie is a paste made from equal quantities of butter and flour mixed together, which is added to liquids to thicken them.

Bicarbonate of soda is a chemical raising agent that produces carbon dioxide.

Bind means to bring the ingredients in a mixture together using a binding ingredient.

Biological catalysts are enzymes, which speed up reactions.

Blanching means immersing fruits or vegetables in boiling water for a short period of time and then cooling rapidly. Blanching stops enzyme activity and helps to retain vitamins.

Blender is a piece of equipment with sharp blades that rotate to cut up food and reduce it to a pulp.

Blood clot is when blood becomes a solid.

Blood sugar level refers to the amount of sugar in your blood.

Blood vessels are the capillaries, veins and arteries.

Body mass index (BMI) is an index of your weight in relation to your height. It is used to classify people into four groups – underweight, healthy, overweight and obese.

Boiling is a method of cooking where foods are cooked in boiling water.

Bread is a combination of flour, yeast, sugar, salt and liquid, which is made into a dough.

Bread knife is a large knife with a serrated blade, used to slice bread, cakes and pastries.

British Lion Scheme is a scheme to vaccinate hens against salmonella and to label eggs with a lion and a 'best before' date.

Brunch is a combined breakfast-lunch meal.

Brunoise means cutting vegetables into tiny dice from julienne strips.

Campylobacter is a type of bacteria and is the main cause of food poisoning in the UK.

Cancer of the bowel is uncontrolled growth of cells in the large intestine.

Caramelisation is the process of changing the colour of sugar from white to brown when heated.

Carbon footprint is a measure of the impact human activities have on the environment in terms of the amount of greenhouse gases produced.

Cardiovascular disease refers to diseases of the heart and blood vessels.

Carriers (of pathogenic bacteria) are people who carry these bacteria, but show no symptoms.

Carving knife is a long thin-bladed knife used to carve both cooked meats and cold meats.

Casserole refers to food that is completely covered in liquid, then cooked in the oven.

Cazeula is a glazed terracotta dish used to make Spanish stews.

Chemical raising agents are raising agents that produce carbon dioxide when they are heated with a liquid.

Cholesterol is a fatty substance found in the blood; it is essential for humans but can be harmful.

Cholesterol-lowering spreads are low-fat spreads that help to keep cholesterol levels low.

Chorleywood Bread Process is the name of the bread-making process used in large bakeries.

Choux pastry is a light, crisp, hollow pastry used to make profiteroles, eclairs and gougeres.

Coagulate is when protein sets, either when heated, or in acidic conditions.

Coagulation is a change in the structure of protein, when proteins set, brought about by heat or acids. This change is irreversible.

Coat means to add another ingredient to create an attractive finish; or to create a protective layer on a food when cooking.

Coeliac is a person suffering from coeliac disease.

Coeliac disease is an auto-immune disease; an sensitivity of gluten.

Cold spots can be found in foods reheated in the microwave, if they are not stirred or turned during the reheating process.

Conduction is when heat travels through solid materials such as metals and food.

Connective tissue gives support and structure to body tissues.

Contaminated is when an unwanted substance is transferred onto another, for example if someone sneezes onto food.

Convection is when heat travels through air or water.

Convection current is the movement of heat in water or in the air.

Cooking with fat uses the convection currents in hot oil or fat to cook food.

Cooking with water uses the convection currents in water to cook food.

Cook's knife is a large general purpose knife with a deep blade, used for cutting, chopping, slicing and dicing.

Coronary heart disease (CHD) is a build-up of fatty deposits in the coronary arteries.

Costing means working out the cost of the ingredients to make your dishes using software packages or manually with a calculator and a supermarket website.

Creaming fat and sugar together adds air.

Cross-contamination means bacteria spreading onto food from another place, for example hands, work surfaces, utensils.

Crush means to crush into tiny pieces with another implement.

Cuisine is a style of food characteristic to a particular country or region.

Culture means our laws, morals, customs and habits.

Curdling is when milk denatures. It develops a slightly lumpy appearance because all the protein in the milk has clumped together.

Defrosted means when frozen food has been removed from the freezer and left to stand in the fridge, until all ice crystals have melted.

Deglazing is to loosen the browned juices on the bottom of the pan by adding a liquid to the hot pan and stirring while the liquid is boiling.

Dehydration is a lack of water.

Demonstrating technical skills means demonstrating skills which you may use when making the final dishes.

Denature is when protein changes shape, either when heated, agitated or in acidic conditions.

Denaturation may be permanent change to protein, which occurs when protein is heated and there is a change in its chemical structure or it may temporary e.g. when egg white foam stands and collapses back to its liquid state.

De-skin means to remove the skin by either putting the fruit or vegetable into boiling water or, for peppers, placing on direct heat.

De-seed means to remove seeds before using.

Developed world refers to nations of the world that are considered more economically and technologically advanced, such as Europe, USA, Japan and Australia.

Developing world refers to nations of the world that are less economically and technologically advanced, such as parts of Africa and Asia.

Dextrinisation is when dry heat turns a starch brown.

Diabetes is a condition when the body's sugar levels cannot be controlled properly.

Dietary diary is a record of all the food and drink consumed over a set period of time.

Digestive system refers to the parts of the body where food is broken down to provide nutrients.

Disinfect means to kill bacteria.

Disposable income is what money is left over for saving or spending after taxes are subtracted from income.

Diverticular disease is a condition where small bulges appear in the large intestine.

Double sugars or disaccharides: two single units of sugar joined together (e.g. sucrose).

Dry-frying refers to heating food on a low heat without any fat or oil.

Dry heat uses convection currents or radiation to cook food.

Durum wheat is a yellowy, high-protein wheat that is grown especially for making pasta.

E. coli is a type of food poisoning bacteria often associated with undercooked meat.

Electromagnetic rays are produced inside a microwave oven and will heat food up by causing water molecules to vibrate.

Elevenses is an old-fashioned name for a mid-morning snack.

Emulsification is the process of using an emulsifier (such as egg yolk) to stabilise an insoluble mixture.

Emulsifier is a substance that will allow two immiscible liquids (substances that do not mix) to be held together.

Emulsion is a mixture of two liquids, made by tiny drops of one liquid spreading evenly through a second liquid.

Energy-dense foods are those which contain a high number of calories per gram (for example biscuits, chocolate).

Enriched foods are foods that have micronutrients added to them to replace those lost during processing.

Environment refers to the air, water and land in or on which people, animals and plants live.

Enzymes are biological catalysts that speed up reactions.

Enzymic browning is when enzymes in food react with oxygen in the air to cause the food to turn brown.

Epithelium contains scent receptors and can identify different smells.

Essential amino acids are amino acids that cannot be made by the body, they must come from food.

Essential fatty acids are required for development and cannot be made by the body.

Evaluation is an overview of what went well and what went wrong, and writing up what was learnt.

Extraction rate is the percentage of flour by weight that is taken from the whole grain to make flour.

Faecal contamination means contaminated with solid waste from humans or animals.

Family budget is the family's income and expenditure of money over a specified time.

Fat-soluble vitamins are vitamins A, D, E, and K which dissolve in fat.

Fat spread is a fatty yellow spread for bread, which contains no more than 60 per cent fat.

Ferment is when yeasts reproduce by feeding on sugar, producing carbon dioxide gas and alcohol.

Fermentation is the process in which yeast produces the gas carbon dioxide.

Fertilisers are chemicals that enhance the soil by introducing nutrients.

Filleting knife is a thin, flexible, narrow-bladed knife used to fillet fish.

Fish fillet is a cut of fish that is free from bone.

Flavour is the combined sense of taste, mouthfeel and aroma.

Fluoride toothpaste is a type of toothpaste that helps to strengthen the enamel on your teeth to prevent decay.

Folding layers into a dough adds air between the layers.

Food allergy is an allergic reaction to a specific food.

Food intolerance is a sensitivity to some foods.

Food miles are the distance that food is transported as it travels from producer to consumer.

Food processor is a piece of equipment with various attachments that can prepare a variety of foods, such as slice and grate vegetables.

Food security is when all people, at all times, have access to enough safe and nutritious food for them to lead an active, healthy life.

Food spoilage is when food loses quality and becomes inedible.

Food tables refers to printed or computer information on nutrients in foods.

Fortified refers to food that has vitamins and minerals added to improve its nutritional value.

Fortification means adding micronutrients to food that were usually not originally in the food.

Fossil fuels are coal, oil or natural gas, formed in the earth from plant or animal remains.

Free radicals are found inside the body and attack healthy cells, which can cause heart disease or cancer.

Free-range production is a method of farming where the animals can have access to outdoor space, rather than being restricted to an enclosure for 24 hours each day.

Free sugars are sugars that are added to food (they are not part of the cell wall of a plant).

Freezer burn is the excessive dehydration and oxidation on the surface of food while stored in the freezer. It is usually caused by inadequate packaging.

Garnishes are decorations on savoury food.

Gelatinisation is the process in which moist heat is applied to starch grains, which swell, increase in size and then break open, releasing amylose, which thickens the mixture around boiling point. Stirring will prevent lumps forming.

Gelation is when a mixture is thickened by starch, and sets on chilling.

Genetically modified refers to foods produced from plants or animals that have had their genetic information changed by scientists.

Global warming is a gradual increase in the overall temperature of the earth's atmosphere caused by increased levels of carbon dioxide and other chemicals in the atmosphere.

Glucose and **galactose** are sugars (single sugars or monosaccharides) found in milk.

Gluten-free means without wheat, rye, barley and sometimes oats.

Grading tests are used to produce a ranking, rating and profiling of a product.

Grate means to make coarse or fine threads by repeatedly rubbing over one of the sides of a grater.

Greenhouses gases are gases that trap heat in the atmosphere; this can cause climate change.

Growth spurt is a rapid increase in height.

Haem iron is iron from animal sources.

Haemoglobin is the part of the red blood cell that carries oxygen around the body.

Healthy diet is a diet low in fat, salt and sugar, and high in fibre.

Heart attack is when the blood supply to the heart is suddenly cut off.

Heart palpitations are when your heart beats suddenly become more noticeable.

Heat stroke is an uncontrolled increase in body temperature.

Hedonic ranking is a preference test, which finds out whether people like or dislike a product.

Hedonic scale is a rating scale (scores) for testing/comparing food samples.

Herbicides are chemicals that destroy weeds.

Hereditary is a condition passed down from parents to their children.

High biological value protein is protein that contains all of the essential amino acids.

High blood cholesterol is a high level of cholesterol in the blood.

High blood pressure is a higher than normal force of blood pushing against the arteries.

High-risk foods are ready to eat moist foods, near-neutral and high in protein; these are most likely to support the growth of bacteria.

Homogenisation is the process of forcing the milk at high pressure through small holes to stop the layer of cream separating out.

Hydration is the supply of water required to maintain the correct amount of fluid in the body.

Hydrogenation is the process in which vegetable oils are 'hardened' to make them solid at room temperature.

Immiscible means not able to be mixed or blended together. Immiscible liquids which are shaken together will eventually separate in to layers. Oil and water are immiscible.

Immune system refers to the parts of your body and processes that protect against disease.

Imported means brought in from a foreign country.

Infuse means to flavour liquid with aromatic ingredients by slowly heating to boiling point and then allowing it to cool. The flavoured liquid is then called an infusion.

Infused liquids are liquids with seasoning, spice, herbs or wine added.

Insoluble fibre is dietary fibre that helps to prevent constipation.

Insulated cold bag is a padded bag used with ice packs to keep food cold.

Intensive farming is a farming system that aims to produce as much yield as possible, usually with the use of chemicals and in a restricted space.

Intestines are part of the digestive system.

Invisible fat is fat that is not clearly seen in food.

Iron deficiency anaemia is caused by a lack of iron.

Jardinière means cutting vegetables into batons.

Julienne means cutting vegetables into matchstick strips.

Kilocalorie is a unit used to measure the energy in food.

Knead means to manipulate dough by pushing it across a work surface and pulling it back. This is essential to stretch the gluten.

Knock back means to knead out the carbon dioxide in risen dough to remove large air pockets to ensure an even texture.

Kwashiorkor is a type of malnutrition linked to a lack of protein and energy.

Kosher refers to food that is allowed to be eaten because it is considered clean (in Judaism).

Lactase is the enzyme that digests lactose.

Lactic acid is formed during the cheese-making process, when lactose is converted into lactic acid.

Lacto-ovo vegetarians are vegetarians who eat no fish, meat and meat products, but eat eggs and dairy foods.

Lacto-vegetarians are vegetarians who eat no fish, meat, meat products or eggs, but eat dairy foods.

Lactose is the sugar naturally found in milk.

Lactose intolerance means you cannot digest lactose.

Layer means to make up a dish with differing ingredients one on top of another.

Lecithin is a natural emulsifier found in egg yolk.

Listeria is a type of food poisoning bacteria that can multiply at fridge temperatures.

Low biological value protein is protein that lacks one or more essential amino acid.

Low-energy foods are foods low in energy and high in water.

Low-fat spread is a yellow fat spread for bread, which contains no more than 40 per cent fat.

Macedoine means cutting vegetables into medium dice.

Magnetron is a device found inside a microwave oven, which produces electromagnetic rays.

Mandatory means required by law.

Margarine is a butter substitute, usually made from vegetable oils/fats; it must contain 80 per cent fat.

Marinade is a highly flavoured liquid, which is used to give flavour, keep food moist and assist in tenderising foods. The liquid can be acidic or a salty solution.

Marinating is the process of soaking meat or vegetables in a strongly flavoured liquid before cooking, to help develop the flavour, tenderise and in some instances colour the food before it is cooked.

Marketing refers to identifying consumers' needs and wants, and using that information to supply consumers with products that match their needs and wants.

Mash means to reduce to a soft mass by using a masher.

Mechanical raising agents are air and steam.

Menopause is when a woman's periods (menstruation) stop, around the age of 50 years.

Menstruation is when a woman has a monthly period.

Microgram is the smallest unit of measurement used to measure micronutrients.

Micronutrients are the nutrients needed in small amounts. Vitamins and minerals are micronutrients.

Micro-organisms are microscopic, tiny organisms; these include yeasts, moulds and bacteria.

Microwave oven is a piece of equipment that heats food, cooks food, defrosts food and cooks frozen or fresh ready meals.

Milling is the process that separates the different parts of the grain.

Mis en place means preparation before starting to cook.

Mix means to combine two or more ingredients together to become one.

Mixer is a machine that primarily whisks and beats.

Modified atmosphere refers to packaging that uses a combination of gases (nitrogen or carbon dioxide) to increase the shelf life.

Modify recipes means to change ingredients or cooking methods to improve a recipe.

Monosodium glutamate is a flavour enhancer, which is a type of food additive.

Moulds are tiny fungi, which produce thread-like filaments. Moulds are a type of micro-organism. They are used in food production to make cheeses, cured sausages and soya sauce.

Mould spores are spores produced by moulds to help the mould spread further.

Mouthfeel is the way a particular type of food feels in the mouth.

Night blindness is caused by a lack of vitamin A, and means you are unable to see well in dim light.

Non-haem iron is iron from vegetable or plant sources.

Nutritional analysis means finding out the nutrients and energy in a recipe, meal or diet.

Nutritional modification means adding ingredients to foods that may improve health.

Obesity is being very overweight.

Oily fish refers to fish in which the oil is distributed throughout the body of the fish.

Olfactory receptors send messages to the brain about the smells.

Olfactory system is the body's 'smell device' and enables you to detect aromas and smells.

Omega 3 fatty acids are polyunsaturated fatty acids, essential for good health.

Organic food refers to food where at least 95 per cent of the ingredients must come from organically produced plants and animals.

Osteoporosis is a condition in adults, where a loss of calcium from bones makes them weak and more likely to break.

Over-nutrition is an oversupply of a nutrient or nutrients.

Oxidation is the loss of water-soluble vitamins on exposure to heat/air.

Paellera is a large round pan with shallow sides used to cook paella.

Paring knife/vegetable knife is a small multi-purpose knife, mainly used for slicing and dicing.

Pasteurisation is the process of prolonging the keeping quality of products such as milk by heating to 72°C for 15 seconds to destroy harmful bacteria.

Pasteurised refers to food that has been heat-treated to kill most micro-organisms.

Peak bone mass is when bones have reached their maximum density by storing nutrients such as calcium.

Peel means to remove thinly the skin of fruits and vegetables using a peeler.

Peer pressure is a feeling that you must do the same things as other people of your age in order to fit in or be liked and accepted.

Pernicious anaemia is a lack of vitamin B12.

Pester power is when children pester adults to buy products.

Pesticides are chemicals that destroy pests: creatures that are harmful to the crops.

Physical activity level (PAL) is the amount of physical activity you do each day, for example sitting, standing, running and exercise.

Plaque is a mixture of bacteria on teeth and the sticky substances produced by them.

Plasticity is the ability of a solid fat to soften over a range of temperatures.

Poaching is a method of cooking where food is cooked in a liquid that is just below boiling point.

Portion size refers to the amount of a food that is recommended for one person to eat in one sitting.

Preference test is used to find out if a product is acceptable to the consumer.

Preservatives are chemicals added to food to increase the shelf life.

Price comparison sites are websites that compare supermarket food prices.

Primary processing refers to the process of changing raw food materials into food that can be eaten immediately or processed further into other food products.

Protein alternatives are products which have been developed for use in food preparation as an alternative to animal protein.

Protein complementation is combining LBV proteins foods to form a HBV protein meal.

Proteolytic enzymes are enzymes that break down the muscle fibres in meat, making it much more tender.

Proving is the last rising of the bread dough in its final shape before it is baked.

Radiation is when heat rays directly heat and cook food.

Raising agent is an ingredient or process that incorporates a gas into a mixture to lighten it; it is added to sweet or savoury mixtures, such as cakes, scones and breads, to make them rise.

Ranking means putting samples in order of preference (for example the one you like best comes first).

Ranking tests are used to measure the strength of a specific sensory property in a number of samples.

Rationed refers to the controlled distribution of scarce resources (food).

Rating test allows people to rate the extent to which they either like or dislike one aspect in a number of similar food products or to rate different aspects of one food product.

Recipe modifications means changes to a recipe to meet a (nutritional or other) need.

Reduction is the process of simmering a liquid over heat until it thickens. It is also the name of the concentrated liquid that forms during this process.

Retinol is vitamin A from animal sources.

Riboflavin is vitamin B2.

Rickets is a condition found in children, where a lack of vitamin D and calcium in the diet causes the bones to soften.

Rind is the outside skin of bacon and gammon.

Roll means to spread out or flatten.

Rubbing in fat into flour adds air.

Salmonella is a type of food poisoning bacteria, sometimes on undercooked meat.

Saturated fatty acids have single bonds on the carbon chain.

Saturated fats contain saturated fatty acids, are usually from animal sources and can be harmful to health.

Sauce is a well-flavoured liquid that has been thickened.

Scissor snip means to cut food with a pair of scissors instead of a knife.

Scoop is a hollow-shaped spoon with a handle.

Scurvy is a lack of vitamin C.

Seasonal foods means foods that are only available at certain times in the year.

Secondary processing refers to the process of changing primary food products into other types of products.

Segment means to peel and pull apart, for example an orange.

Semolina is a coarse-ground flour, which comes from wheat.

Sensory analysis means testing food samples by tasting, touching and visual methods.

Sensory profile test is used to obtain a detailed description of the appearance, taste and texture of a food product.

Sensory qualities refers to the colours, flavours and textures of the dishes/menu.

Shallow frying is a quick method of cooking where a small amount of fat is used to cook food in a frying pan.

Shape means using a knife to create a shape. It also means to give a prepared dough its final shape before proving.

Shortening is the process in which fat coats the flour particles, preventing absorption of water resulting in a crumbly mixture.

Shred means to slice in long, thin strips.

Sieving dry ingredients through a sieve adds air.

Simmering refers to water that is heated to just below boiling point.

Skewer is a long metal or wooden pin used to secure food on during cooking; to skewer is to hold together pieces of food using a metal or wooden pin.

Slaughter means to kill animals for food.

Sodium chloride is the proper name for 'table salt'.

Soluble fibre is dietary fibre that helps to reduce cholesterol.

Spina bifida is a defect in the backbone that can occur in unborn babies if the mother did not eat enough folic acid during pregnancy.

Spore-forming bacteria refers to bacteria that can produce spores, which protect the bacteria from high temperatures, acids and disinfectants. Normal reheating doesn't destroy them.

Starch grains are tiny particles of starch found in some carbohydrates.

Starchy foods are foods high in starch, such as pasta, rice, potatoes and bread.

Starchy carbohydrates are carbohydrates such as bread, rice, potatoes, pasta and chapatis.

Star profile is one method of recording sensory analysis results.

Starter culture is a small quality of harmless bacteria used to start the fermentation of yoghurt or cheese.

Steaming is a method of cooking where food is cooked in the steam coming from boiling water.

Sterilisation is a method of increasing the keeping quality of products by destroying all micro-organisms by heating food to a very high temperature.

Sterilised means heated to kill bacteria, yeasts and moulds.

Stir-frying is a quick method of cooking where small pieces of food are fast-fried in a small amount of oil in a wok.

Stroke is when the blood supply to the brain is cut off.

Sunshine vitamin is another name for vitamin D.

Sustain means to maintain and look after something, for example the environment.

Sustainable environment is one where the demands placed on the environment can be met without reducing its ability to allow all people to live well, now and in the future.

Syneresis usually refers to eggs; if overcooked, the proteins shrink as they coagulate and separate from the watery liquid.

Tagine is a glazed earthenware pot with a distinctive lid. It is also used to describe the food cooked in it.

Tainting is when the flavour/aroma of one food is changed by another stronger food.

Tandoor is a clay oven heated by charcoal used to cook naan bread and tandoori dishes.

Target group is the group you are planning recipes, meals or diets for.

Taste buds detect sweet, sour, salt and bitter tastes.

Temperature danger zone is the range of temperatures between 5°C and 63°C, where most bacteria can easily multiply.

Tenderising meat is a process by which the tough muscle fibres are broken down in order to make the meat more tender to eat.

Thali is a stainless-steel plate on which Indian food is served.

Thiamin is vitamin B1.

Time plan is a step-by-step written timed plan of all the stages of making the final dishes, ideally showing dovetailing where appropriate.

Tooth decay refers to the acids in your mouth that attack tooth enamel.

Triglyceride is the chemical name for a fat molecule.

Ultra heat treatment (UHT) is a process of sterilisation using a high temperature for a very short time.

Umami provides food with a savoury or meaty flavour.

Under-nutrition is eating too little food or too little of a particular nutrient to meet dietary needs.

Unpasteurised milk is milk that hasn't been heat-treated to destroy bacteria.

Unprocessed foods are natural foods that have not been refined, such as wholemeal flour, brown rice, fresh fruits and vegetables.

Unsaturated fatty acids have a double bond on one or more carbon atoms.

Unsaturated fats contain unsaturated fatty acids and are thought to be better for health.

'Use by' date means that food must be consumed by this date to prevent food poisoning.

Vaccinated refers to an injection to prevent infection.

Vegans are vegetarians who eat no fish, no meat, meat products, eggs or dairy foods. Only plant foods are eaten.

Viscosity is the thickness of a liquid.

Visible fat is fat that can be clearly seen in food.

Vitamin drops containing vitamins A, C and D are recommended for children aged 6 months to 5 years in the UK.

Water intoxication is drinking too much water.

Water-soluble vitamins are the B group of vitamins and vitamin C, which dissolve in water.

Whisking at high speed adds air.

Whole grain means the entire seed of the plant – the endosperm, germ and bran.

Wholemeal means that the whole of the cereal grain (for example wheat) has been used, nothing has been taken away.

Wok is a shallow rounded frying pan.

Wraps are fillings that are wrapped up in soft flat breads such as tortillas or pittas.

Yeast is a tiny, single-celled fungus; a type of micro-organism. It is used in bread-making, and it produces carbon dioxide during fermentation.

Index

Page numbers in bold refer to key word definitions.

accompaniments 11
acids
   and enzymic browning 243, 247
   and gelatinisation 216, 217
   and jam-making 395
   marinades 73, 74
   as preservatives 381
   and protein denaturation 206–7
adipose tissue 104
aeration 222, **222**
aerobic 239, **239**, 248
aesthetics 10, **10**
al dente 7, **7**
alcohol intake 179
alcoholic strength by volume 331
allergens 298, 330, **330**
ambient temperature 263, **263**
amino acids 100, **100**, 206
   essential 100, **100**, 101, 102, 427
   non-essential 100, **100**
amylopectin 214, **214**
amylose 214, **214**
anaemia
   iron deficiency 137, **137**, 155, **155**, 158,
      158, 185–6
   pernicious 124, **125**
anaerobic 239, **239**, 248
analyse 170–5, **170**, 414–15, 420, **420**, 423,
   427, 436
   see also nutritional analysis; sensory
      analysis tests
anaphylactic shock 298, **298**
angina 178, **178**
animal welfare 344–6, 348, 354–7
anti-bacterial sprays 255, **255**, 272, **272**
antioxidants **118**, 130–1, 399
apple tarte tatin 27
aroma 8
arrowroot 65
arteries 402, **402**
arthritis 177
assessments 411–51
   non-exam assessment 412–38
   written exam 439–51
au gratin 31, **34**
avocado 247
bacteria
   contamination by 254–61
   definition **238**, 241, **249**
   and food spoilage 238
   freezing 266
   ideal growth conditions 238, 241
   pathogenic 241, 257–61, **257**

   spore-forming 275, **275**
   use in food production 251–2
baking 6, 33, 203
baking blind 79
baking powder 92, 228, **228**
balanced diets 145–65
barbecuing 30, **34**, 203
barley 382
basal metabolic rate (BMR) 168, **168**
batters 92–3
beating 229, **229**
béchamel sauce 68
beef
   beef burgers 273
   beef farming 370
   braised beef 444–7
   cuts of 376–7
beri beri 123, **125**
'best before' dates **249**, 263, 266, 268, **268**,
   330, 351
betacarotene (vitamin A) 119, **119**
beurre manie 8, **9**
bibliographies 415, **415**
bicarbonate of soda 91, 228, **228**
bind 62, **62**
biological catalysts 242, **242**
bitter (taste) 319
blanching **23**, **25**, 26, 52, **52**, 128, **128**, 202,
   242, **242**, 381, 397
blancmange, fruit 97
blend 24
blenders 38–9, **42**
blood clots 178, **178**
blood pressure, high 138, 158, **178**, 179
blood sugar levels 154, **154**, 187
blood vessels 178, **178**, 402
bloodstream 143
BMR *see* basal metabolic rate
BNF *see* British Nutrition Foundation
body mass index (BMI) 176–7, **176**
body temperature 142
body weight 107, 113, 147, 153, 156, 157, 177
   see also obesity
BOGOF *see* buy one get one free
boiling 48, **52**, 202
Bolognese sauce 5
bone health 154, **154**, 182
bowel cancer 114, 115, 158, **158**, 177
braising 37, 202, 204, 444–7
bran 383
brand loyalty 337, 338
bread 82–7, **87**, 208, 211, 233
   bread and butter pudding 98

bread rolls 83, 233
finishing methods 87
and flour 387–8, 417–21
glazing 87
grilling 31
industrial baking 388
ingredients 82, 83
Irish soda bread 91
naan bread 31
pizza 85–6
raising agents 239
recipe 83
regulations 384
roly poly bread 84–5
shaping 84, **87**
breadcrumb and egg coating 58–60
breakfast 147, 302
breakfast cereals, fortified/enriched 404
breast cancer 177
bridge hold 14
British cuisine 300–4
British Lion Scheme 259, **259**
British Nutrition Foundation (BNF) 149
brownies, gluten-free chocolate 297
browning, enzymic 242–3, 246–7, **246**
brunch 302, **302**
brunoise 15, **15**
Buddhists 292
budgets
   family 151, **151**
   see also costing
butter 53, 404
buy one get one free (BOGOF) 337
buying food 262–9, 372
cakes, gluten-free fairy 297
calcium 132–4, 156, 158, 182, 403
   for children and young people 155
   deficiency 133, 182
   dietary reference values 133
   excess 133
   functions 132
   sources 132
calcium phosphate 141, **141**
calzone 252
camplyobacter 258, **259**, 260
cancer 114–15, 156, 157, 158, **158**, 177
canning 377, 378, 381, 398
caramelisation 9, **9**, 219–20, 400, **400**
carbohydrates 109–17
   complex 109
   dietary fibre 109, 114–17
   energy content 166, 167, 169

functional and chemical properties
214–20
functions 109
simple 109
sources 109
see also starch; sugars
carbon dioxide
emissions 366–7
as raising agent 227, 233
carbon footprint **290**, 291, 353, 366, **366**, 370
cardiovascular disease 178–81, **178**
carriers 260, **261**
carrot and raisin salad 41
casseroles 34, **34**
spicy lentil and vegetable 35
cazeula 310, **310**
celebrations 282
cereals 382–6
ceviche 74
char/grill 203
CHD *see* coronary heart disease
cheese 207, 210, 250, 251, 392
cheesecake, lemon 41
Chelsea buns 84, 85
chemical properties of food 206–36
chicken
chicken chow mein 55
chicken tagine 36
contaminated 258
green Thai chicken curry 51
knife skills for 16–17
children
menu planning for 173
nutritional needs 150, 152, 153, 155
and physical exercise 177
chilling 377, 378
Chinese cuisine 311–13
chocolate brownies, gluten-free 297
cholesterol 107, **107**, **402**
foods that lower 402
high blood cholesterol **178**, 179
high density lipoprotein 107
low density lipoprotein 107
cholesterol-lowering spreads 402, **402**
chopping boards 13
Chorleywood Bread Process 388, **388**
choux pastry 94–5, 230
chow mein, chicken 55
Christians 292
claw grip 14
climate change 366–9
coagulation 97, 98, 208–9, **209**, 212, 251, **251**
coat 58–60, **58**
coeliac 295–6, **295**
coeliac disease 162, **162**, 295–6, **295**
cold spots 275, **275**
coleslaw 40
collagen 376, **377**

colour check, visual 7
COMA (Committee on Medical Aspects of
Food Policy) Report 148
combine harvesters 382
composting 350
computer programs, nutritional analysis
173–4
conduction 194, **195**, 196, 198
connective tissue 124, **125**, 376, 377, 378
contamination 238–61, **238**
bacterial 254–61
convection 195, **195**, 196
convection currents 195, **195**, 198
conversion tables 2
cookers 28–37
cooking methods 48–55, 192–205
British 302
Chinese 312
cooking with 'dry' heat 53–5, 198, **199**, 203
cooking with fat 53–5, 199, **199**, 203–4
cooking with water 198, **199**, 202
effects on food 127–9, 193
and food safety 270–5
Indian 315
Italian 307
selection 192, 198–205
Spanish 310
water-based methods using the hob
48–52
cooking times 5–6, 273, 287
cooking water 128
corers 13
cornflour 65, 214
coronary heart disease (CHD) 178, **178**
cost of food 151, 282–3, 285, 288–9
costing 288–9, 422, **422**, 437–9, 448
covering food 268
cream cheese and spinach roulade 89
creaming 222, 223, 229, **229**
crème patisserie 61
cross-contamination 260, 272, **272**
crush **22**, **25**
crystallisation 395, **395**
cuisine 300, **300**
British 300–4
international 305–16
culture 290, **290**
curdling 207, **207**
curry, green Thai chicken 51
custard, baked egg 98
dairy 145, 160–1, 390
dairy alternatives 145
data response questions 443–7
de-seed **23**, **25**
de-skin **23**, **25**
decorations 11, 25
deforestation 368

defrosting 267, 273, **273**, 274
deglazing 69, **69**
dehydration 142, **142**, 144
denaturation/denature 73, **74**, 97, 98, 206–10, **207**, 242, **242**, 243, 251, **251**
dental health 183–4
depression 177
developed world 364, **364**
developing world 364, **364**
dextrin 218, **218**
dextrinisation 7, **7**, 218, **218**
diabetes, type 2 169, 187–8, **188**
dietary diaries 174–5, **175**, 424
dietary reference values (DRVs) 148, 436
calcium 133
dietary fibre 115
fats 107
fluoride 140
iodine 140
iron 137
phosphorus 141
protein 103
salt 138
starch 113
sugar 113
vitamin A 120
vitamin B1 125
vitamin D 121
vitamin E 122
vitamin K 122
water-soluble vitamins 125
diets
analysis 174
balanced 145–65
fat free 334
gluten free 296–7
healthy 145–65, **146**, 284
high fibre 164–5
low fat 334
low salt 334
low sugar 334
Mediterranean 306
modification 171, 372
planning 171
special 160–5
sugar free 334
digestive system 158, **158**
dinner 303
discrimination tests 323
dish preparation 4
disinfect 274, **274**
'display until' dates 330
disposable income 284, **284**
diverticular disease 158, **158**
dough 76–87
bread 82–7
pasta 45, 82, 429
pastry 76–81
DRVs *see* dietary reference values

dry heat 53–5, 203
drying food 381, 399, 400
Durham wheat 389, **389**
dusting 81
E. coli 259, **259**, 260
E numbers 406
eating patterns 302–4, 307, 310, 313, 315
Eatwell Guide 145–6, 152, 156–7, 171, 187
egg(s) 161, 213
    and animal welfare 346
    baked egg custard 98
    barn eggs 346, 356–7
    denaturation 208, 209, 212–13
    as emulsifying agent 70
    enriched caged eggs 346, 356–7
    and foam formation 212–13
    free-range eggs 346, 356–7
    and protein coagulation 212
    as raising agent 88–9
    and salmonella 259
    storage 264
    syneresis 209
    whisking 208
elastin 376, **377**
elderly people, nutritional requirements 150, 157–9
electromagnetic rays 197, **197**
elevenses 302, **302**
emulsification **70**, 71, 224–6
emulsifiers 225, **225**, 406, **406**, 407
    hydrophilic 225
    hydrophobic 225
emulsion sauces 70–1, **71**
emulsions 104, 224, **224**
    oil-in-water 224
    stable 70, 225–6
    water-in-oil 224
endosperm 383, 384
energy claims (food labelling) 334
energy content (food labelling) 333
energy dense foods 157, **157**, 166–7, **166**
energy requirements 146, 166–9, 443–4
    and age 167
    and basal metabolic rate 168
    and energy sources 166–7, 169
    and gender 167
    and health 167, 169
    measuring energy 166
    and physical activity level 168
    and physical activity levels 167
    why you need energy 166
energy sources 166–7, 169
energy use, and food production 366
enriched foods 403–5, **403**
environment 342, **342**
environmental change 366–9
environmental impact of food 342–73
    food waste 349–51
    locally produced food 348

    organic food 347
    packaging 352–3
    Red Tractor Food Assurance Scheme 344
    seasonal foods 343–4, **343**
    transportation 347, 348
enzymes 127, **127**, 128
    definition **238**, **249**
    destruction 242–3
    and food spoilage 238, 242–4, 381
    proteolytic 73, **74**
enzymic browning 26, 242–3, 246–7, **246**
epithelium 320, **320**
equipment
    bacterial contamination 255
    for British cuisine 302
    colour-coding 255, 272
    for international cuisine 307, 310, 312, 315
    use of 38–47
    weighing and measuring 3
essential fatty acids 106, **107**, 147
ethical issues 290
ethylene removers 352
exam, written 439–51
    competition times 439
    data response questions 443–7
    format 439
    general advice 440
    marking scheme 439
    multiple choice questions 439, 441
    open-ended questions 447–51
    questions on recipes 444–7
    short-answer questions 442
extraction rate 384, **385**
faecal contamination 259, **259**
fair testing **323**, 326, 336
Fairtrade 372
fairy cakes, gluten-free 297
falafel, baked 62
family budgets 151, **151**
farming
    beef 370
    fish 368, **368**
    intensive **290**, 291, 355, **355**
    precision 371, **371**
fat free diets 334
fat spreads **403**, 404
fats 104–8, 145
    cooking with 53–5, 199, **199**, 203–4
    deficiencies 107
    dietary reference values 107
    energy content 166, 167, 169
    essential fatty acids 106
    excess 107
    and food labelling 334
    functional and chemical properties 221–6
    functions 104

    invisible 104, **105**
    melting points 223
    monounsaturated fats 106
    plasticity 223
    polyunsaturated fats 106
    reduction 170, 179
    saturated fats 106–7, **106**, 147, 171
    saturated fatty acids 106, **106**
    sources 104–5
    spreading 223
    trans fats 105, **105**
    types of 106–7
    unsaturated fats 106, **106**, 147
    unsaturated fatty acids 106, **106**
    visible 104, **105**
fatty acids 106, 107, 147
ferment/fermentation **87**, 231–2, **231**, 239, **239**, 248, **248**
fertilisers 347, 368, **368**
fibre, dietary 109, 114–17, **115**, 334
    deficiency 115
    dietary reference values 115
    and the elderly 158
    excess 115
    functions 114
    high-fibre diets 164–5
    insoluble fibre 114, **115**, 164, **164**
    reduction 170
    soluble fibre 114, **115**, 164, **164**
    sources 114
'field to fork' 374
filleting 16, 17
finger/poke test 6
fish
    cooking times 5
    fish cakes 59–60
    fish fillet 19, **19**
    fish pie 20
    grilling 31
    knife skills for 19–20
    oily 147, **147**
    primary processing 377–8
    round 19
    structure 378
    sustainability issues 346
    tenderising 74
    types of 377
fish farming 368, **368**
fishing industry 368
fizzy drinks 154, 181
flan rings 78, 79
flavour 8–9, 320, **320**, 400
flavour enhancers 250, 385–6
flavourings 407
flour
    for bread-making 387–8, 417–21
    brown 384, 385
    coating 58
    extraction rate 384, **385**

first break 383
fortified/enriched 384, **385**, 403
gluten content 212
organic 385
and pasta 389
plain 385
production 383–6
as raising agent 88, 90
regulations 384
self-raising 88, 90, 228, 385
stoneground 384, 385
strong 211, 233, 385, 387, 417, 420, 421
as thickener 65, 214
traditional 384
wheatgerm 385
white 384
whole wheat 384
wholemeal 384, 385
zero rating 389
fluoridation 139, **139**
fluoride 139–40
fluoride toothpaste 183, **184**
foam 212–13, **212**
folding 229, **229**
folic acid 123, 125
food access 361–2
food additives 406–7
food allergies 298–9, **298**, 330
food availability 283, 361–2
food carriers 327
food choice 279–340, 448
    British cuisine 300–4
    factors affecting 280–99
    and food labelling 328–36
    international cuisine 305–16
    and marketing 336–8
    sensory evaluation 317–27
food colourings 406, **406**, 407
food costs 151, 282–3, 285, 288–9, 422,
    437–9, 448
food distribution 364–5
food fashions and trends 287
food handler contamination 256
food intolerances 162–3, 294–9, **294**, 330
food investigation task 414–21
food labelling 146, 328–36
    date of minimum durability 330
    and food intolerances/allergies 330
    and food names 329
    and GM foods 360
    health claims 335
    importance 332
    ingredients lists 329
    interpretation 336
    mandatory information 329
    meaning 329–31
    net quantities 330
    nutrient lists 334
    nutrition claims 334
    traffic light labels 333, 336

food miles 290, **290**, 347, **347**
food, nutrition and health 99–146, 176–7
    macronutrients 100–17
    micronutrients 118–41
    water 142–4
food poisoning 449–50
    at-risk groups 257
    methods of control 258–61, 270–6
    prevention 26–7
    sources 254–7
    symptoms 257, **257**, 258
    types of 258–61
food preferences 283
food preparation assessment 412, 422–38
food preparation skills 1–98
    cooker use 28–37
    cooking methods 48–55
    dough 76–87
    food safety precautions 270–5
    general practical skills 2–11
    knife skills 12–21
    marinating 72–5
    preparing, combining and shaping
        56–63
    preparing fruit and vegetables 22–7
    raising agents 88–95
    sauce-making 64–71
    setting mixtures 96–8
    tenderising 72–5
    use of equipment 38–47
food presentation and styling 10–11, 304,
    307, 310, 313, 316
food prices 370, 371, 448–51
    reductions 337
food processing 397–401
food processors 40–1, **42**, 43
food production 354–61, 374–96
    environmental impact 342–73
    methods 354–61
    primary processing 374–86, **375**, 390–1
    secondary processing 374–5, **375**,
        387–9, 391–6
    sustainability issues **342**, 345–6, 362–73
food provenance 341–410, 450–1
    and the environment 342–73
    food processing 397–401
    food production 354–61, 374–96
    sustainability of food **342**, 345–6,
        362–73
    technological developments and
        health 402–8
food safety 237–78, 449–50
    food poisoning 26–7, 254–61, 270–6,
        449–50
    food spoilage 238–61, **238**
    principles of 262–76
food scares 287
food science 191–236
    cooking food 192–205

functional and chemical properties of
    food 206–36
    heat transfer 194–7
food security 362–71, **362**
food shopping 262–9, 372
food spoilage 238–61, **238**
    causes 238
    and enzymes 238, 242–4, 381
    and micro-organisms 238–41
    prevention 26–7
    signs of 246–9
Food Standards Agency (FSA) 148, 406
food tables **170**, 172
food testers 326–7
food use 361–2
food waste 349–51, 372
fortified/fortification **119**, 161, **161**, 384,
    385, 402, **402**, 403–5
fossil fuels 366, **366**
free radicals 130, **131**
free-range food production 346, 354–7, **354**
Freedom Food 345
freezer burn 266, **266**
freezers 266–7
freezing food 351, 377, 378
fridges 264–5
fruit
    chopping 14–15
    Eatwell Guide 145
    enzymic browning 246–7
    and food poisoning 26–7
    fruit blancmange 97
    harvesting 380
    jam-making 394–6
    juice extraction 380
    local 348
    marinating 75
    peeling 380
    preparing 22–7
    preservation 381
    primary processing 379–81
    raw 128
    recommended intake 147
    ripe 127
    seasonal 343–4
    skins 128
    spoilage prevention 26–7
    storage 127
    tropical fruit smoothie 39
    types of 379
    vitamin preservation 127–8
    washing 275
fruit juice 110, 183, 398
fruit sugars 110, **110**, 181
frying food 53–5
    deep frying 204
    dry-frying 53, **55**, 203
    shallow frying 53, **55**, 204
    stir-frying 54–5, **55**, 204
FSA see Food Standards Agency

functional and chemical properties of food 206–36
    carbohydrates 214–20
    fats and oils 221–6
    protein 206–13
    raising agents 227–34, **227**
fungi 239
    see also yeast
galactose 163, **163**
garnishes 10, **10**, 25
GDAs *see* guideline daily amounts
gelatin 376, **376**
gelatinisation 65, **66**, 96, **96**, 214–17, **214**
gelation 96, **96**
gelling agents 394, 395
gels 394, **394**
genes 408, **408**
genetically modified (GM) **290**, 291, 347, 358–60, **359**, 372, 408
germ (wheat) 383, 384
ghee 203
glazes 81, 87
gliadin 211, **212**
global trade 370–1
global warming 347, 353, 366–7, **367**
glucose 112, **112**, 163, **163**, 233
glutamates 319
gluten 211, **211**, 221, 233, 387
    formation 211–12
    gluten balls 417–18, 420–1
    sensitivity to 162, 295–6
gluten free 162, **162**
    gluten-free chocolate brownies 297
    gluten-free diets 296–7
glutenin 211
glycerol 106
glycogen 112, **112**
GM *see* genetically modified
gnocchi 306, 307
goitre 140, **140**
gougeres 94
grading tests 324–5, **324**
grams 2
grate **22**, 25
greenhouse gases 353, 366–7, **366**, 372
grills/grilling 28–31, 203
growth spurts 150, 152, **152**
guacamole 247
guideline daily amounts (GDAs) 333
haemoglobin 156, **156**
Halal meat 292
halloumi 21
    grilled 31
hand washing 270–1
hanging 376, **377**
harvests 380, 382
HATTIE 3
HBV (high biological value) 100–1, **100**, 427, 442
HDL (high density lipoprotein) 107

health
    and food choice 294–9
    and overconsumption of food 169
    and technological developments 402–8
    and vegetarian diets 426
    see also food, nutrition and health; nutritional needs and health
health claims (food labelling) 335
healthy diets 145–65, **146**, 284
    current guidelines 146–9
heart attack 178, **178**
heart disease 107, 130, 156, 157, 169, 178, **178**
heart palpitation 186, **186**
heat stroke 142, **142**
heat transfer 194–7
heat treatments 391, 398, 400–1
heating
    cooking with 'dry' heat 198, **199**, 203
    effect on the sensory characteristics of milk 400–1
    moist heat 220
    removal of heat 96–7
    and vitamins 397–8
hedonic ranking 322, 437
hedonic scale 405, **405**
herbicides 359, **359**, 408, **408**
hereditary 162, **162**
high biological value (HBV) protein 100–1, **100**, 427, 442
high density lipoprotein (HDL) (good cholesterol) 107
high fibre diets 164–5
high-risk foods 241, **241**, 263, 275, **275**
high-speed mixing 388
Hindus 291, 445
hobs 48–55
homogenisation 390, **390**, 401, **401**
hydration 142, **142**, 146, 147
hydrogenation 105, **105**
hyperactivity 407
hypotheses 415, **415**, 418
immiscible liquids 70, **71**, 224, 225
immune system 186, **186**
imported foods 364, **364**
income
    disposable 284, **284**
    household 285
Indian food 314–16
infuse 8, **9**, 68, **69**
infused liquids 49, **52**
ingredients lists 329
insulated cold bags 263, **263**
intensive farming **290**, 291, 355, **355**
international cuisine 305–16
interviews 424
intestines 185, **186**
iodine 140
Irish soda bread 91

iron 135–7, 154, 156, 172, 403
    absorption 135
    for children and young people 155
    deficiency 137
    dietary reference values 137
    excess 137
    functions 135
    haem iron 135, **135**
    iron tablets 185
    non-haem iron 135, **135**, 161, **161**
    sources 135
Islam 292
Italian food 252, 305–7
jam
    jam-making 249, 394–6
    steamed jam pudding 49
jam sugar 395, **395**
jardinière 15, **15**
Jews (Judaism) 291
John West 346
jointing 16
juices 24, 110, 183, 380, 398
julienne 15, **15**
junk food 153
kilocalories (kcal) 166, **166**, 168
kilojoules (kj) 166
kitchen scales 3
knead/kneading 82–4, 86–7, 208, 211, 388–9
knife skills 12–21
knives 12
    bread knives 12, **12**
    carving knives 12, **12**
    cook's knives 12, **12**, 17
    filleting knives 12, **12**
    paring/vegetable knives 12, **12**
    testing for readiness 7
    types of 12
knocking back 82, 83, 87, 388
kosher 291, **291**, 292
kwashiorkor 103, **103**
lactase 163, **163**, 294
lactic acid 251, **251**
lacto-ovo-vegetarians 160, 161, **161**, 426–8, 430, 436
lacto-vegetarians 160, **160**, 426, 427
lactose 251, **251**, 294–5, **294**, 400, **400**
lactose intolerance 163, **163**, 294–5
lasagne 63, 171
layer 61, **62**, 63
LBV (low biological value) 100–1, **100**, 161, 427, 442
LDL (low density lipoprotein) 107
LEAF (Linking Environment and Farming) 372
leaven 239
lecithin 70, 225, **225**, 407, **407**
lemon cheesecake 41
lentil and vegetable spicy casserole 35
lifestyle 286

Linking Environment and Farming (LEAF) 372
lipoproteins 107
liquidisers 38
listeria 260, **261**
locally produced food 348, 372
low biological value (LBV) protein 100–1, **100**, 161, 427, 442
low density lipoprotein (LDL) (bad cholesterol) 107
low energy foods 166–7, **166**
low fat diets 334
low fat spreads 403, **403**, 404
low salt diets 334
low sugar diets 334
loyalty cards 338
lunch 303
macedoine 15, **15**
macronutrients 100–17
    carbohydrates 109–17
    fats 104–8
    protein 100–3
magnetrons 197, **197**
maize (corn) 382
mandatory 329, **329**
margarine 403, **403**, 404
marinades 72, 73, 206, 377, 378
    acidic 73, 74
    citrus marinade 73
    definition **74**, **207**
    marinated peaches 75
    yoghurt marinade 73
marinating 72–5, **74**, 206, **207**
Marine Stewardship Council (MSC) 346
marketing 336–8, **336**, 347
mash **22**, **25**
meal deals 338
meal modification 171
meal nutrition analysis 174
meal planning 150–1, 160–5, 171, 423, 428–35
measuring 2–4
measuring equipment 4
meat
    cooking times 5
    cuts of 376–7
    and food poisoning 254
    grilling 31
    hanging 376, **377**
    knife skills for 18
    price of 370, 371
    primary processing 375–7
    resting 9
    slaughter 254, **254**, 348, 376
    tenderising 72–3
meat alternatives 5, 21, 75, 427
    see also protein alternatives
media 287, 337
medical factors, and food choice 294–9

Mediterranean diet 306
menopause 185, **186**
menstruation 137, 154, **154**, 185
meringue 43, 212
micro-filtration 391, **391**
micro-organisms **238**
    and food spoilage 238–41
    use in food production 250–3
    see also bacteria; mould; yeast
micrograms 118, **118**
micronutrients 118–41, **118**
    minerals 132–41
    vitamins 118–31
microwave ovens 46–7, **46**, 197, 204–5
    combination microwaves 205
milk
    condensed 398, 400
    curdled 207
    denaturation 210
    dried 399, 400
    effect of heating on the sensory characteristics of 400–1
    evaporated 398, 400
    homogenised 390, 401
    primary processing 390–1
    secondary processing 392–4
    ultra heat treatment 391, **391**, 398, 400
    unpasteurised 260, **261**
milk sugar 113, **115**
milligrams 122
milling 251, **251**, 382–4, **383**, 403
mineral deficiencies 133, 137–8, 140–1, 182
minerals 132–41
mis en place 3, **3**
miso 102
mix 58, **58**
mixers 42–3, **42**
modified atmosphere 128, **128**
monosodium glutamate 250, **250**, 407
moral issues 290
mould spores 249, **249**
moulds
    definition **238**, 240, **249**, **250**
    and food spoilage 238, 240, 249
    ideal growth conditions 238, 240
    use in food production 250
mouthfeel 320, **320**
MSC see Marine Stewardship Council
Muslims 292
mycoprotein 5, 102, 427
naan bread 31
National Health Service (NHS) 149
NEA see non-exam assessment
neutral conditions 241, **241**
NHS see National Health Service
nitrates 368, **406**, 407
nocturnal 256
non-exam assessment (NEA) 412–38
    analysis 414–15, 420, **420**, 423, 427, 436

    assessment objectives 413
    completion 412
    evaluation 414–15, 420, **420**, 421, 423, 436
    format 412
    hypothesis 415, **415**, 418
    investigation 414–15, **415**, 417–21
    justification 415, **415**
    marking criteria 413, 414, 422
    menu planning 423, 428–35
    moderation 413
    prediction 415, **415**, 418, 421
    research 413–15, 416, 423–7
    task 1: food investigation 412, 414–21
    task 2: food preparation assessment 412, 422–38
    technical skills 423, 428–35
    time allowed for 412
nutrition 99–146, 176–7
    macronutrients 100–17
    micronutrients 118–41
    water 142–4
nutritional advice 148–9
nutritional analysis 170–5, **175**, 422, **422**, 436, 438
nutritional modification 402, **402**
nutritional needs and health 145–90
    bone health 182
    cardiovascular disease 178–81
    dental health 183–4
    diet, nutrition and health 176–7
    energy needs 166–9
    iron deficiency anaemia 185–6
    making informed choices 145–65
    nutritional analysis 170–5
    type 2 diabetes 187–8
nuts 31
oats 382
obesity 110, 156, 157, 169, 176–7, **176**
    childhood 153
    complications 177
    and diet modification 171
    treatment 177
oils 53, 221–6
olfactory receptors 320, **320**
olfactory system 320, **320**
omega 3 fatty acids 106, 107, 147, **147**
omega 6 fatty acids 106
open-ended questions 447–51
organic food 347, **347**, 385, 450—1
organoleptic qualities 8, **8**, **9**, 318, **318**
osteoporosis 133, **133**, 158, **158**, 182, **182**
ounces 2
ovens 32–7
    see also microwave ovens
over-nutrition 176, **176**
over-ripening 246
overconsumption of food issues 169
overfishing 368

overweight 153, 156, 157
    see also obesity
oxidation 244, **244**
packaging, environmental impact 352–3
paellera 310, **310**
paired preference test 321
PAL *see* physical activity level
palmiers
    puff pastry 81
    savoury 56
pancakes, American-style 93
paneer 21
pasta 306, 307, 428, 429–38
    cooking times 6
    dough 45, 82, 429
    flour 389
    ingredients 82
pasta machines 44–5
pastes 8
pasteurisation 248, **249**, **390**
    milk 390, 391, 393, 400
    pasta 389
    and vitamins 398
pastry 76–81
    choux pastry 94–5, 230
    dusting 81
    filling 81
    finishing methods 81
    flaky pastry 230
    glazing 81
    piping 81
    puff pastry 79–81
    rolling 56
    shortcrust pastry 76–9
pathogens 241, **241**, 257–61, **257**
pavlovas, mini 43
peach(es), marinated 75
peak bone mass 154, **154**
pectin 112, 394, 395, **395**
peel **22**, **25**
peelers 13
peeling 380
peer pressure 287, **287**
pellagra **125**
perishable foods 257, **257**, 263
personal hygiene 270–1
pest contamination 256
pester power 151, **151**
pesticides 347, 359, **359**, 368, **368**, 408, **408**
phosphorus 141
photosynthesis 109
physical activity level (PAL) 168, **168**,
    281, **281**
physical exercise 147, 177, 179
pickling 378
pilaf 37
piping 24, 81
pizza 85–6, 252
plaque 184, **184**

plasticity 223, **223**
poaching 50, **52**, 202
polysaccharides *see* fibre, dietary; starch
population change 370
portion size 150, **150**, 171
portioning 11
poultry
    primary processing 375
    tenderising 72–3
    see also chicken
precision farming 371, **371**
preference (acceptance) tests 321–2, **321**
preparing ingredients and equipment 3–4
    see also food preparation
presentation and styling 10–11, 304, 307,
    310, 313, 316
preservatives **239**, 240, **240**, 406–7, **406**
preserving pans 395, **395**
price comparison sites 151, **151**
price of food 337, 370, 371, 448–51
product placement 337
profiling tests 325
profiteroles 94
protein 100–3, 145
    biological value 100–1, **100**, 161, 427,
        442
    for children and young people 155
    coagulation 208–9
    deficiency 103
    dietary reference values 103
    energy content 166, 167, 169
    excess 103
    functional and chemical properties
        206–13
    functions 100
    high biological value 100–1, **100**,
        427, 442
    low biological value 100–1, **100**, 161,
        427, 442
    nutrition label 334
    sources 101
    use of 97–8
protein alternatives 102, **103**
    see also meat alternatives
protein complementation 101, **101**, 427
protein denaturation 206–13, 251, **251**
    and acids 206–7
    and enzymes 242, **242**, 243
    and heat 208–10
    and mechanical action 208
protein sparers 109
proteolytic enzymes 73, **74**
proving 82, 83, 86, **87**, 388
puff pastry 79–81
quiche Lorraine 77
quinoa 102
Quorn™ 75, 102, 427
radiation 195, **195**, 197, 198
Rainforest Alliance 372

raising agents 88–95, **88**, **227**
    air 227, 229–30
    baking powder 92
    bicarbonate of soda 91
    biological 227, 231–3
    carbon dioxide 227, 233
    chemical 228, **228**
    definition **239**, **250**
    egg 88–9
    flour (self-raising) 88, 90
    functional and chemical properties
        227–34
    mechanical 227, 229–30, **229**
    steam 92–5, 227, 230
    yeast 92, 239, 250
ranking 188, **188**
ranking tests 324, **324**
Rastafarians 292
ratatouille 47
rating tests 324, **324**
rationed 403, **403**
raw food 128, 192
    bacterial contamination 254
    separation from cooked 272
    storage 264
readiness, testing for 7
ready meals 286
recipe modification 170, **170**
recipes
    American-style pancakes 93
    apple tarte tatin 27
    baked egg custard 98
    baked falafels 62
    Bolognese sauce 5
    braised beef 444–7
    braised rice 37
    bread and butter pudding 98
    bread dough 83
    bread rolls 83
    carrot and raisin salad 41
    chicken chow mein 55
    chicken tagine 36
    citrus marinade 73
    costing 288–9
    crème patisserie 61
    fish cakes 59–60
    fish pie 20
    fruit blancmange 97
    gluten-free chocolate brownies 297
    gluten-free fairy cakes 297
    gougeres 94
    green Thai chicken curry 51
    guacamole 247
    Irish soda bread 91
    Italian calzone 252
    jam 396
    lasagne 63
    lemon cheesecake 41
    mini pavlovas 43

mixed vegetable soup 24
modifications 288–9
naan bread 31
nutritional analysis 172–3
pasta dough 45, 82, 430
pizza 85–6
planning 170
profiteroles 94
puff pastry 80
quiche Lorraine 77
ratatouille 47
roasted vegetables 34
roly poly bread 84–5
savoury palmiers 56
savoury scone round 90
shortcrust pastry 77
spicy lentil and vegetable casserole 35
spinach and cream cheese roulade 89
steamed jam pudding 49
Swiss roll 57
tomato sauce 431
trifle 61
tropical fruit smoothie 39
yoghurt 394
yoghurt marinade 73
recycle 342, 350, 352
Red Tractor Food Assurance Scheme 344
reduce 342, 353, 372
reduction 8, **9**, 69, **69**
reference intakes (RIs) 333, 336
refuse 342
reheating food 275, 449–50
religious diets 291–3, 445
rennet 251, **251**, 392
rennin 251
repair 342
research 413–15, 416, 423–7
    primary 416, **416**, 424
    secondary 416, **416**, 424
rethink 342, 350
retinol (vitamin A) 119, **119**
reuse 342, 350, 352
rice 382
    braised rice 37
    cooking times 6
    genetically modified 408
rickets 120–1, **120**, 133, **133**, 182, **182**
rind 18, **18**
ripening 381
RIs see reference intakes
roasting 33–4, 204
roll 56–7, **58**
roulade, spinach and cream cheese 89
roux method 65, 68
RSPCA Assured 345
rubbing in 229, **229**
rubs 289
rye 382
safety issues 43
salad, carrot and raisin 41

salad dressings 70
saliva 143
salmon, steamed 50
salmonella 259, **259**, 260
salt (sodium chloride) 8, 138–9, **180**
    deficiency 138
    dietary reference values 138
    excess 138
    functions 138
    intake reduction 147, 170, 179, 180
    sources 138
salt (taste) 319
salting 377, 378
salt free foods 334
samples, free 337
sauces 64–71
    all-in-one method 65
    béchamel 68
    binding/panada 66
    blended 65
    coating 66
    definition 64, **66**
    emulsion sauces 70–1, **71**
    pouring 66
    reduction sauces 69
    roux method 65, 68
    starch-based sauces 65–8
    velouté 68
    viscosity 65, 66, **66**
sausage 250
savoury 8
Scientific Advisory Committee on Nutrition 148
scissor **22**, **25**
scone round, savoury 90
scoop **22**, **25**
scurvy 124, **125**
sealing 26
seasonal foods 286, **286**, 343–4, **343**, 347, 372
seasoning 8–9
seeds 31
segment **22**, **25**
self-sufficiency 364
'sell by' dates 330
semolina 383, **383**, 389
sensory analysis tests 300–5, 419, 421–2, **422**, 431, 437–8
sensory evaluation 8–11, 317–27
    carrying out 326
    definition 318
    discrimination tests 323
    food samples 327
    food testers 326–7
    grading tests 324
    reasons for carrying out 317
    sensory analysis tests 300–5, 419, 421–2, **422**, 431, 437–8
    smell 320
    taste receptors 318–19

testing environments 326
testing equipment 327
sensory profiling tests 325, **325**
sensory qualities 438, **438**
serving food 273
setting mixtures 96–8
setting point 395, **395**
shape **23**, **25**, 62
    bread 82, 83, 84, **87**
    shortcrust pastry 78
shellfish 5
short-answer questions 442
shortcrust pastry 76–9
shortening 221, **221**, 223
shred **22**, **25**
sieving 229, **229**
Sikhs 292
simmering 51, **52**, 202
skewers 6, 57, **58**
slaughter 254, **254**, 348, 376
smell, sense of 320
smoking 377, 378
smoothie, tropical fruit 39
smoothie makers 38
snip **22**, **25**
sodium chloride see salt
Soil Association 347, 385
soufflés 212
soup, mixed vegetable 24
soup makers 38
sour (taste) 8, 319
soy sauce 250
soya 102
soya milk 102
Spanish cuisine 308–10
special diets 160–5
special offers 337
spina bifida 123, 125, **125**
spinach and cream cheese roulade 89
spore-forming bacteria 275, **275**
stabilisers 406, **406**, 407
Staphylococcus aureus 260
staple foods 382
star profiles 325, 419, 421, **421**
starch 109, **109**, 112–13, 145, 147, **147**, 167, 187, **188**
    deficiency 113
    dietary reference values 113
    excess 113
    and gelatinisation 214–16
    and moist heat 215
    sources of 112
    starch-based sauces 65–8
starch grains 214, **214**
starter cultures 392, 393, **393**
steak, rare 273
steam, as raising agent 92–5
steaming 49, **52**, 202, 204
    methods 49
    steamed jam pudding 49

steamed salmon 50
sterilisation 249, **249**, 391, **391**, 398, 400
stir-frying 54–5, **55**, 204
storing food 257, 262–9, 351, 353, 359
stroke 169, 178, **178**, 179
sucrose 181
sugar free diets 334
sugar syrup 26
sugars 109, **109**, 110–11, 145
    and aeration 222
    caramelisation 219–20
    castor sugar 222
    deficiency 113
    dietary reference values 113
    double sugars (disaccharides) 110, **110**
    excess 113
    free sugars 110, **110**, 113, 147, **147**, 169, 181, **182**, 183–4, 187
    fruit sugar 110, **110**, 181
    and gelatinisation 216, 217
    hidden sugars 111
    intake reduction 147, 179, 181
    jam sugar 395, **395**
    milk sugar 113, **115**
    and moist heat 220
    as preservative 381, 395
    reduction 170, 187–8
    simple sugars (monosaccharides) 110, **110**
    sources 111
    sucrose 181
    and tooth decay 183–4
sunshine vitamin *see* vitamin D
supermarkets 282
supper 303
surveys 424
sustainability **342**, 345–6, 362–73
    food security 362–5, 366–71
    RSPCA Assured 345
sustainable environments 369, **369**
sweating 142
sweet (taste) 8, 319
Swiss roll 57
symptoms 257, **257**, 258
syneresis 209, **209**, 213
tagines 34, 36, **36**
    chicken tagine 36
tainting 264, **264**
tandoor 315
target groups 173, **175**
tarte tatin, apple 27
taste 8
taste buds 8, 318, **318**, 319, 320, **320**
taste receptors 318–19
taste test 7
tea, afternoon 303
technology
    and food production 371–2
    and health 402–8
teenagers, nutritional needs 150, 154–5

tempeh 102
temperature
    ambient 263, **263**
    control of food 262, 273–4
    and food preservation 381
    freezers 266
    fridges 264
    and gelatinisation 216, 217
temperature danger zone 262, **262**, 275, **275**
temperature probes 7, 273–4
tenderising 72–5, **74**
texture 9
textured vegetable protein (TVP) 102, 427
thali 316
thickeners 65
thyroid gland 140, **140**
time constraints 287
time of day 287
time plans 422, **422**, 432, 433–4
tin preparation 4
tofu 21, 75, 102, 427
tomato
    de-skinning, de-seeding and chopping 23
    tomato sauce 431
tongue, map of the 319
tooth decay 110, 113, 140, 171, 183–4, **184**
trade, global 370–1
traffic light labels 333, 336
transportation 347, 348
triangle test 323
trifle 61
triglycerides 106, **106**
TVP *see* textured vegetable protein
ultra heat treatment (UHT) 391, **391**, 398, 400
umami (savouriness) 319, **319**
under-nutrition 176, **176**, 365, **365**
unprocessed foods 154, **154**
'use by' dates 268, **268**, 330, 351
vaccinated 259, **259**
vacuum packs 240, **240**
vegan diets 124, **125**, 160–1, **161**, 426–7
vegetable oils 203
vegetables
    blanching 52
    chopping 14–15
    cooking times 6
    Eatwell Guide 145
    and food poisoning prevention 26–7
    grilling 31
    harvesting 380
    juice extraction 380
    local 348
    marinating 75
    mixed vegetable soup 24
    peeling 380
    preparing 22–7
    preserving 381

    primary processing 379–81
    ratatouille 47
    raw 128
    recommended intake 147
    ripe 127
    roasted 34
    seasonal 343–4
    skins 128
    spicy lentil and vegetable casserole 35
    spoilage prevention 26–7
    storage 127
    types of 379
    vitamin preservation 127–9
    washing 275
vegetarian diet 160–1, 424–38
    dishes for 428–35
    health benefits 426
    motivations 425
    and nutrient deficiencies 426
    types of vegetarian 426
velouté sauces 68
viscosity 65, 66, **66**
visual colour check 7
vitamin A 118–20, 398–9, 404, 408
    antioxidant functions 130–1
    for children and young people 155
    deficiency 120
    dietary reference values 120
    excess 120
    functions 118
    sources 119
vitamin B1 (thiamin) 123, 125, **125**, 398–9, 403
vitamin B2 (riboflavin) 123, 125, **125**
vitamin B3 (niacin) 403
vitamin B12 124, 125, 158
vitamin B group 155, 397–9, 403
vitamin C (ascorbic acid) 124–5, 130–1, 155–6, 158, 388, 397–9
vitamin D 120–1, 156, 158, 182, 398–9, 404
    for children and young people 155
    deficiency 120–1, 182
    dietary reference values 121
    excess 121
    functions 120
    sources 120
vitamin deficiencies 120–1, 122, 123–4, 125
vitamin drops 182, **182**
vitamin E 122, 130–1, 399
vitamins
    effects of cooking methods on 127–9, 202–4
    fat-soluble 118–22, **118**
    and food processing 397–9
    water-soluble 123–30, **125**, 127–9
waist measurements 177
washing
    fruit and vegetables 275
    hand 270–1
waste 143, 257

water 142–6
    bottled 144
    excess 144
    functions 142–3
    and high-fibre diets 165
    lack of 142, 144
    recommended intake 143–4, 146, 147
water intoxication 144, **144**
water soaking 128
water-based cooking methods 48–52, 128
wax coatings 381
weaning 184
weighing 2–4

weight gain 107, 113
weight loss 107, 177
wheat 382, 383–6, 417
    Durham wheat 389, **389**
whisking 208, 229, **229**
whole wheat 384, 417
wholegrain 147, **147**
wholemeal 384, 385, 403, **403**
woks 54, **55**
work surfaces 255, 272
wraps 57, **58**
wrinkle test 395, **395**
yeast 92, 231–3, **231**, 417

aerobic 239, 248
anaerobic 239, 248
definition **238**, 239, **249**
and food spoilage 238, 239, 248
ideal growth conditions 238, 239
types of 231
use in food production 250
yoghurt
    recipe 394
    as tenderiser 73
    types 393
    yoghurt marinade 73
    yoghurt-making 251, 393–4